HIPOXIA: INVESTIGACIONES BÁSICAS Y CLÍNICAS

HOMENAJE A
CARLOS MONGE CASSINELLI

Fabiola LEÓN-VELARDE, Alberto ARREGUI
Editores

IFEA   1993   UPCH

Carátula: Elena Gonzáles

Foto de carátula: Guillermo Hare

© 1993 - IFEA Instituto Francés de Estudios Andinos - Casilla 18-1217, Lima 18, Perú

© 1993 - UPCH Universidad Peruana Cayetano Heredia - Apartado 5045, Lima 100, Perú

ISBN: 84-89302-12-X

Este libro corresponde al Tomo **76** de la serie Travaux de l'Institut Français d'Études Andines (ISSN 0768-424X)

ÍNDICE

COLABORADORES

ARREGUI, Alberto
Departamento de Neurología, Universidad Peruana Cayetano Heredia, Apartado 4314, Lima 100, Peru.

BEALL, Cynthia M.
Department of Anthropology, 238, Mather Memorial Building, Case Western Reserve University, Cleveland, OH, 44106-7125, USA.

BLIGH, John
Department of Cellular and Molecular Physiology, AFRC, Institute of Animal Physiology, Babraham Hall, Cambridge, England CB2 4AT.

BOZZINI, Carlos E.
Cátedra de Fisiología, Facultad de Odontología, Universidad de Buenos Aires y Área de Hematología Experimental, Bio Sidus S.A., Buenos Aires, Argentina.

CABELLO, Gertrudis R.
Departamento de Biología y Salud, Facultad de Ciencias, Universidad de Tarapacá, Arica, Chile.

CAREY, Cynthia
Department of EPO Biology, University of Colorado, Boulder, Colorado, 80309 USA.

CERRETELLI, Paolo
Department of Physiology, CMU, University of Geneva, 1211 Geneva 4, Switzerland.

COUDERT, Jean
Laboratoire de Physiologie, Faculté de Médecine, BP 38, 63001, Clermont-Ferrand, France et

Instituto Boliviano de Biología de Altura, Casilla 717, La Paz, Bolivia.

CHAUCA, Denise
Instituto Veterinario de Investigaciones Tropicales y de Altura, Apartado 4270, Lima, Perú.

ESPINOZA, Mauricio I.
Departamento de Bioquímica y Biología Molecular, Facultad de Ciencias Químicas y Farmacéuticas, Universidad de Chile, Chile.

FRISANCHO, A. Roberto
Center for Human Growth and Development and University of Michigan, Ann Arbor, MI 48104, USA.

GAETE, Cristián, R.
Laboratorio de Fisiología y Fisiopatología del Desarrollo, Departamento de Medicina Experimental, Campus Oriente, Facultad de Medicina, Universidad de Chile, Santiago, Chile.

GARMENDIA, Fausto
Departamento de Endocrinología, Universdad de San Marcos, Lima, Perú.

GONZÁLES, Gustavo F.
Instituto de Investigaciones de la Altura y Departamento de Ciencias Fisiológicas, Universidad Peruana Cayetano Heredia, Apartado 6083, Lima, Perú.

GRASSI, Bruno
Department of Physiology, CMU, University of Geneva, 1211 Geneva 4, Switzerland.

GROVER, Robert F.
University of Colorado School of
Medicine, Denver, Colorado, 216,
Mariposa Circle, Arroyo Grande, CA,
USA.

GUERRA GARCÍA, Roger
Instituto de Investigaciones de la
Altura y Departamento de Ciencias
Fisiológicas, Universidad Peruana
Cayetano Heredia, Apartado 6083,
Lima, Perú.

HEATH, Donald
35, Hesketh Drive, Southport,
Merseyside, U.K. PR9 7JG.

HOCHACHKA, Peter W.
Department of Zoology and Sports
Medicine Division, University of
British Colombia, 6270 University
Boulevard, Vancouver, B.C., Canada,
V6T 2A9.

KAYSER, Bengt
Department of Physiology, CMU,
University of Geneva, 1211 Geneva
4, Switzerland.

LAHIRI, Sukhamay
Department of Physiology, University
of Pennsylvania School of Medicine,
Philadelphia, Pennsylvania, 19104,
USA.

LEÓN-VELARDE, Fabiola
Departamento de Ciencias Fisiológicas
e Instituto de Investigaciones de la
Altura, Universidad Peruana Cayetano
Heredia, Apartado 4314, Lima 100,
Perú.

LLANOS, Anibal J.
Laboratorio de Fisiología y
Fisiopatología del Desarrollo,
Departamento de Medicina Expe-
rimental, Campus Oriente, Facultad
de Medicina, Universidad de Chile,
Santiago, Chile.

MOORE, Lorna G.
Cardiovascular Pulmonary Research
Laboratory, University of Colorado
Health Sciences Center, 4200 Easth 9th
Avenue, Denver, CO 80262, USA and
Department of Anthropology,
University of Colorado at Denver,
Denver, CO 80217, USA.

MORAGA, Fernando
Laboratorio de Fisiología y
Fisiopatología del Desarrollo,
Departamento de Medicina Expe-
rimental, Campus Oriente, Facultad
de Medicina, Universidad de Chile,
Santiago, Chile.

PARER, Julian, T.
Departments of Obstetrics, Gyne-
cology and Reproductive Sciences and
Cardiovascular Research Institute,
University of California, San Francisco,
USA.

PRESSON Jr., Robert G.
Departments of Anesthesiology,
Physiology and Pediatrics, MS 374,
635 Barnhill Drive, Indiana University
Medical School, Indianapolis, Indian
46202, USA.

RAKUSAN, Karel
Department of Physiology, Faculty of
Medicine, University of Ottawa, 451
Smyth, Ottawa, Ontario, Canada K1H
8M5.

RICHALET, Jean-Paul
Professeur de Physiologie, Association
pour la Recherche en Physiologie de
l'Environnement, U.F.R. de Médecine
de Bobigny, 93012, Bobigny, France.

RIQUELME, Raquel A.
Departamento de Bioquímica y
Biología Molecular, Facultad de
Ciencias Químicas y Farmacéuticas,
Universidad de Chile, Chile.

SANHUEZA, EMILIA M.
Laboratorio de Fisiología y Fosiopatología del Desarrollo, Departamento de Medicina Experimental, Campus Oriente, Facultad de Medicina, Universidad de Chile, Santiago, Chile.

SUN, Shinfu
Tibet Institute of Medical Sciences, Lhasa, Tibet Autonomous Region, 850000, China.

SUTTON, John R.
Department of Biological Sciences, Faculty of Health Sciences, The University of Sydney, Sydney, NSW, 2141, Australia.

TENNEY, S. Marsh
Department of Physiology, Dartmouth Medical School, Borwell Building 1, Medical Center Drive, Lebanon, New Hampshire, 03756-0001, USA.

TUREK, Zdenek
Department of Physiology, Faculty of Medicine, University of Nigmegen, Geert Grooteplein N. 21, 6500 HB Nijmegen, Holanda

VARGAS P., Enrique
Instituto Boliviano de Biología de Altura, UMSA, Casilla 641, La Paz, Bolivia.

VILLENA C., Mercedes
Instituto Boliviano de Biología de Altura, UMSA, Casilla 641, La Paz, Bolivia.

WAGNER, Wiltz W.
Departments of Anesthesiology, Physiology and Pediatrics, MS 374, 635 Barnhill Drive, Indiana University Medical School, Indianapolis, Indian 46202, USA.

WEST, John B.
UCSD Department of Medicine, 0623, 9500 Gilman Drive, University of California, San Diego, La Jolla, CA, 92093-0623, USA.

WINSLOW, Robert M.
Department of Medicine, University of California, San Diego, Veterans Affairs Medical Center, 3350 La Jolla Village Drive, San Diego, CA, 92161, USA.

ZAMUDIO, Stacy
Cardiovascular Pulmonary Research Laboratory, University of Colorado Health Sciences Center, 4200 Easth 9th Avenue, Denver, CO 80262, USA, and Department of Anthropology, University of Colorado at Denver, Denver, CO 80217, USA.

PRÓLOGO

Este libro, en honor a Carlos Monge Cassinelli por sus 70 años, reune trabajos de investigadores que estudian la adaptación a la altura con el fin de conocer los mecanismos que permiten a los animales y al hombre vivir y desarrollarse en condiciones de hipoxia aguda o crónica. Se tratan temas relativos al transporte de oxígeno en sus distintos aspectos, la adaptación pulmonar durante el desarrollo, la interacción entre el frío y la hipoxia y la vascularización pulmonar como adaptación a la hipoxia. Además, la etiopatogenia del mal de montaña crónico, la aclimatación a la hipoxia aguda, la hemodinámica uterina en llamas, las alteraciones endocrinas del embarazo y aspectos bioquímicos de la adaptación en aves y mamíferos. Adicionalmente, algunos de los trabajos comparan las poblaciones de los Andes con las de los Himalayas de acuerdo a los diferentes enfoques y disciplinas de cada investigador.

Las estudios de los distintos autores constituyen el estado actual de los conocimientos que nos acercan al entendimiento de la compleja fisiología de la adaptación a la altura, y son un merecido y cálido homenaje a quien dedicó una buena parte de su vida a tratar de entenderla.

Agradecemos al Instituto Francés de Estudios Andinos (IFEA) y a la Universidad Peruana Cayetano Heredia (UPCH) por haber patrocinado la edición de este volumen jubilar. De igual manera a los autores que con gran entusiasmo y espíritu de colaboración se sumaron al homenaje e hicieron posible este volumen que será un recuerdo permanente para Carlos Monge Cassinelli, gran colega, mejor amigo.

Fabiola León-Velarde
Alberto Arregui
Editores

PRESENTACIÓN

Los amigos y discípulos del Dr. Carlos Monge Cassinelli me solicitaron presentar este libro que constituye el homenaje de la Universidad Peruana Cayetano Heredia y del Instituto Francés de Estudios Andinos al destacado investigador peruano.

Carlos Monge Cassinelli es hijo del profesor Carlos Monge Medrano, iniciador en Perú de los estudios biomédicos acerca del efecto de la altura sobre el hombre y los animales y ha continuado profundizando la tarea de su ilustre padre, en una trayectoria académica de sorprendente similitud, y sin parangón en Perú.

Los temas estudiados por Monge Cassinelli han ido cambiando con el transcurso del tiempo; así, a sus estudios iniciales sobre glicemia, lacticidemia y piruvicemia en sujetos de altura, temas de su tesis de bachillerato en medicina, siguieron otros sobre dinámica de fluídos corporales recogidos en su tesis doctoral, ambas en la Universidad Nacional Mayor de San Marcos.

Posteriormente, dirigió su investigación al estudio de la función renal en los nativos de la altura con interesantes hallazgos y luego al incremento del hematocrito con la edad, aspecto aún polémico, que lo acercó a la investigación de la situación de salud de los mineros peruanos, aplicando criterios epidemiológicos a miles de observaciones que no dejan duda sobre la acentuación de la policitemia en función del tiempo de trabajo, y la aparición de síntomas y signos varios.

Esta evolución de Carlos Monge Cassinelli también la tuvieron los iniciadores de los estudios peruanos sobre biomedicina de altura: Carlos Monge Medrano y Alberto Hurtado. En los tres, incluído Monge Cassinelli, ocurre una creciente preocupación por las condiciones de vida de los trabajadores en las inhóspitas alturas de los Andes, en particular la que concierne a los mineros, quienes con su duro esfuerzo aportan significativa proporción de los ingresos del Estado, y por ende de los peruanos en general.

En las tres últimas décadas, Carlos Monge Cassinelli ha acometido el estudio de algunos aspectos de la biofísica en la altitud, reuniendo a jóvenes investigadores, varios de los cuales laboran en otros países, pero que se han sumado a este volumen de homenaje al maestro.

Su preferencia por la biofísica lo acercó a la fisiología comparada y a modelos sencillos como el estudio de los huevos de aves nativas de la altura en los cuales ha realizado importantes demostraciones acerca de cómo se adaptan al pasaje de gases y agua.

Todo lo antes dicho puede deducirse de la revisión del *curriculum vitae* de Carlos Monge Cassinelli, y presentarse mejor que estas carillas. Hay un importante asunto no tratado y es la influencia de Monge Cassinelli en varios miembros de su generación y en numerosos jóvenes que frecuentaron su laboratorio, primero en la Universidad San Marcos, y después en la UPCH. Para ellos «Choclo Monge» es la cabal demostración de que en Perú dedicarse a la investigación biomédica es una opción válida que gana, para quien la practica, el reconocmiento de sus pares y de la sociedad en general. Esta demostración se la debemos muchos, cuénteseme entre ellos, con el valor agregado de proceder de un médico valioso que hubiera triunfado en el ejercicio de la práctica y para quien estaban abiertas todas las puertas en el Perú de los años 50.

Pero lo anterior no es suficiente para explicar la atracción que Carlos Monge Cassinelli ejerció sobre muchos jóvenes médicos y biólogos peruanos, sin duda es una personalidad carismática en el sentido weberiano.

Ésta es una breve descripción de la fructífera vida de Carlos Monge Cassinelli y su repercusión en el desarrollo de la actividad médicocientífica del Perú; pese a su parquedad evidencia lo valioso del hombre a quien la UPCH y sus discípulos rinden homenaje en este volumen.

Roger Guerra García
Rector - Universidad Peruana Cayetano Heredia
Lima, junio de 1993

SEMBLANZA DEL DR. CARLOS MONGE CASSINELLI *

Fabiola León-Velarde S.

Carlos Monge Cassinelli se ha hecho acreedor a una posición especial, tanto en su actividad académica, como en la historia de la fisiología de adaptación a la altura. Hijo de Carlos Monge Medrano, descubridor del Mal de Montaña Crónico (actualmente llamado Enfermedad de Monge) y fundador del Instituto de Biología Andina (IBA, 1930), se vió inmerso desde niño en el mundo del estudio del hombre andino lo que probablemente gravitó decisivamente en su orientación. Sin embargo, fueron sus inclinaciones personales e intensas hacia la investigación, las que lo llevaron a ocupar el lugar que hoy ocupa.

Realizó sus estudios de medicina en la Universidad Nacional Mayor de San Marcos (UNMSM) entre los años 1938 y 1947. Como estudiante de medicina, trabajó intensamente con el Dr. Alberto Hurtado, Director de Investigaciones del Instituto de Biología Andina y fundador del Instituto de Investigaciones de la Altura (IIA, 1961) en fisiología humana (1), llevando a cabo estudios en el habitante de Morococha (4,5400 m). En esta etapa, confirma trabajos preliminares que mostraban disminución de la concentración de glucosa en sangre en condiciones basales y de la concentración de ácido láctico en condiciones de ejercicio en comparación con lo encontrado a nivel del mar. El aporte de su trabajo radica en que da a conocer por primera vez lo que posteriormente sería conocida como «la paradoja del lactato», todavía hoy materia de estudio por la comunidad científica nacional e internacional (3).

Se graduó como médico en la Universidad Nacional Mayor de San Marcos (UNMSM) en 1948. En el mismo año recibió una beca de la Fundación Rockefeller por dos años como investigador médico en el Hospital Johns Hopkins (Escuela de Medicina), donde trabajó con el Dr. Elliot Newman en fisiología renal. Al regreso de John Hopkins, en 1950, fue nombrado

---

* Las referencias bibliográficas entre paréntesis corresponden a la bibliografía citada en el *Curriculum Vitae* del Dr. Carlos Monge C. (página 28 de este volumen).

Profesor Asistente en la UNMSM de Lima, e inició su actividad en el campo de la nefrología. Introdujo el uso del riñón artificial en el Perú, y la enseñanza del capítulo de agua y electrolitos en Medicina y Cirugía (9; 13; 14; 15; 16).

En 1953 pasó un año en la Clínica Cleveland como investigador médico donde desarrolló un método para la medida del hexametonio en sangre, mostrando su distribución extracelular (6). A su regreso desarrolló una intensa actividad de investigación de la función renal en el habitante de las grandes alturas, produciendo el mayor número de contribuciones en este campo en la literatura internacional. Sus trabajos mostraron una correlación inversa entre el hematocrito y el flujo plasmático renal, entre el hematocrito y la función de filtración con autoregulación de la filtración glomerular (27). Demostró que pese a estos cambios glomerulares, las funciones tubulares de concentración, diuresis osmótica, eliminación de protones y de bicarbonato se encontraban normales (24; 38; 39; 40). Hasta el momento estas contribuciones permanecen como únicas en el campo de la fisiología renal. También en este campo, en sus estudios de fisiología comparada, describió por primera vez el papel de la cloaca de la serpiente en la reabsorción de agua y electrolitos (25; 28). Estudió asimismo la reabsorción de agua y electrolitos en bufos (sapos) con ligadura bilateral de uréteres para evaluar su regulación a través de la piel (20). Sumó a este trabajo, experimentos sobre el papel de la vejiga urinaria de bufos estudiados *in-vivo* (23).

En 1961, formó parte del grupo de profesores que decidieron emprender la tarea de crear la Universidad Peruana de Ciencias Médicas y Biológicas (años después Cayetano Heredia), una nueva Escuela de Medicina dedicada a la docencia, el servicio y la investigación.

Algunos años después, se interesó por el estudio de la policitemia de altura, reiniciando trabajos que había llevado a cabo como estudiante de medicina integrando el equipo del Dr. Alberto Hurtado. En 1966 Carlos Monge Medrano y Carlos Monge Cassinelli, son invitados por el editor I. Newton Kugelmass, de la compañia editora Charles L. Thomas, a escribir un libro sobre enfermedades de altura (30), donde por primera vez se presentan ideas conjuntas basadas en la experiencia de ambos autores. Su más importante contribución en este campo ha sido mostrar que el hematocrito se eleva significativamente con la edad en las grandes alturas. Propuso la posibilidad de que la enfermedad de Monge o mal de montaña crónico sea una falta de adaptación de la *población* a las grandes alturas, y no una entidad clínica que afecta a algunos *individuos* (29; 42; 44). Posteriormente, demostró que la normal disminución de la ventilación con la edad va asociada a un aumento del hematocrito, agregando una posible relación causal entre la caída de la ventilación con la edad y la correspondiente elevación del hematocrito (46). El tratar de definir los mecanismos fisiopatológicos que dan lugar a la aparición del Mal de Montaña Crónico ha sido el propósito de su constante interés en los modelos matemáticos, con los que confirmó las correlaciones fisiológicas

mencionadas, indicó que la edad es la causa de la caída de la ventilación y el aumento del hematocrito (50), y cuantificó el concepto de una concentración de hemoglobina óptima (62; 64). Éste ya era manejado por otros autores, mas su modelo brindó una base matemática a los hallazgos experimentales.

En los últimos años, un trabajo de tipo epidemiológico, llevado a cabo por sus asociados, confirma la tendencia de la población minera andina a tener eritrocitosis excesivas para la altura de residencia en función de la edad (92; 108; 111). A pesar de ser su interés principal las ciencias básicas, sus estudios relacionados al efecto de la edad en la eritremia de altura, han contribuido al reconocimiento de que el mal de montaña crónico constituye un problema de salud pública para la población de altura. En este sentido ha planteado la necesidad de expresar los riesgos de pérdida de la salud en la altura en términos exponenciales y no lineares, mostrando su preocupación constante por los mineros, principales víctimas de los efectos negativos de la hipoxia crónica cuanto mayor es la altura de trabajo y/o de residencia; el trabajo, «El Mal de Montaña Crónico y la Salud de la Población Andina», muestra esta preocupación (78).

Como miembro de más de 20 expediciones internacionales a regiones como los Andes peruanos y chilenos en numerosas oportunidades, y a los Himalayas en Nepal en 1985, estudió principalmente tópicos hematológicos como afinidad de la hemoglobina por el oxígeno (75) y la respuesta a la sangría (74), entre otros. Sus conclusiones han sido siempre que la eritremia de altura no es una adaptación adecuada y que el diseño fisiológico del hombre andino corresponde al diseño de nivel del mar. Su clásica gráfica log-log relacionando el P50 al peso animal permite diferenciar estos dos grupos de animales, y muestra que el humano de altura pertenece al grupo de animales de nivel del mar que sólo tienen adaptación fenotípica (48). Estos resultados son extensibles a los animales domésticos que los españoles trajeron a Sudamérica e introdujeron en los Andes.

Con sus asociados de la UPCH demostró que el embrión del ave de altura tiene niveles adaptativos en la cáscara y en la membrana corioalantoidea. Los estudios en la cáscara de aves andinas mostraron cómo la selección natural escoge la reducción de la porosidad hasta una altura cercana a 3,000 m para aumentarla luego, regresando a cifras cercanas a nivel del mar. Estos trabajos pusieron en evidencia la competencia biológica entre agua y oxígeno, en donde la primera es favorecida hasta los 3,000 m de altura, y el segundo a partir de esta altura (67; 84). Los estudios en la membrana corioalantoidea de huevos de la gallareta andina y de nivel del mar, mostraron 2 niveles adaptativos; el primero consiste en una reducción del consumo de oxígeno sin sacrificio del crecimiento embrionario, y el segundo un aumento de la conductancia de la membrana corioalantoidea (87). Mostraron además, que la cámara de aire del huevo de gaviota andina tiene cifras de presión de CO_2 y O_2 semejantes a la de los alveolos pulmonares de humanos residentes de alturas equivalentes. Estos hallazgos los llevaron a concluir que el fenómeno difusivo que se da a través de la cáscara del huevo es suficiente para establecer los valores que aparecen en mamíferos y aves adultos utilizando la respiración pulmonar. Señalan que el proceso convectivo pulmonar más bien se ajusta, y no origina, las cifras basales de presiones parciales de los gases alveolares, y es el proceso difusivo el que las establece.

Para probar si la alta afinidad de la hemoglobina de mamíferos y aves genéticamente adaptados a la altura se encuentra también en ectotermos, en quienes el frío favorece la adaptación, estudió con Hrvoj Ostojic 3 subespecies de bufo de nivel del mar, de 3,100 m y de 4540 m de altura. Encontraron que la afinidad es mayor en los bufo de altura, aún a temperaturas de nivel del mar. A temperatura ecológica la afinidad de la hemoglobina de los bufos de altura aumenta marcadamente (81). Estos trabajos muestran la sensibilidad de la hemoglobina de experimentar cambios genéticos en relación al ambiente hipóxico aún moderado. Un paso significativo en esta interpretación se da cuando sus colaboradores encuentran que gallinas de altura (Taraco, Puno, 3800 m), presentes en el continente Sudamericano tan sólo desde la conquista española, han experimentado un cambio genético traducido por la presencia de hemoglobina de alta afinidad. La importancia de este hallazgo radica en que se muestra por primera vez, en vertebrados, que se puede seleccionar un cambio genético en la molécula de la hemoglobina, en el breve período evolutivo de 500 años (101). Carlos Monge Cassinelli estableció una clara diferencia entre animales con adaptación fenotípica y animales con adaptación genotípica, en quienes la selección opera simultáneamente sobre genes que controlan independientemente los complejos procesos fisiológicos de: la ventilación pulmonar, la afinidad de la hemoglobina por el oxígeno, y la eritremia de altura.

Carlos Monge Cassinelli ha logrado transferir la información de la fisiología comparada de la adaptación natural a la altura a la epidemiología de la enfermedad de Monge, logrando así una integración del conocimiento desde la fisiología básica hasta estudios médicos del mal de montaña crónico. El último artículo de este libro, escrito por Peter Hochachka, de la Universidad de British Columbia describe este proceso dentro de lo que el autor llama: «transferability».

Si bien la actividad académica de Carlos Monge Cassinelli queda apretadamente resumida en los párrafos anteriores, continuar su semblanza sólo en términos impersonales, sería difícil en relación a la riqueza de su personalidad. Ésta se pone de manifiesto ya desde su manera «biológica» de ver la vida y la ciencia. Utiliza frecuentemente el concepto de selección natural, de la teoría evolutiva de Charles Darwin, refiriéndose a los «seleccionados naturalmente para no hacer ciencia». Éstos son para él, quienes abandonan el campo de la investigación científica por las dificultades que ofrece hacer ciencia en el Perú. Los «seleccionados naturalmente», son aquellos con la capacidad de sobreponer a todo, el deseo de hacer investigación, como lo dijo Julio C. Tello en 1922. Este concepto, no es para él un lenguaje simbólico, sino una proposición que ha puesto y sigue poniendo en práctica todos los días de su vida, tal vez muchas veces a costa de sacrificios personales y familiares. En el Perú, como en otros países de Latinoamérica, es una persona extraordinaria quien como Choclo dedica toda una vida a la investigación con absoluto desinterés por el poder al cual pudo acceder sin dificultad en base a sus conocimientos y méritos.

Su pasión por el trabajo de laboratorio, su poco entusiasmo por la actividad administrativa, y su manera horizontal de ver las relaciones humanas y laborales también se expresó claramente cuando ocupaba el cargo de Jefe del Departamento de Medicina. Siempre consideró que el paternalismo y el control autocrático no son indispensables para desarrollar el potencial de un grupo humano, y siendo fiel a su pensamiento decía entonces: «los departamentos acéfalos son los que mejor caminan», dejando el funcionamiento del mismo a cargo de los profesores asistentes, quienes con gran éxito organizaron y manejaron el departamento, continuando él, en el ejercicio de su pasión, la investigación.

El compromiso con la ciencia Monge lo consiguió sin aspaviento alguno, con la dedicación intensa que pone en cada uno de sus experimentos, por más rutinarios que éstos sean, y en transmitir sus conocimientos a sus alumnos con esa claridad y sencillez propia de quien no necesita hacer inútiles alardes, pero sí tiene en cambio mucho que enseñar. Lo mostró en su afán de no perder ni un minuto de contacto con su laboratorio, cuando éste se encontraba en remodelación; él no pudo dejar de trabajar; fue una imagen propia de la realidad fantástica de García Marquez, verlo entre cemento, ladrillos, martillazos y una decena de obreros, fumando su pipa y pensando en algún modelo teórico (o tal vez en su propia filosofía de la vida), sin parar, porque su dedicación a la ciencia, más allá del tiempo y condiciones razonables, es independiente de todo factor externo.

No quisiera terminar sin expresar que ha sido, y sigue siendo, un placer trabajar con Choclo desde hace 18 años; nunca lo ví dejar de trabajar a pesar de los tremendos problemas sociales y económicos del Perú. Me enseñó a conocer lo que es ser científico, en un medio donde la ciencia se confunde fácilmente con el voluntarismo; su trayectoria es ejemplo de lo que es posible hacer en investigación, aún cuando otras personas lo asumen como imposible. Aprendí mucho de él, no sólo como científico, sino también, y tal vez lo más importante, como ser humano. Considero que la recopilación de las contribuciones más importantes en el campo de fisiología de adaptación a la altura en este volumen jubilar, es el mejor tributo que podemos rendirle al maestro, al colega, al amigo.

Lima, junio de 1993

CURRICULUM VITAE

Nombre: Carlos Monge Cassinelli.
Fecha de nacimiento: Primero de setiembre de 1921.

EDUCACIÓN

Abril 1938 - Marzo 1940: Estudios prémedicos, Facultad de Medicina, Universidad de San Marcos, Lima, Perú.

Abril 1940 - Marzo 1947, Estudios de medicina, Facultad de Medicina, Universidad de San Marcos, Lima, Perú.

Setiembre 1948 - Setiembre 1950, Fellow, Departamento de Medicina, The Johns Hopkins Hospital, Baltimore, Maryland, USA.

Marzo 1953 - Diciembre 1953, Research Fellow, Cleveland Clinic and F.E. Bunts Educational Institute, Cleveland, Ohio, USA.

POSICIONES ACADÉMICAS

1948-1950, Instructor, Facultad de Medicina, Universidad de San Marcos, Lima, Perú.

1950-1958, Profesor Asistente, Facultad de Medicina, Universidad de San Marcos, Lima, Perú.

1958-1962, Profesor Asociado, Facultad de Medicina, Universidad de San Marcos, Lima, Perú.

1962-1985, Profesor Principal de Medicina, Departamento de Medicina, Universidad Peruana Cayetano Heredia, Lima, Perú.

1962 - hasta la fecha, Investigador Principal, Instituto de Investigaciones de la Altura, Universidad Peruana Cayetano Heredia, Lima, Perú.

1963, Profesor visitante, Departamento de Medicina, Vanderbilt University, Nashville, Tennessee, USA.

1966, Profesor visitante, Departamento de Medicina, The Johns Hopkins School of Medicine, Baltimore, Maryland, USA.

1970-1973, Rector, Universidad Peruana Cayetano Heredia, Lima, Perú.

1982-1986, Profesor Invitado, University of Miami School of Medicine, Miami, Florida, USA.

1986, Profesor Visitante, Institut fur Cardiologie und Physiologie, University of Erlangen, Alemania.

1985 - 1991, Profesor Principal de Fisiología, Departamento de Ciencias Fisiológicas, Universidad Peruana Cayetano Heredia, Lima, Perú.

1991-hasta la fecha, Profesor Investigador en este mismo departamento.

RECONOCIMIENTOS, NOMBRAMIENTOS Y OTROS HONORES:

1948-1950, Fellow, Rockefeller Foundation, The Johns Hopkins School of Medicine, Baltimore, Maryland, USA.

1953, Fellow, Cleveland Clinic, Cleveland, Ohio, USA.

1956, Miembro, Academia de Medicina, Lima, Perú.

1956, Fellow en Educación Médica, Rockefeller Foundation, Brasil.

1957, Premio Nacional de Cultura, Lima, Perú.

1957, Fellow, Kellog Foundation, Educación Médica, Colombia.

1961, Fellow en Nefrología, Rockefeller Foundation

1964, Fellow, Rockefeller Foundation, Fisiología renal, Brasil.

1972, Premio Cultural Andrés Bello, Caracas, Venezuela.

1973, Fellow, Churchill College, Department of Physiology, University of Cambridge, Cambridge, UK.

1975, Scholar, The Johns Hopkins University, Baltimore, Maryland, USA.

1976 - 1983, Comité de investigación, Organización Panamericana de la Salud, Washington, D.C., USA.

1978, Miembro Honorario, American College of Physicians.

1979, Scholar, Fogarty International Center, National Institutes of Health, Bethesda, Maryland, USA.

1980, Honorary Faculty Member, University of Alabama, Birmingham, Alabama, USA.

1980 - 1981, Scholar in Residence, Fogarty International Center, National Insitutes of health, Bethesda, Maryland, USA.

1983, Miembro Honorario de la Academia de Medicina, Chile.

1983, Miembro Fundador, Academia de Ciencias de Latino América.

1992, Palmas Magisteriales en el Grado de Amauta, Lima, Perú.

PUBLICACIONES

ABSTRACTOS

1. MONGE-C., C., R. LOZANO, C. MARCHENA, J. WHITTEMBURY & C. TORRES. 1968. Kidney function in the high altitude native [Abstract]. International Symposium on Altitude and Cold. Aspen, Colorado. Sept. 2-6.

2. RENNIE, D. B., R. LOZANO, C. MONGE-C., F. SIME & J. WHITTEMBURY. 1970. Renal hemodynamics and oxygenation in Peruvian natives living permanently at 4300 meters (14,200 feet) [Abstract]. *J. Clin. Invest.* 49: 792.

3. WINSLOW, R. M., C. MONGE-C., N. J. STATHAM, C. C. GIBSON, S. CHARACHE & J. WHITTEMBURY. 1978. Variable blood oxygen affinity in natives of high altitude [Abstract]. Am. Soc. Hematology.

4. CORREA, A. M., C. MONGE-C. & J. WHITTEMBURY. 1979. Hematología corporal y cerebral en ratones blancos aclimatados a la hipoxia hipobárica equivalente a 4,500 m de altura (Abstracto 152). *In: II Jornadas científicas: programa y abstractos.* Lima: Universidad Peruana Cayetano Heredia, , p. 182.

5. LEÓN-VELARDE, F., C. MONGE-C. & J. WHITTEMBURY. 1979. Metabolismo energético máximo en ratones blancos aclimatados a la hipoxia hipobárica equivalente a 4,500 m de altura (Abstracto 149). *In: II Jornadas científicas: programa y abstractos.* Lima: Universidad Peruana Cayetano Heredia, p. 179.

6. MONGE-C., C., F. LEÓN-VELARDE & J. WHITTEMBURY. 1979. Ventajas de la hipoxia hipobárica experimental intermitente como modelo de aclimatación a la altura. Consideraciones teóricas (Abstracto 151). *In: II Jornadas científicas: programa y abstractos.* Lima: Universidad Peruana Cayetano Heredia, p. 181.

7. MORÁN, O., H. OSTOJIC & C. MONGE-C. 1979. Afinidad de la hemoglobina por el oxígeno en tres subespecies de anuros (Abstracto 146). *In: II Jornadas científicas: programa y abstractos.* Lima: Universidad Peruana Cayetano Heredia, p. 176.

8. MORÁN, O., H. OSTOJIC & C. MONGE-C. 1979., Efecto de la temperatura sobre la afinidad de la hemoglobina por el oxígeno en tres subespecies de Bufo spinolosus (Abstracto 147). *In: II Jornadas científicas: programa y abstractos.* Lima: Universidad Peruana Cayetano Heredia, p. 177.

9. MORÁN, O., H. OSTOJIC & C. MONGE-C. 1979. Efecto del pH en la afinidad de la hemoglobina por el oxígeno en tres subespecies de anfibios (Abstracto 148). *In: II Jornadas científicas: programa y abstractos.* Lima: Universidad Peruana Cayetano Heredia, p. 178.

10. KROUSKOP, R. W., E. G. BROWN, F. E. MCDONNELL, R. M. WINSLOW, C. MONGE-C., N. J. STATHAM & F. H. SARNSQUIST. 1982. Continuous measurement of oxygen transport [Abstract]. *In: Hypoxia: man at altitude*, edited by J. R. Sutton, N. L. Jones and C. S. Houston. New York: Thieme-Stratton, p. 200.

11. WINSLOW R. M., C. MONGE-C. & N. J. STATHAM. 1982. In vivo blood oxygen affinity in high altitude natives [Abstract]. *In: Hypoxia: man at altitude*, edited by J. R. Sutton, N. L. Jones and C. S. Houston. New York: Thieme-Stratton, p. 202.

12. CARRILLO, A. P., A. BRYCE, F. AMAT Y LEÓN, C. MONGE-C., M. ROITMAN, C. DEL RÍO & C. SOTO. 1983. M-mode echocardiographic study in healthy men born and living at high altitude [Abstract]. *J. Am. Coll. Cardiol.* 1: 592.

13. LEÓN-VELARDE, F., J. WHITTEMBURY, C. CAREY, H. RAHN & C. MONGE-C. 1983. Modification of eggshell conductance to gases in avian eggs laid at high altitudes [Abstract]. *In: Hypoxia, exercise, and altitude.* Proceedings of the Third Banff International Hypoxia Symposium, edited by J. R. Sutton, C. S. Houston and N. L. Jones. New York: Alan R. Liss, p. 462-463.

14. CAREY, C., F. LEÓN-VELARDE, G. CASTRO & C. MONGE-C. 1985. Adaptation of avian eggs to high altitudes in the Peruvian Andes (Abstract 18). Fourth Joint Meeting of the Wilson Ornithological Society and the Cooper Ornithological Society. University of Colorado, Boulder.

15. LEÓN-VELARDE, F., C. MONGE-C. & J. WHITTEMBURY. 1985. Consumo de oxígeno y respiración mitocondrial en ratones sometidos a hipoxia hipobárica intermitente (Resumen 199). *In: III Jornadas científicas.* Lima: Universidad Peruana Cayetano Heredia, p. 238.

16. CAREY, C., F. LEÓN-VELARDE & C. MONGE-C. 1987. Physiological adaptations of avian embryos and morphological adaptations of eggshells to low barometric pressure in the Peruvian Andes (Abstract 57.6). *Physiologist* 30: 195.

17. LEÓN-VELARDE, F., C. MONGE-C., A. VIDAL, M. CARCAGNO, M. CRISCUOLO, A. ARREGUI & C. E. BOZZINI. 1989. Eritropoyetina inmuno-reactiva en suero de mineros sanos nativos de Cerro de Pasco (4,300 m) (Abstracto 286). Medicina (B. Aires) 49: 494.

18. ESPINOZA, D., F. LEÓN-VELARDE, M. RIVERA CH., A. PALACIOS, M. VARGAS & C. MONGE-C. 1990. Hemoglobina de alta afinidad en gallinas de altura (Resumen 11). *In: VI Jornadas Científicas.* Lima: Univ. Peruana Cayetano Heredia, p. 84.

19. IZAGUIRRE, V., M. VARGAS, F. LEÓN-VELARDE, A. ARREGUI & C. MONGE-C. 1990. Efecto del Prazosin (bloqueador a1) sobre la respuesta del hematocrito a la hipoxia (Resumen 12). *In: VI Jornadas Científicas.* Lima: Univ. Peruana Cayetano Heredia, p. 85.

20. LEÓN-VELARDE, F., C. MONGE-C., A. ARREGUI & C. STANLEY. 1990. Increased prevalence of excessive erythrocytosis with age in healthy high altitude miners (Abstract 20). *In: Hypoxia: the adaptations*, edited by J.R. Sutton, G. Coates and J.E. Remmers. Toronto: B.C. Decker, p. 280.

21. LEÓN-VELARDE, F., C. MONGE-C., A. VIDAL, M. CARCAGNO, M. CRISCUOLO, A. ARREGUI & C. E. BOZZINI. 1990. Eritropoyetina inmuno-reactiva en mineros de Cerro de Pasco (4,300 m) con policitemia excesiva. (Resumen 7). *In: VI Jornadas Científicas.* Lima: Univ. Peruana Cayetano Heredia, p. 80.

22. LEÓN-VELARDE, F., A. PALACIOS, M. VARGAS & C. MONGE-C. 1990. Afinidad de la hemoglobina por el O_2 y equilibrio ácido-base en patos (*Cairina moschata*) llevados a la altura a la semana de nacidos y al año de edad (Resumen 10). *In: VI Jornadas Científicas*. Lima: Univ. Peruana Cayetano Heredia, p. 83.

23. LEÓN-VELARDE, F., R. TAPIA & C. MONGE-C. 1990. Desarrollo e hipertrofia cardíaca en patos (*Cairina moschata*) llevados a la altura (4,300 m) a la semana de nacidos y al año de edad (Resumen 6). *In: VI Jornadas Científicas*. Lima: Univ. Peruana Cayetano Heredia, p. 78.

24. PALACIOS, A., F. LEÓN-VELARDE & C. MONGE-C. 1990. Transporte de oxígeno en embriones de pato muscovy (*Cairina moschata*) (Resumen 9). *In: VI Jornadas Científicas*. Lima: Univ. Peruana Cayetano Heredia, p. 82.

25. RIVERA CH., M., D. ESPINOZA & C. MONGE-C. 1990. Efecto del cianato de sodio sobre la afinidad de la hemoglobina por el oxígeno y la respuesta eritrocítica en hipoxia crónica (Resumen 8). *In: VI Jornadas Científicas*. Lima: Univ. Peruana Cayetano Heredia, p. 81.

26. RIVERA CH., M., M. VARGAS, O. DUNIN-BORKOWSKI, F. LEÓN-VELARDE, L. HUICHO, & C. MONGE-C. 1990. Efectos metabólicos del cianato de sodio en ratones a nivel del mar y en condiciones de hipoxia hipobárica intermitente crónica (Resumen 5). *In: VI Jornadas Científicas*. Lima: Univ. Peruana Cayetano Heredia, p. 77.

27. LEÓN-VELARDE, F., A. ARREGUI & C. MONGE-C. 1991. Fisiopatología del mal de montaña crónico. (Physiopathology of chronic mountain sickness) [Abstract]. *In: VI Reunión Científica Anual*, Sociedad Chilena de Ciencias Fisiológicas, Santiago.

28. MONGE-C., C., F. LEÓN-VELARDE & C. E. BOZZINI. 1991. Chronic mountain sickness: excessive erythrocytosis and/or excessive hypoxemia [Abstract]. *In: Neurobiology and cell physiology of chemoreception: abstracts*. International Symposium on Arterial Chemoreception, Chieti, IT, in Press.

LIBROS Y ARTÍCULOS

1. HURTADO, A., H. ASTE, C. MERINO, T. VELÁSQUEZ, C. MONGE-C. & C. REYNAFARJE. 1947. Physiological characteristics of flight personnel. *J. Aviation Med.* 18: 406.

2. MONGE-M., C., L. CONTRERAS, M. T. VELÁSQUEZ, C. REYNAFARJE & C. MONGE-C. 1948. Physiological adaptations of dwellers in the tropics. *In: Proceedings of the Fourth International Congresses on Tropical Medicine and Malaria.* Washington, DC: U.S. Government Printing Office, p. 136-147.

3. MONGE-C., C. 1949. Glucosa, ácido láctico y ácido pirúvico a nivel del mar y en la altura (Tesis Bachiller). *An. Fac. Med. (Lima)* 32: 1-28, .

4. NEWMAN, E. V., M. MERREL, A. GENECIN, C. MONGE-C., W. R. MILNOR & W. P. MCKEEVER. 1951. The dye dilution method for describing the central circulation. An analysis of factors shaping the time concentration curves. *Circulation* 4: 735, .

5. MONGE-C., C. & A. CAZORLA T. 1952. Valores normales de sodio y potasio en suero sanguíneo. *An. Fac. Med. (Lima)* 35: 303-307.

6. MONGE-C., C., A. C. CORCORAN, F. DEL GRECO & I. H. PAGE. 1954. Volume of distribution of hexamethonium in nephrectomized dogs. *Am. J. Physiol.* 178: 256.

7. MONGE-M., C., J. VELLARD, C. MONGE-C. & A. CAZORLA T. 1954. Aclimatación en los Andes: antropología fisiológica comparada del hombre del altiplano (Forma y función del torax). *Perú Indígena* 5: 9-21.

8. MONGE-C., C., A. CAZORLA T., G. WHITTEMBURY M., Y. SAKATA B. & C. RIZO-PATRÓN. 1955. A description of the circulatory dynamics in the heart and lungs of people at sea level and at high altitude by means of the dye dilution technique. *Acta Physiol. Latinoam.* 5: 198-210.

9. WHITTEMBURY M., G., M. RAMÍREZ V., J. FERNÁNDEZ Ñ. & C. MONGE-C. 1955. A normographic system for calculation of water requirements. *Acta Physiol. Latinoam.* 5: 117-121.

10. FERNÁNDEZ Ñ., J., M. RAMÍREZ V., G. WHITTEMBURY M. & C. MONGE-C. 1956. El método de microdifusión de Conway: su aplicación a la determinación de amoniaco, úrea y nitrógeno no proteico. *Rev. Patol. Clin. (Lima)* 1: 50-58.

11. MONGE-C., C. 1956. La acción hipotensora del nitroprusiato. Aplicaciones terapéuticas. *An. Fac. Med. (Lima)* 39: 1330-1332.

12. WHITTEMBURY M., G., A. CAZORLA T. & C. MONGE-C. 1956. Description of the circulatory dynamics in the heart and lungs in mitral stenosis by means of the dye dilution technique. *Acta Physiol. Latinoam.* 6: 15.

13. FERNÁNDEZ Ñ., J., G. WHITTEMBURY M., M. RAMÍREZ V. & C. MONGE-C. 1957. Variaciones del potasio plasmático en la sangre conservada a diferentes temperaturas. *Rev. Patol. Clin. (Lima)* 1: 48-56.

14. WHITTEMBURY M., G., M. RAMÍREZ V., J. FERNÁNDEZ Ñ. & C. MONGE-C. 1957. The use of high resistance voltmeters in the determination of biological chlorides. *Acta Physiol. Latinoam.* 7: 76.

15. WHITTEMBURY M., G., J. FERNÁNDEZ Ñ., M. RAMÍREZ V. & C. MONGE-C. 1958. On the artificial kidney. 1. Testing of the disposable Kolff-Coil kidney. *Acta Physiol. Latinoam.* 8: 1.

16. MONGE-C., C. 1959. La insuficiencia renal glomerular. (Evaluación cuantitativa e inter-relaciones funcionales) (Tesis Doctoral). *An. Fac. Med. (Lima)* 42: 547-579.

17. MONGE-C., C., M. RAMÍREZ V., J. FERNÁNDEZ Ñ., E. & HORNA C. 1959. Relationships between serum creatinine with endogenous creatinine clearance and urinary creatinine. Acta Physiol. Latinoam. 9: 50, .

18. MONGE-C., C., C. TORRES, J. FERNÁNDEZ Ñ. & M. RAMÍREZ V. 1959. *Relación funcional entre creatinina, úrea y sulfatos inorgánicos en la insuficiencia renal glomerular.* XXI Congreso Internacional de Ciencias Fisiológicas. Buenos Aires, Argentina.

19. MONGE-C., C., C. TORRES & M. RAMÍREZ V. 1961. Interrelationships between serum creatinine, urea, sulphate and endogenous creatinine clearance in man. *Acta Physiol. Latinoam.* 11: 4-9.

20. MONGE-C., C. 1962. Effect of bilateral ligature of ureters on the concentration of sodium, potassium, urea and total solutes in the plasma of toads. *Nature (Lond.)* 193: 1183.

21. MONGE-C., C. & E. FERNÁNDEZ (Introd. by CARLOS MONGE-M.). 1962. Effect of cyanide on the double perfused toad kidney. *Fed. Proc.* 21: 2.

22. RAMÍREZ V., M. & C. MONGE-C. 1962. Glycerine extract of water melon (*citrulus vulgaris*) seeds as a source of urease. *Acta. Physiol. Lationam.* 12: 210.

23. MONGE-C., C. 1963. Water balance in toads: role of the urinary bladder. *Acta Physiol. Latinoam.* 13: 255-259.

24. MONGE-C., C., R. LOZANO & A. CARCELÉN. 1964. Renal excretion of bicarbonate in high altitude natives and in natives with chronic mountain sickness. *J. Clin. Invest.* 43: 2303-2309.

25. JUNQUEIRA, L.C.U., G. MALNIC & C. MONGE-C. 1964. Note on the function of the ophidian cloaca. *An. Acad. Bras. Cienc.* 36: 311-312.

26. MONGE-C., C., R. LOZANO & J. WHITTEMBURY. 1965. Effect of blood-letting on chronic mountain sickness (Letter). *Nature (Lond.)* 207: 770.

27. LOZANO R. & C. MONGE-C. 1965. Renal function in high-altitude natives and in natives with chronic mountain sickness. *J. Appl. Physiol.* 20: 1026-1027.

28. JUNQUEIRA, L. C. U., G. MALNIC & C. MONGE-C. 1966. Reabsortion function of the ophidean cloaca and large intestine. *Physiol. Zool.* 39: 151.

29. MONGE-C., C. 1966. Natural acclimatization to high altitudes: clinical conditions. *In: Life at high altitudes.* Washington, DC: Pan American Health Organization, p. 46-48.

30. MONGE M., C. & C. MONGE-C. 1966. *High altitude diseases: mechanism and management.* Springfield, Il: Charles C. Thomas.

31. MONGE M., C. & C. MONGE-C. 1967. Adaptación biológica de las sociedades sud americanas a las grandes alturas. *Peru Indígena* 26: 1-20.

32. MONGE M., C. & C. MONGE-C. 1967. Mal de montaña crónico. *In: 8° Congreso Internacional de Medicina Interna.* Buenos Aires: Bartolomé U. Chiesino, p. 305-315.

33. MONGE M., C. & C. MONGE-C. 1968. Adaptation to high altitude. *In: Adaptation of domestic animals,* edited by E.S.E. Hafez. Philadelphia: Lea & Febiger, p. 194-201.

34. MONGE M., C. & C. MONGE-C. 1968. Adaptación de los animales domésticos: adaptación a las grandes alturas. *Arch. Inst. Biol. Andina* 2: 276-291.

35. WHITTEMBURY, J., R. LOZANO & C. MONGE-C. 1968. Influence of cell concentration in the electrometric determination of blood pH. *Acta Physiol. Latinoam.* 18: 263-265.

36. WHITTEMBURY, J., R. LOZANO, C. TORRES & C. MONGE-C. 1968. Blood viscosity in high altitude polycythemia. *Acta Physiol. Latinoam.* 18: 355-359.

37. LOZANO R., C. TORRES, C. MARCHENA, J. WHITTEMBURY & C. MONGE-C. 1969. Response to metabolic (ammonium chloride) acidosis at sea level and at high altitude. *Nephron* 6: 102-109.

38. MONGE-C., C., R. LOZANO, C. MARCHENA, J. WHITTEMBURY & C. TORRES. 1969. Kidney function in the high-altitude native. *Fed. Proc.* 28: 1199-1203.

39. TORRES C., R. LOZANO, J. WHITTEMBURY & C. MONGE-C. 1970. Effect of angiotensin on the kidney of the high altitude native. *Nephron* 7: 489-498 .

40. RENNIE, D. B., R. LOZANO, C. MONGE-C., F. SIME & J. WHITTEMBURY. 1971. Renal oxygenation in male Peruvian natives living permanently at high altitude. *J. Appl. Physiol.* 30: 450-456.

41. RENNIE, D. B., E. A. MARTICORENA, C. MONGE-C. & L. SIROTZKY. 1971. Urinary protein excretion in high-altitude residents. *J. Appl. Physiol.* 31: 257-259.

42. WHITTEMBURY, J. & C. MONGE-C. 1972. High altitude, haematocrit and age. *Nature (Lond.)* 238: 278-279.

43. GUERRERO, C., T. KIRCHHAUSEN, V. DIAZ LAU, C. MONGE-C. & J. WHITTEMBURY. 1973. PH intracelular de músculo de pata de rata. *Anales Científicos (Lima)* 11: 14-1.

44. MONGE-C., C. & J. WHITTEMBURY. 1973. Homo montanus. *Bild Wiss.*: 251-256.

45. MONGE-C., C. & J. WHITTEMBURY. 1974. Increased hemoglobin-oxygen affinity at extremely high altitudes (Letter). *Science* 186: 843.

46. SIME, F., C. MONGE-C. & J. WHITTEMBURY. 1975. Age as a cause of chronic mountain sickness (Monge's disease). *Int. J. Biometeorol.* 19: 93-98.

47. ZEUTHEN, T. & C. MONGE-C. 1975 Intra- and extracellular gradients of electrical potential and ion activities of the epithelial cells of the rabbit ileum in vivo recorded by microelectrodes. *Philos. Trans. R. Soc. Lond. [Biol.].* 71: 277-281.

48. MONGE-C., C. & J. WHITTEMBURY. 1976. High altitude adaptations in the whole animal. *In: Environmental physiology of animals,* edited by J. Bligh, J. L. Cloudsley-Thompson and A. G. MacDonald. New York: John Wiley & Sons, p. 289-308.

49. MONGE-C., C. & J. WHITTEMBURY. 1976. Acclimatization of man and animals in the Andes. *In: Anthropologie des populations andines.* Paris: INSERM, p. 143-144.

50. MONGE-C., C. & J. WHITTEMBURY. 1976. Chronic mountain sickness. *Johns Hopkins Med. J.* 139: 87-89.

51. ZEUTHEN T. & C. MONGE-C. 1976. Electrical potential and ion activities in the epithelial cell layer of the rabbit ileum in vivo. *In: Ion and Enzyme Electrodes in Biology and Medicine.* Munchen: Urban & Schwarzenberg, p. 345-350.

52. MONGE-C., C. & C. VIDAL. 1977. La enseñanza de la medicina interna en la formación del médico. *Educ. Med. Salud (Lima)* 11: 375-388.

53. WHITTEMBURY, J. & C. MONGE-C. 1977. Cerebral blood-flow in polycythemia (Letter). *Lancet* 2: 923-924.

54. MONGE-C., C. 1978. Ecology and health. *Bull. Pan Amer. Health Organ.* 12: 7-10.

55. MONGE-C., C. 1979. La nutrición del paciente grave. *Diagnóstico (Perú)* 3: 28-29.

56. MORÁN, O., J. WHITTEMBURY, C. MONGE-C. & A. M. CORREA. 1979. Hipertrofia cardíaca en ratones sometidos a hipoxia intermitente. *Arch. Biol. Andina* 9: 13-20.

57. GONZÁLEZ, E., C. GUERRERO, C. MONGE-C. & J. WHITTEMBURY. 1980. Comparison of the use of nicotine and 5,5' - dimethyl - 2,4 - oxazolidinedione (DMO) in the measurement of red blood cell pH. *Acta Cient. Venez.* 31: 131-136.

58. GONZÁLEZ, E., C. MONGE-C. & J. WHITTEMBURY. 1980. Ionization constants of 5,5' - dimethyl - 2,4 - oxazolidinedione (DMO) and nicotine at temperatures and NaCl concentrations of biological interest. *Acta Cient. Venez.* 31: 128-130.

59. MONGE-C., C. & J. WHITTEMBURY. 1980. High-altitude research. *In: Biomedical research in Latin America: background studies,* edited by C. V. Kidd. Washington, DC: U.S. Department of Health, Education, and Welfare, p. 189-203. (NIH Publication, 80-2051).

60. WINSLOW, R. M., C. MONGE-C., N. J. STATHAM, C. G. GIBSON, S. CHARACHE, J. WHITTEMBURY, O. MORÁN & R. L. BERGER. 1981. Variability of oxygen affinity of blood: human subjects native to high altitude. *J. Appl. Physiol.* 51: 1411-1416.

61. KEYNES, R. J., G. W. SMITH, J. D. H. SLATER, M. M. BROWN, S. E. BROWN, N. N. PAYNE, T. P. JOWETT & C. MONGE-C. 1982. Renin and aldosterone at high altitude in man. *J. Endocrinol.* 92: 131-140.

62. MONGE-C., C. & J. WHITTEMBURY. 1982. Chronic mountain sickness and the physiopathology of hypoxemic polycythemia. *In: Hypoxia: man at altitude,* edited by J. R. Sutton, N. L. Jones and C. S. Houston. New York: Thieme-Stratton, p. 51-56.

63. MONGE-C., C. 1983. *La salud de la población: Tarea multidisciplinaria.* Seminario «Investigaciones para políticas de investigación». Chincha. Consejo Nacional de Población. Lima, Perú.

64. MONGE-C., C. 1983. Hemoglobin regulation in hypoxemic polycythemia. *In: Adjustment to high altitude,* edited by E. C. Chamberlayne and P. G. Condliffe. Bethesda, Md: U.S. Department of Health and Human Services, p. 53-56. (NIH Publication, 83-2496).

65. BONAVIA, D., F. LEÓN-VELARDE, C. MONGE-C., M. I. SÁNCHEZ-GRIÑÁN & J. WHITTEMBURY. 1984. Tras las huellas de Acosta 300 años después, consideraciones sobre su descripción del «Mal de altura». *Histórica (Lima)* 8: 1-31.

66. LEÓN-VELARDE, F., J. WHITTEMBURY, C. CAREY & C. MONGE-C. 1984. Shell characteristics of eggs laid at 2,800 m by hens transported from sea level 24 hours after hatching. *J. Exp. Zool.* 230: 137-139.

67. LEÓN-VELARDE, F., J. WHITTEMBURY, C. CAREY & C. MONGE-C. 1984. Permeability of eggshells of native chickens in the Peruvian Andes. *In: Respiration and metabolism of embryonic vertebrates,* edited by R. S. Seymour. Dordrecht, NL: Dr. W. Junk, p. 245-257.

68. BONAVIA, D., F. LEÓN-VELARDE, C. MONGE-C., M. SÁNCHEZ-GRIÑÁN & J. WHITTEMBURY. 1985. Acute mountain sickness: critical appraisal of the Pariacaca story and on-site study. *Respir. Physiol.* 62: 125-134.

69. BROWN, E. G., R. W. KROUSKOP, F. E. MCDONNELL, C. MONGE-C. & R. M. WINSLOW. 1985. A technique to continuously measure arteriovenous oxygen content difference and P50 in vivo. *J. Appl. Physiol.* 58: 1383-1389.

70. CASTILLO, C., J. WHITTEMBURY, O. MORÁN, A. BARCLAY, M. MUÑOZ & C. MONGE-C. 1985. Un modelo de hipoxia hipobárica intermitente en ratones: el ratón de Morococha. *Vultur* 1: 1-11.

71. CASTRO, G., C. CAREY, J. WHITTEMBURY & C. MONGE-C. 1985. Comparative responses of sea level and montane Rufous-collared sparrows, Zonotrichia capensis, to hypoxia and cold. Comp. Biochem. Physiol. [A] 82: 847-850.

72. MONGE-C., C. 1985. Bases biológicas del proceso de aclimatación a la altura. *Vultur* 1: 1-11.

73. MONGE-C., C. 1985. Alberto Hurtado Obituary. *Physiologist* 28: 100.

74. WINSLOW, R. M., C. MONGE C., E. G. BROWN, H. G. KLEIN, F. SARNQUIST, N. J. WINSLOW & S. S. MCKNEALLY. 1985. Effects of hemodilution on O_2 transport in high-altitude polycythemia. *J. Appl. Physiol.* 59: 1495-1502.

75. WINSLOW, R. M., C. MONGE-C., N. J. WINSLOW, C. G. GIBSON & J. WHITTEMBURY. 1985. Normal whole blood Bohr effect in Peruvian natives of high altitude. *Respir. Physiol.* 61: 197-208.

76. BONAVIA, D. & C. MONGE-C. 1986. Apuntes para la historia de la medicina americana: el soroche. *Histórica (Lima)* 10: 175-189.

77. LEÓN-VELARDE, F., J. WHITTEMBURY & C. MONGE-C. 1986. Oxidative phosphorylation of liver mitochondria from mice acclimatized to hypobaric hypoxia. *Int. J. Biometeorol.* 30: 283-289.

78. MONGE-C., C. & E. SALINAS. 1986. *El mal de montaña crónico y la salud de la población andina.* Lima: INANDEP: p. 23.

79. MOORE, L. G., P. BRODEUR, O. CHUMBE, J. D'BROT, S. HOFMEISTER & C. MONGE-C. 1986. Maternal hypoxic ventilatory response, ventilation, and infant birth weight at 4,300 m. *J. Appl. Physiol.* 60: 1401-1406.

80. CAREY, C., F. LEÓN-VELARDE, G. CASTRO & C. MONGE-C. 1987. Shell conductance, daily water loss, and water content of Andean gull and Puna ibis eggs. *J. Exp. Zool. Suppl.* 1: 247-252.

81. WINSLOW, R. M. & C. MONGE-C. 1987. *Hypoxia, polycythemia, and chronic mountain sickness.* Baltimore, Md: Johns Hopkins.

82. BLUME, F. D., R. SANTOLAYA, M. G. SHERPA & C. MONGE-C. 1988. Anthropometric and lung volume measurements in Himalayan and Andean natives. *Faseb J.* 2: A1281 (N° 5727).

83. MONGE-C., C. 1988. Medical research in the Andes. *Ann. Sports Med.* 4: 245-254.

84. MONGE-C., C., F. LEÓN-VELARDE & G. GÓMEZ DE LA TORRE. 1988. Laying eggs at high altitude. *News Physiol. Sci.* 3: 69-71.

85. WINSLOW, M. R., K. W. CHAPMAN, C. G. GIBSON, A. MURRAY, C. MONGE-C. & F. D. BLUME. In press. Linkage between ventilation and erythropoiesis in sherpas native to 3700 m altitude. *Am. Soc. Hematol.* 30th annual meeting, 1988.

86. BONAVIA, D. & C. MONGE-C. 1989. Notas sobre la historia de la medicina peruana: una interpretación errónea del «Mal de altura». *Histórica (Lima)* 13: 1-7.

87. CAREY, C., F. LEÓN-VELARDE, O. DUNIN-BORKOWSKI, T. L. BUCHER, G. GÓMEZ DE LA TORRE, D. ESPINOZA & C. MONGE-C. 1989. Variation in eggshell characteristics and gas exchange of montane and lowland coot eggs. *J. Comp. Physiol. [B]* 159: 389-400.

88. CAREY, C., F. LEÓN-VELARDE, O. DUNIN-BORKOWSKI & C. MONGE-C. 1989. Shell conductance, daily water loss, and water content of Puna teal eggs. *Physiol. Zool.* 62: 83-95.

89. HOCHACHKA, P. W., G. O. MATHESON, P. S. ALLEN, C. STANLEY, D. C. MCKENZIE, J. SUMAR-KALINOWSKI, C. MONGE-C. & W. S. PARKHOUSE. 1989. *Andes (Altitude-adaptation in native-highlanders during exercise stress): strategy and organization of study.*

90. MONGE-C., C. 1989. Animal adaptation to low-oxygen Andean gradient. *Interciencia* 14: 7.

91. MONGE-C., C. 1989. William J. Harrington and medicine in Latin America. *Am. J. Med.* 87: 7N-8N.

92. MONGE-C., C., F. LEÓN-VELARDE & A. ARREGUI. 1989. Increasing prevalence of excessive erythrocytosis with age among healthy high-altitude miners (Letter). *N. Engl. J. Med.* 321: 1271.

93. WINSLOW, R. M., K. W. CHAPMAN, C. G. GIBSON, M. SAMAJA, C. MONGE-C., E. GOLDWASSER, M. SHERPA, F. D. BLUME, & R. SANTOLAYA. 1989. Different hematologic responses to hypoxia in Sherpas and Quechua Indians. *J. Appl. Physiol.* 66: 1561-1569.

94. ARREGUI, A., F. LEÓN-VELARDE & C. MONGE-C. 1990. Mal de montaña crónico entre mineros de Cerro de Pasco: evidencias epidemiológicas y fisiológicas. *Rev. Med. Herediana (Lima)* 1: 35-39.

95. CAREY, C., F. LEÓN-VELARDE & C. MONGE-C. 1990. Eggshell conductance and other physical characteristics of avian eggs laid in the Peruvian Andes. *Condor* 92: 790-793.

96. HOCHACHKA, P. W., G. O. MATHESON, W. S. PARKHOUSE, J. SUMAR-KALINOWSKI, C. STANLEY, C. MONGE-C., D. C. MCKENZIE, J. MERKT, S. F. P. MAN, R. JONES & P. S. ALLEN. 1990. Path of oxygen from atmosphere to mitochondria in Andean natives: adaptable versus constrained components. In: *Hypoxia: the adaptations*, edited by J. R. Sutton, G. Coates and J. E. Remmers. Toronto: Decke, p. 72-74.

97. MONGE-C., C. 1990. Regulación de la concentración de hemoglobina en la policitemia de altura: modelo matemático. *Bull. Inst. fr. études andines* 19: 455-467.

98. MONGE-C., C., D. BONAVIA, F. LEÓN-VELARDE & A. ARREGUI. 1990. High altitude populations in Nepal and the Andes. In: *Hypoxia: the adaptations*, edited by J. R. Sutton, G. Coates and J. E. Remmers. Toronto: Decker, p. 53-58.

99. WINSLOW, R. M., K. W. CHAPMAN & C. MONGE-C. 1990. Ventilation and the control of erythropoiesis in high-altitude natives of Chile and Nepal. *Am. J. Hum. Biol.* 2: 653-662.

100. HOCHACHKA, P. W., G. O. MATHESON, W. S. PARKHOUSE, J. SUMAR-KALINOWSKI, C. STANLEY, C. MONGE-C., D. C. MCKENZIE, J. MERKT, S. F. P. MAN, R. JONES & P. S. ALLEN. 1991. Inborn resistance to hypoxia in high altitude adapted humans. *In: Response and adaptation to hypoxia: organ to organelle*, edited by S. Lahiri, N. S. Cherniack, and R. S. Fitzgerald. New York: Oxford Univ. Press, p. 191-194.

101. LEÓN VELARDE, F., D. ESPINOZA, C. MONGE-C. & C. DE MUIZON. 1991. A genetic response to high altitude hypoxia: high hemoglobin-oxygen affinity in chicken (*Gallus gallus*) from the Peruvian Andes. *C. R. Acad. Sci. Ser.* III 313: 401-406.

102. LEÓN-VELARDE, F., C. MONGE-C., A. VIDAL, M. CARCAGNO, M. CRISCUOLO, & C. E. BOZZINI. 1991. Serum immunoreactive erythropoietin in high altitude natives with and without excessive erythrocytosis. *Exp. Hematol.* 19: 257-260.

103. MONGE-C., C., R. GUERRA-GARCÍA & F. LEÓN VELARDE. In press. Fisiología y fisiopatología de la altura. *In: Fisiología humana*, edited by C. R. Douglas. Sao Paulo.

104. MONGE-C., C. & F. LEÓN-VELARDE. 1991. Physiological adaptation to high altitude: oxygen transport in mammals and birds. *Physiol. Rev.* 71: 1135-1172.

105. MONGE, E. & C. MONGE-C. 1991. Gastrointestinal endoscopy and arterial oxygen desaturation in high-altitude hospitals (Letter). *Am. J. Gastroenterol.* 86: 787.

106. RIVERA CH., M., O. DUNIN-BORKOWSKI, F. LEÓN-VELARDE, L. HUICHO, M. VARGAS & C. MONGE-C. 1991. Metabolic effects of cyanate on mice at sea level and in chronic hypobaric hypoxia. Life Sci. 49: 439-445.

107. LEÓN-VELARDE, F., L. HUICHO, L., & C. MONGE-C. 1992. Effects of cocaine on oxygen consumption and mitochondrial respiration in normoxic and hypoxic mice. Life Sci. 50:213-218.

108. MONGE-C., C., A. ARREGUI & F. LEÓN-VELARDE. 1992. Pathophysiology and epidemiology of Chronic Mountain Sickness. *Int J Sports Med,* ; 13(Suppl 1): S79-S81.

109. LEÓN-VELARDE F., J. SANCHEZ, A.X. BIGARD, A. BRUNET, C. LESTY & C. MONGE-C. 1993. High altitude tissue adaptation in Andean coots: Capillarity, fiber area, fiber type and enzymatic activities of skeletal muscle. *J. of Comp. Physiol.* B 163(1): 52-8.

110. BONAVIA, D. & C. MONGE-C. El Hombre Andino. *In: Las Sociedades Originarias* (T. Rojas J .Murra eds). Vol I. General History of Latin America.UNESCO. En prensa.

111. LEÓN-VELARDE, F.,A., ARREGUI, C., MONGE-C. & H., RUIZ & RUIZ 1993. Aging at high altitudes and the risk of chronic mountain sickness. *J of Wild Med* 4: 183-188.

I.

FISIOLOGÍA

CARDIORESPIRATORIA

INFLUENCE OF DEVELOPMENTAL ACCLIMATIZATION TO THE ATTAINMENT OF FUNCTIONAL ADAPTATION TO HIGH ALTITUDE

A. Roberto Frisancho

Abstract

Investigations conducted in the Andes and the Himalayas have permitted us to postulate that the normal functional adaptation that characterizes the high altitude native is acquired through growth and development in a hypoxic environment. The present article summarize the findings related to respiratory function and aerobic capacity. The comparisons have been made between andeans, tibetans, ethiopians europeans and americans. Chest dimensions and lung volume enhancement of high altitude natives appears to be established by early childhood, the difference between high altitude (HAN) and low altitude (LAN) natives are merely maintained during childhood and adolescence. The same forced vital capacity of HAN is attained by the LAN when acclimatized to high altitude during growth. In contrast LAN acclimatized as adults had significantly lower vital capacities than HAN. Normal oxygen consumption, ventilation and maximun pulse rate are achieved by LAN migrants residing at high altitude as a result of adaptations acquired during the period of growth. In contrast, when LAN acclimatized to high altitudes as adults, attained significantly lower aerobic capacities than the HAN. From these studies emerges the conclusion that differences between HAN and LAN in physiological performance and morphology of the organs of the oxygen transport system are caused in part by adaptations acquired during the developmental period. Morphological traits such as skeletal dimensions are affected more by ethnicity and energy availability than by high altitude hypoxia.

Key words: High altitude, developmental acclimatization, developmental adaptation, respiratory function, lung volume, growth, development, aerobic capacity, exercise.

Resumen

Las investigaciones llevadas a cabo en los Andes y en los Himalayas nos han permitido postular que la normal adaptación funcional que caracteriza al nativo de la altura es adquirida durante el crecimiento y desarrollo en un ambiente hipóxico. Este artículo resume los hallazgos relacionados a la función respiratoria y la capacidad aeróbica. Se comparan estas variables entre andinos, tibetanos, etíopes, europeos y americanos. El aumento de las dimensiones torácicas y del volumen pulmonar de los nativos de altura se establece aparentemente muy temprano en la niñez, la diferencia entre los nativos de altura (HAN) y los de nivel del mar (LAN) simplemente se mantiene durante la niñez y la adolescencia. Cuando en los LAN, el proceso de aclimatación a la altura ocurre durante el crecimiento, éstos logran la misma capacidad vital forzada que los HAN. Por el contrario, los LAN aclimatados ya en la etapa adulta, tienen capacidades vitales significativamente menores que los HAN. Asímismo, los LAN residentes de altura muestran consumos de oxígeno, ventilación y frecuencias respiratorias máximas normales como producto de las adaptaciones adquiridas durante el periodo de crecimiento. Sin embargo, cuando los LAN se aclimatan a la altura como adultos, muestran capacidades aeróbicas significativamente menores. Los resultados de estos estudios indican que las diferencias de rendimiento físico, fisiológicas y morfológicas del sistema de transporte de oxígeno entre los HAN y los LAN se deben en parte a adaptaciones adquiridas durante el desarrollo. Los rasgos morfológicos como las dimensiones óseas se ven afectadas más por factores étnicos y de disponibilidad de energía, que por la hipoxia propia de los ambientes de altura.

Palabras claves: Altura, aclimatación y desarrollo, adaptación y desarrollo, función respiratoria, volumen pulmonar, crecimiento, desarrollo, capacidad aeróbica, ejercicio.

Résumé

    Les recherches menées dans les Andes et en Himalaya nous ont permis de postuler que l'adaptation normale fonctionnelle qui caractérise la personne née en altitude est acquise au cours de la croissance et du développement dans un milieu hypoxique. Cet article rend compte des découvertes sur la fonction respiratoire et la capacité aérobie. Les variables sont comparées entre les cas andins, tibétins, éthiopiens, européens et américains. L'augmentation des dimensions thoraciques et du volume pulmonaire des populations nées en altitude, survient apparemment très tôt au cours de l'enfance; la différence entre ceux qui sont nés en altitude (HAN) et ceux qui naissent au bord de la mer (LAN) se maintient simplement au cours de l'enfance et de l'adolescence. Chez les LAN, quand le processus d'acclimatation à l'altitude survient au cours de la croissance, la capacité vitale forcée arrive à être la même que chez les HAN. Cependant, les LAN qui se sont adaptés au cours de l'âge adulte, ont des capacités vitales beaucoup moins importantes que les HAN. De même, les LAN résidant en altitude ont des consommations d'oxygène, une ventilation et des fréquences respiratoires maximales normales suite aux adaptations acquises au cours de la croissance. Cependant, quand les LAN s'acclimatent à l'altitude au cours de l'âge adulte, leur capacité aérobie sont nettement inférieures. Les résultats de ces études indiquent que les différences de rendement physique, physiologiques et morphologiques du système de transport d'oxygène entre les HAN et les LAN sont dues en partie aux adaptations acquises au cours du développement. Aussi bien les caractéristiques morphologiques que les dimensions osseuses varient plus en fonction des facteurs ethniques et de disponibilité d'énergie que de l'hypoxie propre des milieux d'altitude.

Mots clés : Altitude, acclimatation et développement, adaptation et développement, fonction respiratoire, volume pulmonaire, croissance, développement, capacité aérobique, exercice.

INTRODUCTION

    After the initial effects of and responses to high altitude, usually characterized by the onset and disappearance of the symptoms of acute mountain sickness, gradual adaptive responses develop, some of which require months or many years for complete development. The various systemic and cell responses, which together permit the organism to function normally with low oxygen availability, develop at different rates. Some increase progressively for many months; others reach an early peak and then subside; and others require exposure during the organism's period of growth and development. During the last years investigations conducted in the Andes and the Himalayas have permitted us to postulate that the normal functional adaptation that characterizes the high altitude native is the result of adaptive responses acquired during the period of growth and development. Hence, the purpose of the present article is to summarize the findings related to respiratory function and aerobic capacity.

CHEST SIZE

High Altitude Natives

A distinguishing feature of the highland native is an enlarged thorax (28). As shown by studies done in the central and southern highlands of Peru and Chile the increased chest size of the highland native is acquired through rapid and accelerated growth, especially after the end of childhood (14, 19, 16, 17, 27, 3, 42, 39, 40, 9, 26). Studies of an Ethiopian population (9, 26) indicate that the trend toward greater chest size is also present among highland children and adults. These studies show that at a given age the highland boys and girls have a larger chest size than their low-altitude counterparts. Similarly, the highland adult Ethiopians have a greater maximum chest circumference than their low-altitude counterparts. Furthermore, evaluations of the anthropometric measurements of migrant groups demonstrated that the enlarged chest size of the highland Ethiopian could be attained by lowland natives who migrated to high altitude (26). An study conducted among the Bod natives of the mountains of Ladakh situated at 3514 m in India demonstrated that the growth in chest circumference of the highlanders is significantly faster than the low-altitude Indian norm. Adult Sherpas also exhibit an enlarge thorax (41). Thus, it would appear that, with the exception of the Russians from the Tien Shan Mountains (37), high altitude natives are characterized by a rapid growth in chest dimension resulting in a relatively large adult chest size.

Europeans

That prolonged residence at high altitude can result in enlarge chest size is also inferred from the fact that United States adult women who resided at Pikes Peak for 2 1/2 months exhibited an increase in maximum chest circumference despite a significant reduction in subscapular skinfold thickness (25). Furthermore, data of European migrants residing in La Paz (3,600 m) Bolivia indicated that lifelong exposure to chronic hypoxia resulted in an average expansion of chest depth of 1.2 to 1.8 cm (23, 22).

LUNG VOLUME

Andean

As shown in Figure 1 highland natives have larger lung volumes and residual volumes than sea level natives when adjustments are made for differences in body size (29, 30, 21, 15, 4). Various investigations indicate that the greater forced vital capacity (FVC) of highland natives is acquired through a rapid and accelerated growth (28, 14, 19, 16, 17, 40, 9, 26, 34, 41, 37, 25, 23, 22, 29, 30, 21, 15, 4). In view of the fact that during childhood at sea level growth in lung volume is associated with an enhanced quantity of alveolar units and alveolar surface area (12), the rapid growth in lung volume at high altitude is probably also associated with an enhanced quantity of alveolar units and alveolar surface area. Since there is a direct relationship between alveolar surface area and rate of oxygen diffusion from the lungs to the capillary bed, the rapid growth in lung volume at high altitude may reflect an adaptation to high-altitude hypoxia.

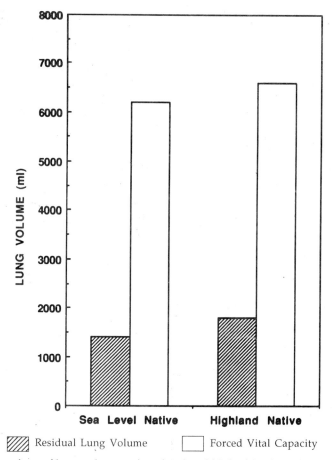

Fig. 1 - Comparison of lung volumes of sea level and high-altitude natives. Lung volume, especially residual lung volume, is increased among highland natives (29).

Himalayans (Tibetans)

Studies of Tibetans who were born and raised above 3600 m and Hans who were born at sea sea level and acclimatized to high altitude during adulthood (38, 11) are presented in Figure 2. This figure shows that the high altitude native Tibetans had both a larger forced vital capacity and residual lung volumes than the sea level natives Hans.

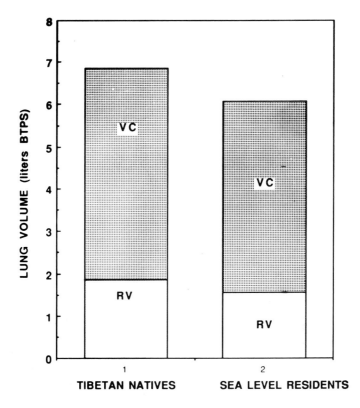

Fig. 2 - Comparison of lung volumes of high altitude natives (Tibetans) and sea-level natives (Hans) residing at high altitudes in the Himalayas. Adapted from ref. 3.

Ethiopians

Investigations in Ethiopia demonstrated that highlanders living above 3000 m have a significantly greater forced vital capacity than their lower altitude counterparts. Furthermore, evaluation of the respiratory function of migrant groups demonstrated that the enlarged forced vital capacity of the highland Ethiopian can be acquired by lowland natives who migrate to high altitudes (9, 26).

Thus, high altitude natives irrespective of the geographic region have larger lung volumes than low altitudes.

Europeans

Comparison of European highland children residing at high altitude (La Paz, Bolivia) with lowlanders indicated that exposure to chronic hypoxia resulted in an average increase in forced vital capacity of 150-300 ml (23, 22). Furthermore, data of European migrants indicated that lifelong exposure to chronic hypoxia resulted in an average expansion of 288 to 384 ml in forced vital capacity (23, 22).

In summary, the above studies suggest that children of European ancestry growing under conditions of chronic hypoxia exhibit an enhancement of chest size lung volumes. However, as indicated by Greksa and Beall (22) there is little evidence to suggest that European children exhibit an accelerated development of chest size and lung volumes during childhood and adolescence. On the other hand, the enhancement of chest dimensions and lung volumes of high altitude natives appears to be established by early childhood, and therefore the difference between high altitude and low altitude natives are merely maintained during childhood and adolescence. Since the magnitude of the hypoxia induced expansion of chest size and lung volumes among European children is much smaller than the range of variation found high altitude populations suggest that the distinctive thorax of high altitude Andean natives is mediated by genetic factors.

Developmental aspects of lung volume

Current evidence suggests that the enlarged lung volume of the high-altitude native results from adaptations acquired during the developmental period (21, 15, 32, 5). As shown in Figure 3 the sea level natives who were acclimatized to high altitudes during growth, when adjustments were made for variations in body size, attained the same forced vital capacity as the high-altitude natives. In contrast sea level natives (Peruvian and white United States subjects) acclimatized as adults had significantly lower vital capacities than high-altitude natives.

The hypothesis that the enlarged lung volume of high-altitude natives results from developmental adaptation is supported by experimental studies on animals. Various studies (6, 1, 7, 10, 2) have demonstrated that young rats, after prolonged exposure to high-altitude hypoxia (3450 m), exhibited an accelerated proliferation of alveolar units and accelerated growth in alveolar surface area and lung volume. In contrast adult rats, after prolonged exposure to high-altitude hypoxia, did not show changes in quantity of alveoli and lung volume (1, 7, 10). Figure 4 shows that rats acclimatized to a high altitude from birth to the age of 131 days develop a greater lung volume than sea level controls. In contrast adult rats, who were the mothers of the young rats studied, were acclimatized to a high altitude for the same number of days and had lung volumes similar to the sea level controls. These findings suggest that in experimental animals and humans the attainment of an enlarged lung volume at high altitude is probably mediated by developmental factors.

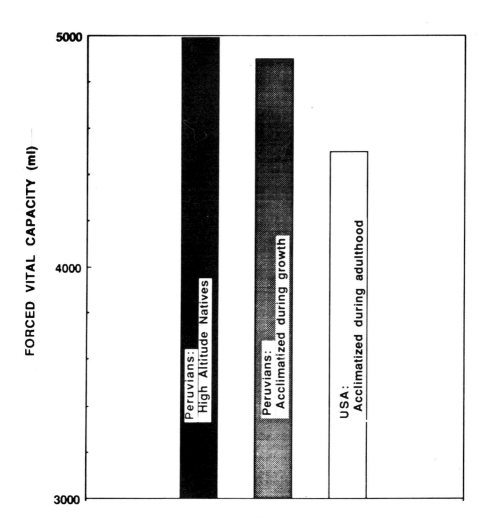

Fig. 3 - Comparison of forced vital capacity of high-altitude natives, Peruvian sea level subjects acclimatized to high altitude during growth, and United States sea level subjects acclimatized to high altitude during adulthood. Acclimatization to high altitude during growth results in lung volumes similar to those of high-altitude native (Based on data from ref. 20).

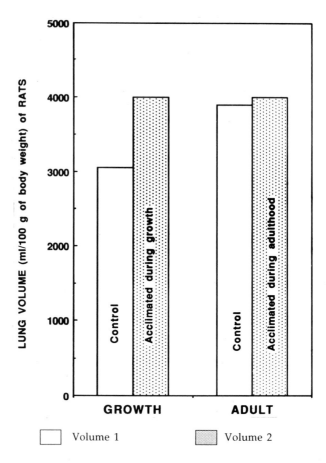

Fig. 4 - Comparison of lung volume of rats raised at sea level and acclimatized to high altitude during growth and during adulthood. Like humans, acclimatization to high altitude during growth results in enlargements of lung volumes (Based on data from ref. 6).

WORK CAPACITY AND MAXIMAL OXYGEN INTAKE

Functional Meaning of Measurements of Aerobic Capacity

It is generally agreed that the maximum oxygen, intake per unit of body weight (or aerobic capacity) during maximal work is a measure of the individual's work capacity because it reflects the capacity of the working muscles to use oxygen and the ability of the cardiovascular system to transport and deliver oxygen to the tissues.

Reduction of Aerobic Capacity among Sea Level Natives

Table 1 summarizes the available data on maximum oxygen consumption during exercise. These data indicate that the maximum aerobic capacity of well-trained sea level subjects, when expressed as percent of the sea level values, declined by 11% for every 1000 m (3000 feet) ascended beyond 1500 m (5000 feet). Similarly, studies among sea level newcomers to high altitude demonstrated a reduction in aerobic capacity of 13% to 22% (8). It must also be noted that the observed decreases in aerobic capacity at high altitude are influenced very little by physical conditioning.

Table 1. Comparison of maximum aerobic power (VO_2 max: ml/kg/min) attained by samples tested at high and low altitudes (LA).

				VO_2 max (ml/kg/min)		
					Attained or	
		Tested at	Time at	Attained at	expected at	D
Sample	N	Altitude (m)	Altitude	Altitude	Sea Level	(%)
Sedentary or Untrained						
Sedentary-U.S.	12	4000	4 weeks	38.1	50.4	24.4
Urban-Bolivia	28	3600	Life	46.0	40-50	0.0
Rural-Chile	37	3650	Life	46.4	40-50	0.0
Rural-Peru	8	4000	Life	51.8	40-50	0.0
Rural-Peru	5	4000	10 years	49.2	40-50	0.0
Urban-Peru	20	3400	2-15 years	46.3	40-50	0.0
Urban-Peru	8	4350	2 weeks	49.0	53.6	8.6
Urban-Peru	5	4540	23 weeks LA	50.0	50.2	0.4
Active						
Urban-Bolivia	29	3700	Life	37.7	50-60	0.0
Urban-Peru	28	4500	Life	51.2	50-60	0.0
Urban-Peru	20	3750	Life	50.9	50-60	0.0
Trained or Athletes						
Athletes-U.S.	6	4000	7 weeks	49.0	63.0	22.2
Athletes-U.S.	6	3090	2 weeks	59.3	72.0	17.6
Athletes-U.S.	5	3100	4 weeks LA	45.5	61.7	26.3
Athletes-Peru	10	3700	6 months	55.0	70.0	21.4

Source: Adapted from ref. 20.

In fact the decrease in aerobic capacity at high altitude has been observed to be proportional to the extent of training; athletes show the greatest decrease, sedentary individuals the least, and active subjects an intermediate decrease (8, 31, 36, 24, 33). Thus, sea level natives as judged by their inability to recuperate their work capacity attain only a partial functional adaptation to high altitude.

Normal Aerobic Capacity among High Altitude Natives

As shown by measurements of oxygen consumption during maximal exercise the aerobic capacity of high-altitude natives is comparable to that attained by lowland natives tested at sea level (8, 31, 36, 24, 33) (see Table 1). Thus, high altitude natives as judged by their ability to attain an aerobic capacity similar to that at sea level have acquired a full (complete) functional adaptation to high altitude.

Developmental Component

As demonstrated by studies of sea level migrants residing at high altitude, the attainment of a normal aerobic capacity at high altitude is the result of adaptations acquired during the period of growth (15, 20). As shown in Figure 5 sea level subjects, when acclimatized to high altitude during childhood and adolescence, attained an aerobic capacity (maximum oxygen intake) that was equal to that of the highland natives. In contrast sea level natives (Peruvian and white United States subjects), when acclimatized to high altitudes as adults, attained significantly lower aerobic capacities than the highland natives. Evaluations of the data indicated that in the sea level subjects who were acclimatized young the volume of air ventilated per unit of oxygen consumed (ventilation equivalent), maximum pulse rate, and the volume of oxygen consumption per pulse rate were comparable to those of the highland natives. On the other hand, the lowland subjects (Peruvian and United States) attained significantly higher ventilation ratios and lower heart rates than the highland natives (15, 20). From these investigations it appears that the attainment of normal aerobic capacity at high altitude is influenced by adaptations acquired during the developmental period (15, 36).

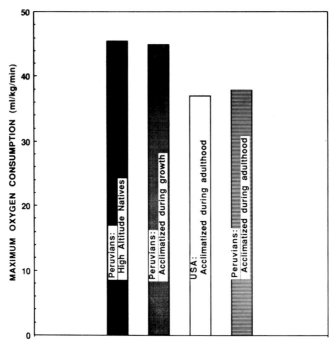

Fig. 5 - Comparison of aerobic capacity among subjects acclimatized to high altitude during growth and adulthood and subjects native to high altitude. Acclimatization to high altitude during developmental period is associated with attainment of aerobic capacity similar to high-altitude native. (Based on data from ref. 20).

Studies of Tibetans indicate that the aerobic capacity (maximum oxygen intake) of high altitude native Tibetans was higher than the Hans who were born at sea level and acclimatized to high altitude after the age of 8 years (43). However, in this study the proportion of smokers (45%) among the sea level Hans was much higher that in the Tibetans (38%). Therefore, the lower aerobic capacity of the Hans probably reflects the negative effects of smoking rather than differences in the process of acclimatization to high altitude. In other words, if the comparison would have included either the same proportion of smokers (or excluded the smokers) the sea level Hans would have attained a similar aerobic capacity as the high altitude Tibetan natives, which would suggest a developmental role on the attainment of full functional adaptation to high altitude.

CONCLUSION

Acclimatization to high-altitude hypoxia is a complex phenomenon that develops through the modification and synchronized interdependence of the respiratory, circulatory, and cardiovascular systems to improve oxygen delivery and oxygen utilization. As judged by evaluations of oxygen intake during maximal exercise the sea level native who have resided for as long as 2 years have acquired only a partial acclimatization to high altitude. In contrast, the high altitude native or those raised at high altitude during growth and development have acquired a full acclimatization to high altitude.

The available information suggests that full acclimatization to high altitude is acquired through growth and development in a hypoxic environment. The hypothesis that developmental adaptations account for most part of the differences in physiological performance and morphology between fully and partially acclimatized residents living at high altitudes is supported by the evidence. It is also based on the well-grounded assumption that the respective contributions of genetic and environmental factors vary with the developmental stage of the organism. In general, the earlier the developmental stage, the greater the environment influence of the environment. Furthermore, studies on chemoreceptor sensitivity indicate that the hyposensitivity that characterizes the high-altitude native is acquired during growth and development (13). From these studies emerges the conclusion that differences between highland and sea level native in physiological performance and morphology of the organs of the oxygen transport system are caused in part by adaptations acquired during the developmental period. This does not mean, however, that all physiological characteristics exhibited by the high altitude native are due to developmental adaptive responses. For example, it is now generally accepted that the attainment of low systemic blood pressure at high altitude does not depend on developmental factors because it can be acquired by long-term residency at high altitude (35). Furthermore, we do not know the developmental modifications that occur within each component of the oxygen transport system (such as ventilation, pulmonary diffusion, and oxygen delivery to the tissues) that enable a sea level native to attain a complete functional adaptation to high altitude. Similarly, it is not known whether other sea level populations who do not have indigenous admixture such as the Peruvian populations can acquire a full functional adaptation. Future research must be addressed at answering these questions, for they have importance to all areas concerned with the organism's coping with low oxygen availability.

During growth and development environmental factors are constantly conditioning and modifying the expression of inherited potentials. The environmental influences felt by the organism depend on the type of stress imposed and especially on the age at which the individual is subjected to the stress. Hence, the respective contributions of genetic and environmental factors vary with the developmental stage of the organism; in general, the earlier the age, the greater the environmental influence (18). Thus, it would be surprising if developmental processes did not influence the functional performance and morphology of the high-altitude native. However, the principle of developmental sensitivity and plasticity does not necessarily imply greater adaptive responses in all biological parameters, which may depend on the developmental stage of the organism, the type of organism, and the particular functional process that is affected. Homeostatic interdependence does not imply uniform correlations for all physiological and morphological variables. The finding that acclimatization to high altitude in humans and experimental animals results in an enhancement of respiratory volumes and pulmonary diffusing capacity without the direct participation of chest dimensions, with which one would expect to be associated, is a good example of the organism's functional plasticity and independent response of morphological traits. In other words, successful acclimatization to high altitudes depends primarily on the adjustments and synchronized interdependence of environmentally modifiable functions that related to oxygen transport such as the respiratory and circulatory functions and less on morphological traits such as skeletal dimensions that affected more by ethnicity and energy availability than by high altitude hypoxia.

REFERENCES

1. BARTLETT, D. 1972. Postnatal development of the mammalian lung. *In*: R. Goss, ed. *Regulation of organ and tissue growth*. Academic Press, Inc., New York.

2. BARTLETT, D., Jr. & REMMERS, J.E. 1971. Effects of high altitude exposure on the lungs of young rats. *Respir. Physiol.* 13: 116-125.

3. BEALL, C.M., BAKER, P.T., BAKER, T.S. & HAAS, J.D. 1977. The effects of high altitude on adolescent growth in southern Peruvian Amerindians. *Hum. Biol.* 49: 109-124.

4. BOYCE, A.J., HAIGHT, J.S.J., RIMMER, D.B. & HARRISON, G.A. 1974. Respiratory function in Peruvian Quechua Indians. *Ann. Hum. Biol.* 1: 137-148.

5. BRODY, J.S., LAHIRI, S., SIMPSER, M., MOTOYAMA, E.K. & VELÁSQUEZ, T. 1977. Lung elasticity and airway dynamics in Peruvian natives to high altitude. *J. Appl. Physiol.* 42: 245-251.

6. BURRI, P.H. & WEIBEL, E.R. 1971. Morphometric estimation of pulmonary diffusion capacity, Part 2. Effect of PO_2 on the growing lung. Adaptation of the growing rat lung to hypoxia and hyperhypoxia. *Respir. Physiol.* 11: 247-264.

7. BURRI, P.H. & WEIBEL, E.R. 1971. Morphometric evaluation of changes in lung structure due to high altitudes. *In*: R. Porter and J. Knight, eds. *High altitude physiology. Cardiac and respiratory aspects*. Churchill Livingstone, Edinburgh.

8. BUSKIRK, E.R. 1976. Work performance of newcomers to the Peruvian highlands. *In*: P.T. Baker and M.A. Little, eds. *Man in the Andes: a multidisciplinary study of high-altitude Quechua natives*. Dowden, Hutchinson, & Ross, Inc., Stroudsburg, Pa.

9. CLEGG, E.J., PAWSON, I.G., ASHTON, E.H. & FLINN, R.M. 1972. The growth of children at different altitudes in Ethiopia. *Philos. Trans. R. Soc. Lond. (Biol.)* 264: 403-437.

10. CUNNINGHAM, E.L., BRODY, J.S. & JAIN, B.P. 1974. Lung growth induced by hypoxia. *J. Appl. Physiol.* 37: 362-366.

11. DROMA, T.S., MCCULLOUGH, R.G., MCCULLOUGH, R.E., ZHUANG, J.G., CYMERMAN, A., SUN, S.F., SUTTON, J.R., RAPMUND, G. & MOORE, L.G. 1991. Increased vital and lung capacities in Tibetan compared to Hans residents of Lhasa (3,658 m). *Am. J. Phys. Anthrop.* 86: 341-351.

12. DUNNILL, M.S. 1962. Postnatal growth of the lung. *Thorax* 17: 329-333.

13. FORSTER, H.V., DEMPSEY, J.A., BIRNBAUM, M.L., REDDAN, W.G., THODEN, J., GROVER, R.F. & RANKIN, J. 1971. Effect of chronic exposure to hypoxia on ventilatory response to CO_2 and hypoxia. *J. Appl. Physiol.* 31: 586-592.

14. FRISANCHO, A.R. 1969. Human growth and pulmonary function of a high altitude Peruvian Quechua population. *Hum. Biol.* 41: 365-379.

15. FRISANCHO, A.R. 1975. Functional adaptation to high altitude hypoxia. *Science* 187: 313-319.

16. FRISANCHO, A.R. 1976. Growth and functional development at high altitude. *In*: P.T. Baker and M.A. Little, eds. *Man in the Andes: a multidisciplinary study of high altitude Quechua natives*. Dowden, Hutchinson & Ross, Inc., Stroudsburg, Pa.

17. FRISANCHO, A.R. 1978. Human growth and development among high altitude populations. *In*: P.T. Baker, ed. *The biology of high-altitude peoples*. Cambridge University Press, New York.

18. FRISANCHO, A. R. 1981. *Human Adaptation: A Functional Interpretation*. University of Michigan Press, Ann Arbor, MI 48105.

19. FRISANCHO, A.R. & BAKER, P.T. 1970. Altitude and growth: a study of the patterns of physical growth of a high altitude Peruvian Quechua population. *Am. J. Phys. Anthropol.* 32: 279-292.

20. FRISANCHO, A.R., MARTÍNEZ, C., VELÁSQUEZ, T., SÁNCHEZ, J. & MONTOYE, H. 1973. Influence of developmental adaptation on aerobic capacity at high altitude. *J. Appl. Physiol.* 34: 176-180.

21. FRISANCHO, A.R., VELÁSQUEZ, T. & SÁNCHEZ, J. 1973. Influences of developmental adaptation on lung function at high altitude. *Hum. Biol.* 45: 583-594.

22. GREKSA, L.P. & BEALL, C.M. 1989. Development of chest size and lung function at high altitude. *In*: M.A. Little and J.D. Haas, eds. *Human population biology.* Oxford University Press, New York, pp. 222-238

23. GREKSA, L.P., SPIELVOGEL, H., PAZ-ZAMORA, M. & CÁCERES, E. 1988. Effect of altitude on the lung function of high altitude residents of European ancestry. *Am. J. Phys. Anthropol.* 75: 77-85.

24. GROVER, R.F., REEVES, J.T., GROVER, E.B. & LEATHERS, J.S. 1967. Muscular exercise in young men native to 3,100 m altitude. *J. Appl. Physiol.* 22:555-564.

25. HANNON, J.P., SHIELDS, J.L. & HARRIS, C.W. 1969. Anthropometric changes associated with high altitude acclimatization in females. *Am. J. Phys. Anthropol.* 31: 77-84.

26. HARRISON, G.A., KUCHEMANN, G.F., MOORE, M.A.S., BOYCE, A.J., BAJU, T., MOURANT, A.E., GODBER, M.J., GLASGOW, B.G., KOPEC, A.C., TILLS, D. & CLEGG, E.J. 1969. The effects of altitudinal variation in Ethiopian populations. *Philos. Trans. R. Soc. Lond. (Biol)* 256B: 147-182.

27. HOFF, C. 1974. Altitudinal variations in the physical growth and development of Peruvian Quechua. *Homo* 24: 87-99.

28. HURTADO, A. 1932. Respiratory adaptation in the Indian natives of the Peruvian Andes. Studies at high altitude. *Am. J. Phys. Anthropol.* 17: 137-165.

29. HURTADO, A. 1964. Animals in high altitudes: resident man. *In*: D.B. Dill, E.F. Adolph, and C.G. Wilber, eds. *Handbook of physiology, vol. 4. Adaptation to the environment.* American Physiological Society, Washington, D.C.

30. HURTADO, A., VELÁSQUEZ, T., REYNAFARJE, C., LOZANO, R., CHÁVEZ, R., ASTE-SALAZAR, H., REYNAFARJE, B., SÁNCHEZ, C. & MUÑOZ, J. 1956. *Mechanisms of natural acclimatization: studies on the native resident of Morococha, Peru, at an altitude of 14,000 feet.* Rep. 56-1. U.S. Air Force School of Aviation Medicine, Randolph Field, Texas.

31. KOLLIAS, J., BUSKIRK, E.R, AKERS, R.F., PROKOP, E.K., BAKER, P.T. & PICON-REATEGUI, E. 1968. Work capacity of long-time residents and newcomers to altitude. *J. Appl. Physiol.* 24: 792-799.

32. LAHIRI, S., DELANEY, R.G., BRODY, J.S., SIMPSER, M., VELÁSQUEZ, T., MOTOYAMA, E.K. & POLGAR, C. 1976. Relative role of environmental and genetic factors in respiratory adaptation to high altitude. *Nature* 261: 133-135.

33. LAHIRI, S., MILLEDGE, J.S., CHATTOPADHYAY, H.P., BHATTACHARYYA, A.K. & SINHA, A.K. 1967. Respiration and heart rate of Sherpa highlanders during exercise. *J. Appl. Physiol.* 23: 545-554.

34. MALIK, S.L. & SINGH, I.P. 1978. Growth trends among male Bods of Ladakh—a high altitude population. *Am. J. Phys. Anthropol.* 48:171-176.

35. MARTICORENA, E., RUIZ, L., SEVERINO, J., GALVEZ, J. & PEÑALOZA, D. 1969. Systemic blood pressure in white men born at sea level: changes after long residence at high altitudes. *Am. J. Cardiol.* 23: 364-368.

36. MAZESS, R.B. 1969. Exercise performance of indian and white high altitude residents. *Hum. Biol.* 41: 494-518.

37. MIKLASHEVSKAIA, N.N., SOLOVYEVA, V.S. & GODINA, E.Z. 1972. Growth and development in high-altitude regions of Southern Kirghizia, U.S.S.R. *Vopros Anthropologii* 40: 71-91.

38. MOORE, L.G., ZHUANG, J.G., MCCULLOUGH, R.G., CYMERMAN, A., DROMA, T.S., SUN, S.F., PING, Y. & MCCULLOUGH, R.E. 1991. Increased lung volumes in Tibetan high altitude residents. *Am. J. Phys. Anthrop.* 12(abstract): 134.

39. MUELLER, W.H., SCHULL, V.N., SCHULL, W.J., SOTO, P. & ROTHHAMMER, F. 1978. A multinational Andean genetic and health program: growth and development in an hypoxic environment. *Ann. Hum. Biol.* 5: 329-352.

40. MUELLER, W.H., YEN, F., ROTHHAMMER, F. & SCHULL, W.J. 1978. A multinational Andean genetic and health program. VI. Physiological measurements of lung function in a hypoxic environment. *Hum. Biol.* 5: 489-541.

41. SLOAN, A.W. & MASALI, M. 1978. Anthropometry of Sherpa men. *Ann. Hum. Biol.* 5: 453-458.

42. STINSON, S. 1978. Child growth, mortality and the adaptive value of children in rural Bolivia. Ph.D. Thesis. University of Michigan, Ann Arbor, Mich.

43. SUN, S.F., DROMA, T.S., ZHUANG, J.G., TAO, J.X., HUANG, S.Y., MCCULLOUGH, R.G., MCCULLOUGH, R. E., REEVES, C.S., REEVES, J.T. & MOORE, L.G. 1990. Greater maximal O_2 uptakes and vital capacities in Tibetan than Han residents of Lhasa. *Respiration Physiology* 79: 151-162.

VENTILATORY CHARACTERISTICS OF PERUVIAN AND TIBETAN WOMEN AND MEN NATIVE TO HIGH ALTITUDE

Stacy Zamudio, Shinfu Sun, Lorna G. Moore

Abstract

Comparisons between Andean and Himalayan residents are of interest for determining whether strategies of adaptation vary by region and/or duration of high-altitude residence. We report measurements of resting ventilation, hypoxic and hypercapnic ventilatory responses in a small number of Peruvian and Tibetan women and men. We found little difference in resting ventilation, hypoxic or hypercapnic ventilatory responsiveness between lifelong Peruvian and Tibetan high-altitude residents. Males, but not females, differed in their hyperoxic ventilation, with Peruvian men decreasing their breathing during hyperoxia and Tibetans showing no change. The women had lower hypoxic ventilatory responses than the men at both high-altitude locations. Comparison of the end-tidal PO_2 and PCO_2 levels observed in our subjects with those reported previously using a Rahn-Otis diagram revealed that both the Peruvian and Tibetan values were close to the acclimatized newcomer curve. Our Peruvian values were closer to the acclimatized newcomer curve than most other Andean studies, while the Tibetan values are in accordance with those of prior Himalayan reports. Needed are studies using identical techniques in carefully selected and sufficiently large numbers of Andean and Himalayan high-altitude residents that sources of experimental error within and between subjects, the range of variation within each population by age and by gender, and the influence of factors known to alter ventilatory response such as metabolic rate and temperature, can be controlled and/or documented.

Key words: Pulmonary ventilation, Andean populations, Tibetan populations, high altitude women.

Resumen

Las comparaciones entre residentes andinos y tibetanos son de interés para determinar si las estrategias de adaptación varían de región a región y/o con la duración de la residencia en la altura. Reportamos medidas de ventilación en reposo, y respuestas ventilatorias hipóxicas e hipercápnicas en un número pequeño de mujeres y hombres del Tibet y los Andes. Encontramos pocas diferencias en la ventilación de reposo y en las respuestas ventilatorias hipóxicas o hipercápnicas entre residentes permanentes de altura del Tibet y los Andes. Los hombres, pero no las mujeres, difieren en su hiperventilación hiperóxica, teniendo los peruanos una disminución de su respiración durante la hiperoxia, cosa que no muestran los tibetanos. Las mujeres tienen respuestas ventilatorias hipóxicas menores que la de los hombres de ambas localidades. La comparacion de los niveles de PO_2 y PCO_2 observados en nuestros sujetos con la de aquellos reportados anteriormente usando el diagrama de Rahn-Otis, revela que los valores peruanos y tibetanos se aproximan a los de la curva de un recien llegado. Nuestros valores peruanos están más cerca de la curva del recién llegado que los reportados en otros estudios realizados en los Andes, mientras que los valores tibetanos están de acuerdo con otros realizados en el Himalaya. Se necesitan estudios que utilicen técnicas idénticas en residentes de altura de los Andes e Himalayas seleccionados adecuadamente y en número suficiente, de manera tal que el error experimental dentro y entre los individuos, el rango de variación entre cada población por edad y sexo, y la influencia de factores que alteran la respuesta ventilatoria - como la tasa metabólica y la temperatura- puedan ser controlados y/o documentados.

Palabras claves: Ventilación pulmonar, población andina, población tibetana, mujeres de altura.

Résumé

Les comparaisons entre résidents andins et tibétains permettent de déterminer si les stratégies d'adaptation varient d'une région à l'autre et /ou avec la durée de la résidence en altitude. Nous rendons compte des mesures de ventilation au repos, et des réponses ventilatoires hypoxiques et hypercapniques chez un petit nombre d'hommes et de femmes du Tibet et des Andes. Nous avons trouvé peu de différence dans la ventilation au repos et dans les réponses ventilatoires hypoxiques et hypercapniques chez les résidents permanents en altitude du Tibet et des Andes. Les hommes, mais non les femmes, diffèrent dans leur hyperventilation hyperoxique, les péruviens souffrant d'une diminution de la respiration au cours de l'hyperoxie, ce qui n'arrive pas avec les tibétains. Les réponses ventilatoires hypoxiques des femmes sont moindres que celles des hommes des deux endroits. La comparaison des niveaux de PO_2 et PCO_2 entre nos sujets et ceux examinés antérieurement en utilisant le diagramme de Rahn-Otis, révèlent que les valeurs péruviennes et tibétaines se rapprochent de ceux de la courbe d'un nouvel arrivé. Nos valeurs péruviennes sont plus proches de la courbe du nouvel arrivé que celles consignées dans d'autres études réalisées dans les Andes, tandis que les valeurs tibétaines sont en accord avec d'autres réalisées dans l'Himalaya. Il serait nécessaire d'avoir des études qui utilisent des techniques identiques pour les résidents en altitude des Andes et de l'Himalaya, convenablement sélectionnés et en nombre suffisant pour que l'erreur expérimentale dans et chez les sujets, le type de variation entre chaque population par âge et par sexe, et l'influence des facteurs qui altèrent la réponse ventilatoire - comme le taux de métabolisme et la température - puissent être controlés et/ou documentés.

Mots clés : Ventilation pulmonaire, population andine, population tibétaine, femme vivant en altitude.

INTRODUCTION

Over 50 million people live at high altitude worldwide. While populations have lived successfully for generations in the Andean and Himalayan regions, limited archaeological and paleontological data suggest that there has been longer human habitation on the Tibetan Plateau than in the Andean region (5, 14, 20, 29). Evidence stemming from studies of pregnancy and neonatal life as well as in adults suggests that Tibetans may be better-adapted to altitude than Andean highlanders (3, 6, 7, 8, 18, 19, 21, 28, 30).

Comparisons between Andean and Himalayan residents are of interest for determining whether strategies of adaptation vary by region and/or numbers of generations of high-altitude residence. However, few studies have been performed in Andean and Himalayan residents by the same investigators using the same study techniques, and fewer still have included women in the study samples. In order to begin to compare Andean and Tibetan high-altitude residents of both sexes, we report here our measurements of resting ventilation, hypoxic and hypercapnic ventilatory responses in 31 Peruvian and 40 Tibetan men and women. While the sample sizes are too small to permit generalizations about regional differences in high-altitude adaptation, the information obtained is instructive about how such a comparison should be carried out.

MATERIALS AND METHODS

Subjects

Peruvian subjects resided in Cerro de Pasco, Peru (elevation 4300 m, barometric pressure 455 mmHg). Tibetan subjects were residents of Lhasa, Tibet Autonomous Region, China (elevation 3658 m, barometric pressure 490 mmHg). All subjects gave informed consent to study procedures approved by the University of Colorado Health Sciences Center Institutional Review Board and were healthy as judged by medical history and physical exam. One Peruvian female, 7 Peruvian males, and 12 Tibetan males smoked cigarettes (0.4, 0.2 ± 0.1 and 2.7 ± 0.7 pack years, respectively). All Peruvian subjects were born and raised at 4300 m, and were of Indian or Mestizo ancestry. The Tibetans were born and had always lived at an altitude $\geq$ 3658 m and were of Tibetan descent without known low-altitude progenitor.

Equipment and study techniques

Measurements were conducted at the High Altitude Research Laboratory in Cerro de Pasco, Peru in October 1982 - March 1983 and the Tibet Institute of Medical Sciences in Lhasa, Tibet Autonomous Region, China from August 1987 - July 1991. Forced vital capacity was measured in standing subjects using a recording spirometer (8 or 13 liters; Warren Collins, Braintree, MA). The remaining ventilatory measurements were performed in resting, seated subjects while they breathed through a bidirectional respiratory valve (Koegel Y valve, San Antonio, TX, in Peru and model 1400, Rudolph, Kansas City, MO, in Tibet) from which PO_2 and PCO_2 were sampled continuously by fuel cell O_2 analyzer (model 101, Applied Technical Products, Denver CO) and infrared CO_2 analyzer (Model LB-2, Beckman Instruments, Fullerton, CA). Gas analyzers were calibrated before each set of room air, hypoxic, or hyperoxic measurements with gases analyzed on-site by the Scholander technique. Arterial O_2 saturation (SaO_2) was monitored using an ear oximeter (model 47201A, Hewlett-Packard, Waltham, MA). Ventilation was measured in Peru by collecting expired gases in a recording 13-liter spirometer (Collins, Braintree, MA) and in Tibet by a dry gas flowmeter during room air breathing and hyperoxia (model RAM 9200, Rayfield, Waitsfield, VT). Ventilation was measured using the 13-liter spirometer (Collins, Braintree, MA) during hypoxic and hypercapnic ventilatory tests in both locations. The electrical signals from the fuel cell O_2 analyzer, ear oximeter, and CO_2 infrared analyzer were recorded on multi-channel strip chart recorders (Soltec model S-4202, Sun Valley, CA and Cole Palmer model 142, Chicago IL in Peru; Prime Line Model R304, San Francisco, CA in Tibet). Electrocardiograms were recorded in all subjects (Model 500, Sanborn, Waltham, MA).

Subjects came to the laboratory after having fasted for ≥ 4 hours. Forced vital capacity was measured in triplicate and the highest value accepted. After the subject had been seated in a chair at rest for 20 min, minute ventilation, end-tidal O_2 and CO_2 tensions and arterial O_2 saturation were monitored for ≥ 5 min or until values became stable. The arterial O_2 saturation values reported are those obtained while the subjects breathed through a mouthpiece; measurements obtained without a mouthpiece in place were similar.

The isocapnic hypoxic ventilatory response was measured in duplicate using a rebreathing system (17). Progressive hypoxia was induced over 10 min by having the subject rebreathe in a closed circuit from a spirometer that initially contained 70% O_2 in nitrogen in Peru and room air in Tibet. As the subjects consumed the O_2 in the spirometer, the end-tidal PO_2 and arterial O_2 saturation were reduced to approximately 40 mmHg or 70% respectively. Isocapnia was maintained at the subject's eucapnic value by regulating the amount of expired gas shunted through the cannister containing CO_2 absorber. Ventilation, end-tidal gas tensions, and arterial O_2 saturation were averaged over 30-s intervals. Curves relating ventilation to end-tidal PO_2 are hyperbolic and were analyzed for each run in each subject by fitting the data to the hyperbolic equation: $V_E = V_0 + A/(P_{ET}O_2 - 32)$, where V_E was in l/min BTPS, V_0 was the ventilation asymptote, A was the shape parameter, and 32 was the $P_{ET}O_2$ asymptote. The relationship of V_E and arterial O_2 saturation is linear and was described by the slope $\Delta V_E/\Delta SaO_2$. The hypoxic ventilatory response A and $DV_E/DSaO_2$ were averaged from duplicate measurements made on two separate days in Peru and from duplicate measurements on one day in Tibet. The mean $\pm$ SEM of differences in the A value between measurements on a given day was 8 ± 7, 1 ± 10, 5 ± 10, and 3 ± 8 for Peruvian women and men and Tibetan women and men, respectively.

To measure resting ventilation during hyperoxia, the subject breathed from a bag containing 70% O_2. End-tidal gas sampling was discontinued and CO_2 was absorbed from the inspired air while the subject breathed from the spirometer for 3-5 min. Arterial O_2 saturation remained at 98-100% throughout the test.

The hypercapnic ventilatory response was measured using a modified rebreathing technique (23). Sufficient O_2 was added to the spirometer to maintain $P_{ET}O_2 > 150$ mmHg. As the subject rebreathed, a progressive rise in end-tidal PCO_2 of 10-15 mmHg occurred within 7-10 min. Curves relating V_E to $P_{ET}CO_2$ were linear and were analyzed by fitting data to the linear equation: $V_E = S (P_{ET}CO_2 - B)$ where S is the slope $\Delta V_E / \Delta P_{ET}CO_2$ and B is the X-intercept. Hypercapnic responses on separate days were averaged for Peruvian subjects.

In Peru, the order of the testing consisted of measuring resting ventilation, end-tidal gases, and arterial O_2 saturation during room air breathing followed by the hyperoxic ventilation, the two isocapnic hypoxic ventilatory response tests and the hypercapnic ventilatory test. The same sequence was followed in Tibet except that hyperoxic ventilation was measured before the hypercapnic ventilatory response. The total testing time was 2 - 3 hours.

Statistics

Values in figures and tables are means $\pm$ standard error of the mean (SEM). Two-sample (Student's) t tests were used to compare all subjects between the two altitudes. One-way analysis of variance with specific contrasts was used to compare women with men at each location. Similar techniques were used to compare women with women and men with men (*i.e.* same sex comparisons) at the two locations. Results were considered significant when $p < 0.05$.

RESULTS

Comparison between locations

The Peruvians and Tibetans were similar in age but the Peruvians were shorter and had a smaller body surface area than the Tibetans (Table 1). The Peruvian women were slightly older and the Peruvian men were slightly younger than their Tibetan counterparts. Within each gender, the Peruvians were shorter and heavier than the Tibetans but had equivalent body surface area (Table 1).

Forced vital capacity was lower in the Peruvians than the Tibetans but similar when calculated per cm height (Table 1). Forced vital capacity did not differ in the Peruvian and Tibetan women or in the Peruvian and Tibetan men (Table 1).

Room air ventilation and respiratory frequency were similar in the entire sample Peruvians and Tibetans (Table 1). The Peruvian men tended to have a a larger tidal volume than the Tibetan men either when absolute values were considered (p=0.06, Table 1) or when tidal volume was expressed relative to body size (0.44±0.02 *vs.* 0.38±0.02 l BTPS/m² BSA, p<.05)]. Respiratory frequency also tended to be lower in the Peruvian than the Tibetan men (p=0.08, one-tailed test). Consistent with their higher altitude of residence, the Peruvians had lower end-tidal O_2 tensions and arterial O_2 saturations than the Tibetans (Table 1).

Tabla 1 - Group and ventilatory characteristics.

	All Peruvians	All Tibetans	Women		Men	
			Peru	Tibet	Peru	Tibet
n	31	40	21	13	10	27
Altitude (meters)	4300	3658	4300	3658	4300	3658
Age (years)	24 ± 1	23 ± 0	25 ± 1	22 ± 1*	20 ± 1†	23 ± 1*
Height (cm)	153 ± 1	163 ± 1*	149 ± 1	156 ± 2*	162 ± 2†	167 ± 1*†
Weight (kg)	54 ± 1	53 ± 1	53 ± 1	49 ± 1*	57 ± 2†	55 ± 1†
Body surface area (m²)	1.50 ± 0.02	1.56 ± 0.02*	1.46 ± 0.02	1.47 ± 0.02	1.60 ± 0.03†	1.61 ± 0.01†
Forced vital capacity (l BTPS)	3.96 ± 0.15	4.45 ± 0.14*	3.51 ± 0.8	3.41 ± 0.12	4.95 ± 0.19†	4.96 ± 0.10†
FVC (ml/cm ht)	26 ± 1	27 ± 1	23 ± 0	22 ± 1	31 ± 1†	30 ± 1†
Room air ventilation						
Ventilation (l BTPS/min)	10.2 ± 0.3	11.1 ± 0.4	9.5 ± 0.4	10.1 ± 0.5	11.6 ± 0.4†	11.50 ± 0.5
(l BTPS/min/m² BSA)	6.8 ± 0.2	7.1 ± 0.2	6.5 ± 0.2	6.9 ± 0.3	7.3 ± 0.2	7.1 ± 0.3
Respiratory frequency (breaths/min)	18 ± 1	19 ± 1	18 ± 1	20 ± 1	17 ± 1	19 ± 1
Tidal volume (l BTPS)	0.59 ± 0.02	0.59 ± 0.02	0.54 ± 0.02	0.50 ± 0.01	0.71 ± 0.04†	0.62 ± 0.03†
End-tidal PO_2 (mmHg)	58.7 ± 0.8	67.2 ± 0.5*	58.3 ± 1.0	68.8 ± 1.1*	59.5 ± 0.9	66.5 ± 0.4*
End-tidal PCO_2 (mmHg)	31.0 ± 0.5	31.5 ± 0.5	31.0 ± 0.7	30.7 ± 0.7	31.0 ± 0.8	31.9 ± 0.6
Arterial O_2 saturation (%)	84.7 ± 0.6	89.2 ± 0.3*	83.9 ± 0.7	89.0 ± 0.5*	86.4 ± 0.6†	89.3 ± 0.3*
Heart rate (beats/min)	76 ± 2	74 ± 2	75 ± 2	75 ± 2	77 ± 3	73 ± 3
Hypoxic ventilatory response						
Hyperoxic V_E (l BTPS/min)	9.0 ± 0.4	11.3 ± 0.4*	8.8 ± 0.6	9.8 ± 0.5	9.6 ± 0.4	11.8 ± 0.5*†
(l BTPS/min/m² BSA)	6.0 ± 0.3	7.2 ± 0.3*	6.1 ± 0.4	6.8 ± 0.4	6.0 ± 0.3	7.4 ± 0.3*
A value (per m² BSA)	42 ± 7	59 ± 8	28 ± 7	27 ± 6	68 ± 10†	76 ± 11†
Δ V_E/Δ SaO_2 (per m² BSA)	-0.105 ± 0.035	-0.234 ± 0.030*	-0.023 ± 0.032	-0.112 ± 0.020	-0.268 ± 0.052†	-0.292 ± 0.039†
Hypercapnic ventilatory response						
S value (per m² BSA)	0.80 ± 0.08	0.82 ± 0.06	0.84 ± 0.11	0.66 ± 0.07	0.73 ± 0.07	0.89 ± 0.07
B (mmHg)	24.6 ± 1.1	21.0 ± 1.2*	25.1 ± 1.4	18.0 ± 2.0*	23.7 ± 1.7	22.5 ± 1.6

Abbreviations: FVC, forced vital capacity; V_E, minute ventilation; BSA, body surface area; SaO_2, arterial oxygen saturation

* p<.05 comparison between all Peruvians vs. all Tibetans; Peru vs. Tibet females, or Peru vs. Tibet males
† p<.05 comparison of Peru females vs. Peru males, or Tibet females vs. Tibet males

Ventilation during hyperoxia (inspired $PO_2 > 250$ mmHg) was lower in the Peruvians than the Tibetans (Table 1). Hyperoxic ventilation was similar in Peruvian and Tibetan women but smaller in Peruvian than Tibetan men. The Peruvian men decreased their ventilation during hyperoxia (-1.1 ± 0.3 1 BTPS/m^2 BSA) whereas values did not change in the Tibetan men (0.2 ± 0.3 1 BTPS/min/m^2 BSA). The hypoxic ventilatory response A values were similar in the Peruvians and Tibetans (Table 1, Figure 1). The Tibetan men had more A values in the higher range and a greater coefficient of variation than the Peruvian men (0.73 vs 0.44, Figure 1). The greater $\Delta VE/\Delta SaO_2$ in all the Tibetans compared with all the Peruvians was due to differences in gender composition of the samples at the two locations since Tibetan and Peruvian females or Tibetan and Peruvian males had similar values (Table 1, Figure 2). Hypercapnic ventilatory sensitivity was similar in the Peruvian and Tibetan subjects (Table 1, Figure 3). The Peruvian women had a higher CO_2 intercept (B value) than the Tibetan women but values were similar in the men (Table 1).

Comparisons between genders

The women were shorter, lighter and had less body surface area than the men. Forced vital capacity was lower in the women than the men whether expressed in absolute values or normalized for height (Table 1).

Room air ventilation relative to body surface area was similar in the women and men (Table 1). The Peruvian women had lower tidal volume normalized for body size than the Peruvian men ($0.37+0.02$ *vs.* 0.44 ± 0.2 1 BTPS/m^2 BSA, p <0.05). Values were similar in Tibetan women and men. Arterial O_2 saturation was lower in Peruvian women than men but similar in Tibetan women and men (Table 1). Respiratory frequency, end-tidal PO_2, end-tidal PCO_2, and heart rate were similar in the women and men at both locations (Table 1).

Hyperoxic ventilation normalized for body surface area was similar in women compared with men at both locations (Table 1). The hypoxic ventilatory response A and $\Delta V_E/\Delta SaO_2$ values were lower in the women than the men whether expressed as absolute values or per m^2 body surface area (Table 1, Figures 1 and 2). The difference stemmed from a shift to lower values in the entire distribution of A values (Figure 1). Hypercapnic ventilatory sensitivity and the CO_2 intercept (B value) were similar in women and men (Table 1, Figure 3).

DISCUSSION

We found little difference in resting ventilation, hypoxic or hypercapnic ventilatory responsiveness between lifelong Peruvian and Tibetan high-altitude residents. At each location, women had lower hypoxic ventilatory responses than men. The differences between women and men were greater than the differences between locations.

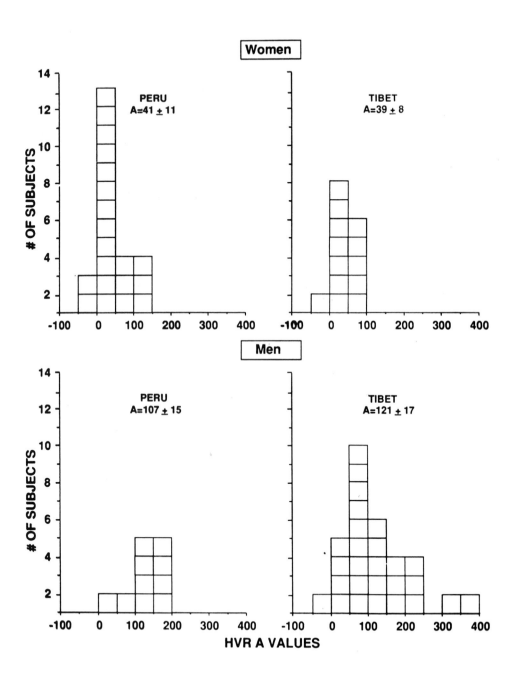

Fig. 1 - Histogram of individual hypoxic ventilatory response (HVR) A values. HVR did not differ in Peruvians compared with Tibetans, but was greater in men than women at each location (p<0.05).

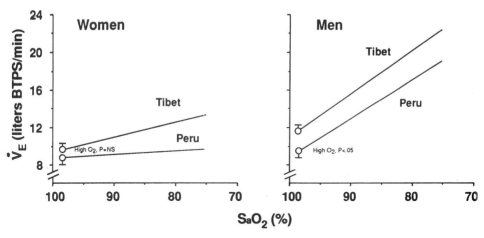

Fig. 2 - The slope of the change in minute ventilation (VE) in response to the change in arterial O_2 saturation (SaO_2) was similar in Peruvians and Tibetans when data are compared by gender. The response slope was greater in men than women at both locations. Hyperoxic ventilation (open circles) was similar in the two groups of women, but was higher in Tibetan compared with Peruvian men.

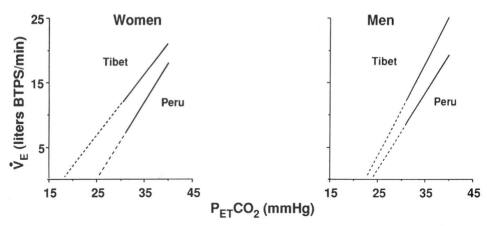

Fig. 3 The slope of the change in minute ventilation (VE) in response to the change in end-tidal PCO_2 ($PETCO_2$) was similar in Peruvians and Tibetans, and in men compared with women at each location.

The limitations of our study stemmed from differences in altitude, the unequal numbers of females and males in the two samples, and from the small sample sizes. Because of their higher altitude of residence, the Peruvians had lower end-tidal PO_2 and arterial O_2 saturation values. There were more women than men in the Peru sample and more men than women in the Tibet sample. For variables such as forced vital capacity which differed between women and men, the larger number of women in the Peruvian sample and the larger number of men in the Tibetan sample caused forced vital capacity to differ when comparing all the subjects at the two locations. Likewise, the

Tibetans' higher $\Delta VE/\Delta SaO_2$ was due to the male's higher values and the larger proportion of men in the Tibetan than the Peruvian sample.

Samples ranging from 10 to 27 persons were studied at the two locations. The question of what constitutes an adequate sample size and how representative samples are to be obtained requires some knowledge of the range of variation in the parameters of interest. With respect to hypoxic ventilatory responsiveness, previous studies in Andean or Himalayan high-altitude residents were done long ago using different techniques (e.g. the potentiation of the ventilatory response to CO_2 at various inspired PO_2, the relationship between alveolar PCO_2 and PO_2 among individuals living at different altitudes, and the effect of O_2 administration on ventilation during exercise). Since these techniques involve multiple ventilatory stimuli, they do not permit identification of the effect of hypoxia *per se* on ventilation. We chose a well-established methodology for measuring hypoxic ventilatory response which can be used in a field setting. However, additional studies are required to address questions of reproducibility within and between subjects over time, the effects of gender and of age, and the influence of factors such as metabolic rate or exercise training which are known to modify hypoxic ventilatory response at low altitude (1).

Our findings indicated that the Peruvians were shorter and heavier than the Tibetans but had equivalent body surface area when data were considered by gender. When normalized for height or body surface area, the two groups had similar forced vital capacity and resting ventilation in keeping with our previous report (6). A tendency existed for the Tibetan men to have a different ventilatory pattern than the Peruvian men insofar as the Tibetans had a smaller tidal volume and a trend toward a higher respiratory frequency (p = 0.08). This high-frequency respiratory pattern among Tibetans agrees with an earlier report in Sherpas (9).

Using the data obtained from the same Tibetan men as in the present report, we have previously reported that male Tibetans had hypoxic ventilatory responses similar to those of low-altitude residents, greater than those of lifelong high-altitude residents of Colorado, and similar or greater than those of Sherpas native to 2,200 m but studied at 1377 m (30). Qualitative comparisons suggested that the male Tibetans' values were greater than those observed in lifelong Peruvian or Bolivian high-altitude residents (12, 13). The similarity observed between the male Tibetans and the male Peruvians in the present report does not support the assertion that the Tibetans have higher ventilatory responses than Andean high-altitude natives. Of interest, however, were the differences observed in the distribution of the hypoxic ventilatory response A values and in the hyperoxic ventilatory responses in the Tibetan *vs* the Peruvian men. The Tibetans exhibited a greater range of variation and had more A values in the higher range than the Peruvian men. Since sample sizes differed and a similar tendency was not observed among the women, it is not clear whether differences in the variability of hypoxic ventilatory

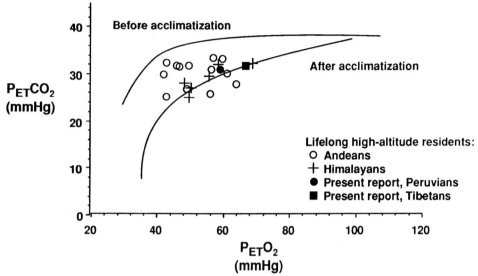

Fig. 4 - A Rahn-Otis diagram showing the relationship between end-tidal PCO_2 (PETCO$_2$) and end-tidal PO_2 (PETO$_2$) before and after acclimatization. Subjects before acclimatization were studied within one hour of ascent (22). The values of lifelong altitude residents in the Andes and the Himalayas are plotted in relation to the curve established for acclimatized newcomers 4 days to 1-2 years after ascent (data summarized 30).

responsiveness exist in the two locations. With brief hyperoxia ($P_IO_2 > 250$ mmHg), the Peruvian men decreased their ventilation whereas Tibetan men did not. We and others have observed a paradoxical hyperventilatory response to hyperoxia in Tibetans (9, 30). This is supported here by the absence of a fall in minute ventilation but is better documented by the fall in end-tidal PCO_2 reported previously (30). Thus, while the hypothesized differences in hypoxic ventilatory responsiveness between the Tibetan and Peruvian men were not supported, further study is warranted in larger-sized samples before concluding whether or not population differences in hypoxic as well as hyperoxic ventilatory responsiveness exist.

Previous studies of female high-altitude residents are extremely limited. At low altitude, women hyperventilate (have lower end-tidal and arterial CO2 tensions) compared with men (1). However, there are not clear differences in hypoxic and hypercapnic ventilatory response between women and men despite the stimulatory effects of female hormones on ventilatory drives (1, 27, 24). Little is known concerning gender differences in acclimatization to high altitude. There is some indication that women are less susceptible than men to high-altitude pulmonary edema but not to acute mountain sickness (11). Among prior studies of lifelong high-altitude residents, nearly all include only male subjects. Cudkowicz is among the few to have included both women and men, although only a total of 14 female residents of two altitudes (3600 and 5200 m) were studied (4). He found that the women hypoventilated relative to the men at both altitudes, having higher end-tidal PCO_2 and lower end-tidal PO_2 values (4). Our comparisons of Peruvians and Tibetans revealed that the women had lower hypoxic ventilatory responses than the men at both locations. Finding a low hypoxic ventilatory response among the high-altitude women was unexpected given the stimulatory effects of female hormones on ventilatory responsiveness (10, 24) and the infrequency with · which chronic mountain sickness develops among women (15, 16, 21). However, the role of a low hypoxic ventilatory response in the etiology of chronic mountain sickness is unclear.

To compare the levels of resting ventilation observed with published values for high-altitude residents, we plotted the Peruvian and Tibetan end-tidal PO_2 and PCO_2 on a Rahn-Otis diagram (Figure 4). The Peruvian and Tibetan values were close to the curve established for acclimatized newcomers. Inspection of the range of reported values revealed that our Peruvian values were closer to the acclimatized newcomer curve than most other Andean studies, while the Tibetan values were in accordance with those of prior Himalayan reports. The position of the Peruvian and Tibetan samples on the Rahn-Otis curve agreed with the similarity in hypoxic ventilatory responsiveness between the two locations but does not accord with previous reports of hypoventilation in Andean and in some Himalayan lifelong high-altitude residents (reviewed in 30). The source of the difference between this and previous reports is not clear. It is not likely to be due simply to smaller sample sizes, younger-aged subjects, or lower altitudes of residence since blunting has been observed at lower altitudes than those of the present report (12), in similarly-aged subjects and in equally small sample sizes (4). Needed are carefully controlled studies of the within-day and between-day variation in alveolar ventilation as well as in hypoxic ventilatory responsiveness.

Further comparisons between Tibetan and Andean high-altitude inhabitants are of interest in light of recent studies suggesting that Tibetans may be better-adapted to altitude than Andean highlanders. Tibetan newborns are protected from high-altitude intrauterine growth retardation (18, 28). They have higher levels of arterial O_2 saturation in the neonatal and early infancy periods than Han («Chinese») newborns at 3658 m (19) which may be protective against the development of subacute infantile mountain sickness (25). Pulmonary artery pressures measured in small numbers of Tibetans are within the sea-level normal range and respond minimally to added hypoxia or near-maximal exercise (7). Autopsy data suggests that the muscularization of pulmonary arteries observed in Andeans is absent in Tibetan residents of Ladakh (2, 8). Monge's disease (chronic mountain sickness, *soroche*) (15, 16, 21) may also be less common among Himalayan than North or South American high-altitude residents, perhaps explaining the tendency toward lower hemoglobin concentration at a given altitude (3, 26).

The limited data of this report does not support the existence of differences in the levels of resting ventilation, hypoxic or hypercapnic ventilatory responsiveness in lifelong, healthy, male and female residents of Cerro de Pasco, Peru compared with those of Lhasa, Tibet Autonomous

Region. However, the present studies are not definitive because of limitations due to the small numbers of not-necessarily representative subjects that were studied. Needed are studies using identical techniques in carefully selected and sufficiently large numbers of persons that sources of experimental error within and between subjects and the range of variation within each population by age and by gender can be documented. Further, such studies need to be conducted under conditions in which factors known to influence ventilation and HVR (*e.g.* metabolic rate, temperature) can be carefully controlled. Genetic markers should be sampled so the degree of admixture and information on population history can be obtained. Studies should be extended to include older-aged persons so that age-related changes in hypoxic ventilatory response in relation to the appearance of the age-associated syndrome of chronic mountain sickness can be addressed in both genders. Once this information is obtained, future studies can be designed to determine whether any differences observed between Himalayan and Andean high-altitude inhabitants are due to innate (genetic) or acquired (environmental) influences.

ACKNOWLEDGEMENTS

The cooperation of our subjects, the people of Cerro de Pasco and Lhasa, and the assistance of our colleagues at the Universidad Peruana Cayetano Heredia and the Tibet Institute of Medical Science in Lhasa, is gratefully acknowledged. This research was supported by NIH CHD HD-000681, NIH HLBI HL-14985, NSF BNS 8919645, U.S. Army DAMD 17-87-C7202, and AHA 80-837.

REFERENCES

1. AITKIN, M.L., FRANKLIN, J.L., PIERSON, D.J. & SCHOENE, R.B. 1986. Influence of body size and gender on control of ventilation. *J. Appl. Physiol.* 60: 1894-1899.
2. BANCHERO, N., SIME, F., PEÑALOZA, D., CRUZ, J., GAMBOA, R. & MARTICORENA, E. 1966. Pulmonary pressure, cardiac output and arterial oxygen saturation during exercise at high altitude and at sea level. *Circulation* 33: 249-262.
3. BEALL, C.M., STROHL, K.P. & BRITTENHAM, G.M. 1983. Reappraisal of Andean high altitude erythrocytosis from a Himalayan perspective. *Semin. Respir. Med.* 5: 195-210.
4. CUDKOWICZ, L., SPIELVOGEL, H. & ZUBIETA, G. 1972. Respiratory studies in women at high altitude (3,600 m or 12,200 ft and 5,200 m or 17,200 ft). *Respiration* 29: 393-426.
5. DENELL, R.W., RENDELL, H.M. & HAILWOOD, E. 1988. Late Pliocene artifacts from northern Pakistan. *Curr. Anthropol.* 29: 495-498.
6. DROMA, R., MCCULLOUGH, R.G., MCCULLOUGH, R.E., ZHUANG, J., CYMERMAN, A., SUN, S., SUTTON, J.R. & MOORE, L.G. 1991. Increased vital and total lung capacities in Tibetan compared to Han residents of Lhasa (3658 m). *Am. J. Phys. Anthropol.* 86: 341-351.

7. GROVES, B.M., DROMA, T., SUTTON, J.R., MCCULLOUGH, R.G., MCCULLOUGH, R.E., ZHUANG, J., RAPMUND, G., SUN, S., JANES, C. & MOORE, L.G. 1993. Minimal hypoxic pulmonary hypertension in normal Tibetans at 3,658 m. *J. Appl. Physiol.* In press,

8. GUPTA, M.L., RAO, K.S., ANAND, I.S., BAERJEE, A.K. & BOPARAI, M.S. Lack of smooth muscle in the small pulmonary arteries of the native Ladakhi - Is the Himalayan highlander adapted? *Am. Rev. Respir. Dis.*. Submitted.

9. HACKETT, P.H., REEVES, J.T., REEVES, C.D., GROVER, R.F. & RENNIE, D. 1980. Control of breathing in Sherpas at high and low altitude. *J. Appl. Physiol.* 49: 374-379.

10. HANNHART, B., PICKETT, C.K. & MOORE, L.G. 1990. Effects of estrogen and progesterone on carotid body neural output responsiveness to hypoxia. *J. Appl. Physiol.* 68: 1909-1916.

11. HONIGMAN, B., THEIS, M.K., KOZIOL-MCLAIN, J., ROACH, R., YIP, R., HOUSTON, C. & MOORE, L.G. 1993. Acute mountain sickness in a general tourist population at moderate altitudes. *Ann. Int. Med.* In press.

12. LAHIRI, S., MILLEDGE, J.S. & SORENSEN, C. 1972. Ventilation in man during exercise at high altitude. *J. Appl. Physiol.* 32: 766-769.

13. LEFRANCOIS, R., GAUTIER, H.& PASQUIS, P. 1968. Ventilatory oxygen drive in acute and chronic hypoxia. *Respir. Physiol.* 4: 217-228.

14. MACNEISH, R.S. & BERGER, R.P. 1970. Megafauna and man from Ayacucho, highland Peru. *Science* 166: 975-977.

15. MONGE-C., C. 1976. Chronic mountain sickness. *Johns Hopkins Med. J.* 139: 87-89.

16. MONGE-M., C. & MONGE-C.,C. 1966. *High-Altitude Diseases: mechanism and management*. Springfield, Il: Charles C. Thomas.

17. MOORE, L.G., BRODEUR, P., CHUMBE, O., D'BROT, J., HOFMEISTER, S. & MONGE, C. 1986. Maternal hypoxic ventilatory response, ventilation and infant birth weight at 4,300 m. *J. Appl. Physiol.* 60: 1401-1406.

18. MOORE, L.G. 1990. Maternal O_2 transport and fetal growth in Colorado, Peru, and Tibet high-altitude residents. *Am. J. Hum. Biol.* 2: 627-637.

19. NIERMEYER, S., PING, Y,. SHANMINA, O., DROLKAR, O. & MOORE, L.G. In Press. Adequate arterial O_2 saturation in native but not newcomer newborns at high altitude. *Pediatr. Res.*

20. NUÑEZ, L. 1983. Paleoindian and archaic cultural periods in the arid and semiarid regions of Northern Chile. *Adv. World Archaeol.* 2: 161-203.

21. PEI, S.X., CHEN, X.J., SI REN, B.Z., LIU, Y.H., CHENG, X.S., HARRIS, E.M., ANAND, I.S. & HARRIS, P.C. 1989. Chronic mountain sickness in Tibet. *Q. J. Med.* 71: 555-574.

22. RAHN, H. & OTIS, A.B. 1949. Man's respiratory response during and after acclimatization to high altitude. *Am. J. Physiol.* 157: 445-462.

23. READ, D.J.C. 1967. A clinical method for assessing the ventilatory response to carbon dioxide. *Australas. Ann. Med.* 16: 20-32.

24. REGENSTEINER, J.G., WOODARD, W.D., HAGERMAN, D.D., WEIL, J.V., PICKETT, C.K., BENDER, P.R. & MOORE, L.G. 1989. Combined effects of female hormones and metabolic rate on ventilatory drives in women. *J. Appl. Physiol.* 66: 808-813.

25. SUI, G.J., LIU, Y.H., CHENG, X.S., ANAND, I.S., HARRIS, E., HARRIS, P. & HEATH, D. 1988. Subacute infantile mountain sickness. *J. of Pathol.* 155: 161-170.

26. WINSLOW, R.M., CHAPMAN, K.W., GIBSON, C.C., SAMJA, M., MONGE, C.C., GOLDWASSER, E., SHERPA, M., BLUME, F.D. & SANTOLAYA, R. 1989. Different hematologic responses to hypoxia in Sherpas and Quechua Indians. *J. Appl. Physiol.* 66: 1561-1569.

27. WHITE, D.P., DOUGLAS, N.J., PICKETT, C.K., WEIL J.V. & ZWILLICH, C.W. 1983. Sexual influence on the control of breathing. *J. Appl. Physiol.* 54: 874-879.

28. ZAMUDIO, S., DROMA, T., YONZON, K., AHARYA, G., ZAMUDIO, J.A., NIERMEYER, S.N. & MOORE, L.G. 1993. Protection from intrauterine growth retardation in Tibetans at high altitude. *Am. J. Phys. Anthropol.* In Press.

29. ZHIMIN, A. *et al.* 1982. Paleoliths and microliths from Sheja and Shuanghu, Northern Tibet. *Current Anthropol.* 23: 493-499.

30. ZHUANG, J., DROMA, T., SUN, S., JANES, C., MCCULLOUGH, R.E., MCCULLOUGH, R.G., CYMERMAN, A., HUANG, S.Y., REEVES, J.T. & MOORE, L.G. 1993. Hypoxic ventilatory responsiveness in Tibetan compared with Han residents of 3,658 m. *J. Appl. Physiol.* 74(1): In press.

GOLDEN AGE OF HIGH ALTITUDE PHYSIOLOGY

Sukhamay Lahiri

Abstract

The evolving views of the Monges' with respect to adaptation of high altitude natives have been reviewed in the context of the observations during the past several decades. The consensus is that, confronted with low oxygen pressure gradients (air to cells) from birth, the high altitude natives (HN) develop particular defense strategies. Two of these have to do with the two well-known oxygen sensitive tissues: peripheral chemoreceptors and erythropoietin producing tissues. Both can and do respond differently in the HN than the sea level natives. Peripheral chemoreceptor dependent control of ventilation due to hypoxia is blunted. The strategy seems to be saving metabolic energy and an increased tolerance of hypoxia.

That was the golden age when most of these high altitude studies were accomplished. A new age should be in sight.

Key words: Hypoxia, high altitude physiology, chemoreceptors, ventilation.

Resumen

Se revisa el desarrollo de los puntos de vista de los Monge con respecto a la adaptación de los nativos de altura en el contexto de las observaciones y hallazgos que han tenido lugar en las últimas décadas. El consenso es que, confrontados con bajos gradientes de presión de oxígeno (del ambiente a las células) desde el nacimiento, los nativos de altura (HN) desarrollan estrategias particulares de defensa. Dos de éstas están relacionadas con los dos bien conocidos tejidos sensibles al oxígeno: los quimiorreceptores periféricos y los tejidos productores de eritropoyetina. Ambos pueden, y efectivamente responden desigualmente en los HN con respecto a los nativos de nivel del mar. El control de la ventilación con respecto a la hipoxia se encuentra hiporeactivo. La estrategia pareciera ser el ahorro de energia metabólica y un aumento de tolerancia a la hipoxia.

Esa fue la edad de oro, cuando la mayoría de estos estudios en altura fueron llevados a cabo. Una nueva edad debería estar a la vista.

Palabras claves: Hipoxia, fisiología de altura, quimiorreceptores, ventilación.

Résumé

Cet article passe en revue les points de vue de Carlos Monge, père et fils sur l'adaptation des personnes nées en altitude dans le contexte des observations et découvertes des dernières décennies. Il y a un consensus sur le fait que, confrontés à de faibles gradients de pression d'oxygène (du milieu ambiant aux cellules) depuis la naissance, les personnes nées en altitude (HN) développent des stratégies particulières de défense. Deux d'entre elles sont en relation avec les deux tissus particulièrement sensibles à l'oxygène: les chémorécepteurs périphériques et les tissus producteurs d'érythropoïétine. Tous les deux peuvent répondre, et le font effectivement, mais de façon différente chez les HN et chez les personnes nées au niveau de la mer. Le contrôle de la ventilation par rapport à l'hypoxie est hyporéactif. Il semblerait que la stratégie soit celle de l'économie de l'énergie métabolique et une augmentation de tolérance à l'hypoxie.

Ça, c'était l'âge d'or, au moment où se menaient la majorité des études sur l'altitude. Un nouvel âge devrait être en vue.

Mots clés : Hypoxie, physiologie d'altitude, chémorécepteurs, ventilation.

The end of the second world war witnessed a new surge of research in high altitude physiology, stimulated by the scientific interest developed partly due to necessity during the war. Public and government interest in many countries made research funds available. The conjoint interest and efforts created the golden age of high altitude research beginning in the late forties. That period is now over. The Andean high altitudes in South America being the densely populated had the greatest need and provided the most incentive for medical research. The Peruvian and other laboratories in the Andes were more prominent in this organized venture, and the Monges' in Peru, father and son played an eminent role. I was fortunate to come to know both the Monges in 1967 in Lima, Peru. Since then, I returned to the Andes several times for high altitude research and my plan is to recount some of the scientific endeavor in this publication, celebrating the 70th birth anniversary of Professor Carlos Monge C. Since another part of my high altitude ventures concern medical and mountaineering expeditions in the Himalayas, glimpses of that experiences will also be included. Altogether, high altitude studies took me six times (1960, 1961, 1964, 1972, 1980, 1987) to the Himalayas, twice to the Peruvian (1967, 1975) and once (1986) to the Chilean Andes (14). A part of these studies concerns the view of senior Monge that physiologic patterns of high altitude natives are different from the newcomers to high altitude, a view not shared by junior Monge. Although there were signs of reconciliation between the Monges' lately, the controversy has not been resolved and deserves further attention. However, geopolitical and economic changes have impaired the research progress, and after the first round of scientific surge the research has dwindled, and transition from the level of integrative biology to that of cells and molecules has been slow.

BIRTH, LIFE AND OXYGEN

Before birth, arterial PO_2 of a fetus at any altitude is lower than that in the normal adult. At birth, all newborns are hypoxemic. It is only after birth that arterial PO_2 increases, most at sea level and least at highest altitudes, and then a wide difference is established in arterial PO_2 between sea level and high altitude natives. At the stage of early extra-uterine development, biological make-up of cells undergoes explosive changes. Accordingly it is a reasonable assumption that continuing cellular hypoxia would leave an important imprint on its function, because oxygen in many instances is a metabolic and molecular determinant. Lack of adequate cellular observations makes it impossible to judge and predict the mechanism of effect of hypoxia but emphasizes the need for exploration of the pathways by which this all important molecules regulate living processes.

Because the cells find themselves in a quantitatively different oxygen environment, one may postulate that there may be a quantitative but not a qualitative difference in the cellular make up between altitudes. There is obviously other environmental and ecological factors which would influence the behavior of the organism at high altitude but low oxygen pressure cannot be avoided by external adjustment (e.g., clothing, shelter, food, etc.) leaving the only option of internal adjustment.

A reasonable hypothesis regarding the speed of cellular adjustment after birth is that the most change in arterial PO_2 at sea level would lead to most responses whereas smaller change at high altitudes would lead to slower and least responses. Testing the hypothesis requires aserial comparative measurements which are rare. More recently Hanson et al. (4) and Hertzberg et al. (5) reported that continued hypoxia after birth in kittens and rats respectively delayed development of hypoxic ventilatory chemoreflex. Previously it was shown that continued hypoxemia in the children with congenital cyanotic heart disease had blunted ventilatory response to hypoxia (2) and thath surgical correction of cyanosis improved the response (1). The cyanosis with heart disease however is not an ideal model of chronic hypoxia alone.

Prolonged hypoxia however may not totally suppress the developmental physiology. It has beeb found that within the first decade of life at high altitude the hypoxic chemoreflex develops, and subsequently it declines (10). It has also been found that the blunted response in the high altitude natives reverses upon years of residence at sea level (10). Blunted ventilatory response to hypoxia has also been observed in the adult Sherpa high altitude natives in the Himalayas (7). Although Hackett et al. (3) found that blunting of ventilatory response to hypoxia was age-dependent in Sherpas, they expressed a different interpretation. However, comparative study of the young high altitude natives in the Chilean Andes and in Nepal Himalayas confirmed their blunted ventilatory response to hypoxia (9). Taken together, it is clear that the high altitude natives develop blunted ventilatory response to hypoxia which is not reversible in a short time. Lowlanders after prolonged residence at high altitude may develop similar characteristics which appear to be more readily reversible.

Thus, prolonged hypoxia after birth leads to ventilatory attributes which are different from those at sea level. These attributes are shared by both natives of and residents at high altitude. It is in this area perhaps that Carlos Monge Cassinelli came close to the view of his father (15) but subtle and important differences persist.

In the context it is appropriate to note in that Hochachka with his colleagues (6, 11) have provided fresh evidence in favor of the hypothesis that the Andean highlanders do not change over their metabolic pattern (brain and cardiac and skeletal muscles) to the sea level type in several works at sea level. These fundamental observations have given a new dimension to the legend that the high altitude natives are more tolerant to hypoxia of high altitude. Conceptually it makes sense that they are better adapted to their own environment for survival than the newcomers. Incidentally, egg shells of birds native to high altitudes do not share the same strategy of pore-size adaptation to chronic hypoxia as those from sea level with respect to oxygen and water diffusive properties (12).

Like carotid body which is concerned with O_2 transport by convection of air and blood, another specially oxygen sensitive tissue is that which produces erythropoietin and increases oxygen transport capacity by increased erythropoiesis. Chronic hypoxia stimulates both the tissues. The two secondary responses (ventilation and erythropoiesis) are divergent. Excessive responses of the two tissues in the human natives to the Andes have been described (13, 15). One may not be dependent on the other but high altitude natives with high blood hematocrit always show blunted ventilatory response to hypoxia. Hypoventilation however would contribute to a greater hypoxemia and a stronger stimulus for erythropoiesis. Blunted ventilatory response to hypoxia may be associated with the carotid body hypertrophy but the latter is not the cause. The chemosensory response of hypertrophied carotid body is not blunted, and blunted ventilatory response to hypoxia may be found with normal carotid body function (8). The ventilatory response of chemodectoma patient is not known, although their prevalence in the Andes has been described (15). The functional status of carotid body in the high altitude natives still remains unknown.

The physiological characteristic of high altitude natives both in the Andes and Himalayas are different from those of the sea level natives at high altitudes in many subtle ways. These ways are manifested in their legendary performance in soccer field in the Andes and mountain climbing in the high Himalayas, as in their ability to tolerate long breath hold. The extra ability of «tolerance» perhaps makes them different from the newcomers to high altitudes. The mechanism of this tolerance to hypoxia is perhaps the key to the successful adaptation of the high altitude natives as supported by Hochachka's study.

It was on our expedition to Ollague and Ancanquilcha in 1986 that I came to know Carlos Monge-C. as Choclo. He is a walking history of Andean physiology and politics. He is also a storehouse of stories. He would have an interesting stories to tell had he not left Ollague by day and been with us on a midnight freight train, crawling through the cold and thin air of the Andes on March 11, 1986. After about two hours, the train stopped on a mountain top station, the highest in Chile, for shunting and refueling. We came out of the wagon for relief, and there was the spectacular night sky over the Andes with Halley's comet in it. He missed observing the comet with stunning effect but we missed his comraderie.

ACKNOWLEDGEMENT

I am grateful to Ms. Valerie Johnson for her secretarial assistance.

REFERENCES

1. BLESA, M.I., LAHIRI, S., RASHKIND, W.J. & FISHMAN, A.P. 1977. Normalization of the blunted ventilatory response to acute hypoxia in congenital cyanotic hearth disease. *N Engl J Med* 296: 237-241.

2. EDELMAN, H.H., LAHIRI, S., CHEARNIACK, N.S. & FISHMAN, A.P. 1970. The blunted ventilatory response to hypoxia in cyanotic congenital heart disease. *N Engl J Med* 282(8): 405-411.

3. HACKETT, P., REEVES, J.T., REEVES, C.D. & GROVER, R.F. 1980. Control of breathing in Sherpas at low and high altitude. *J. Appl. Physiol.* 49: 374-379.

4. HANSON, M.A., KUMAR, P. & WILLIAMS, B.A. 1989. The effect of chronic hypoxia upon the development of respiratory chemoreflexes on the newborn kitten. *J Physiol. (London)*411: 563-574.

5. HERTZBERG, T., HELLSTROM, S., HOLGERT, H., LAGERCRANTZ, H. & PEQUIGNOT, J.M. 1992. Ventilatory response to hyperoxia in newborn rats born in hypoxia - possible relationship to carotid body dopamine. *J. Physiol. (London)* 450: 645-654.

6. HOCHACHKA, P.W., MATHESON, G.O., PARKHOUSE, W.S., SUMAR-KALINOWSKI, J., STANLEY, C., MONGE, C., McKENZIE, D.C., MERKT, J., MAN, S.F.P., JONES, R. & ALLEN, P.S. 1991. Inborn resistance to hypoxia in high altitude adapted humans. *In*: S. Lahiri, N.S. Charniak & R.S. Fitzgerald (eds), *Reponse and adaptation to hypoxia: organ to organelle*. Oxford: University Press: 191-194.

7. LAHIRI, S. 1984. *In*: J. B. West & S. Lahiri (eds), High Altitude and Man. Bethesda: *Am. Physiol. Soc.*: 147-162.

8. LAHIRI, S. 1991. Oxygenbiology of peripheral chemoreceptors. *In*: S. Lahiri & N.S. Cherniack & R.S. Fitzgerald (eds), *Reponse and adaptation to hypoxia: organ to organelle.*, Oxford: University Press: 95-106.

9. LAHIRI, S. & DATA, P.G. 1992. Chemosensitivity and regulation of ventilation during sleep at high altitudes. *Intl. J. Sports Med.* 13: S31-S33.

10. LAHIRI, S., DELANEY, R.G., BRODIE, J.S., VELÁSQUEZ, T., MOTOYAMA, E.K. & POLGAR, G. 1976. Relative role of environmental and genetic factors in respiratory adaptation to high altitude. *Nature* 261: 133-135.

11. MATHESON, G.O., ALLEN, P.S., ELLINGER, D.C., HANSTOCK, C.C., GHEORGHIU, D., McKENZIE, D.C., STANLEY, C., PARKHOUSE, W.S. & HOCHACHKA, P.W. 1991. Skeletal muscle metabolism and work capacity: a 31P-NMR study of Andean natives and lowlanders. *J. Appl. Physiol.* 70: 1963-1976.

12. MONGE-C., C. & LEÓN-VELARDE, F. 1991. Physiological adaptation to high altitude: Oxygen transport in mammals and birds. *Physiol. Rev.* 71: 1135-1172.

13. MONGE-M., C. & MONGE-C., C. 1966. *High altitude diseases: mechanisms and management*. Springfield: Charles C. Thomas.

14. SANTOLAYA, R.B., LAHIRI, S., ALFARO, R.T. & SCHOENE, R.B. 1989. Respiratory adaptation in the highest Sherpa mountaineers. *Respir. Physiol.* 77: 253-262.

15. WINSLOW, R. M. & MONGE-C., C. 1987. *Hypoxia, polycythemia and chronic mountain Sickness*. Baltimore: Johns Hopkins University Press.

GAS EXCHANGE RESERVE DURING HYPOXIA: ROLE OF CAPILLARY RECRUITMENT

Wiltz W. Wagner, Jr., Robert G. Presson, Jr.

Abstract

Using *in vivo* microscopy we studied the response of the pulmonary microcirculation in the upper lung of dogs to whole lung hypoxia. Unexpectedly, increasingly severe hypoxia consistently raised the level of recruited capillaries. From a series of studies, it was determined that the recruitment was not caused by pulmonary vein constriction, increased left atrial pressure, or increased cardiac output. Rather the pulmonary arterial hypertension resulting from precapillary constriction caused blood flow to be redistributed from the dependent lung to the upper lung where capillary recruitment occurred. The newly perfused capillaries added to the surface area for gas exchange. Work was then begun using video microscopy to determine whether the opening patterns of recruited capillaries were stable or variable. Using an isolated canine lobe, the pump was set to perfuse half of the capillaries. Then the pump was turned of and all of the capillaries closed. By cycling the pump through six on-off cycles, we could determine whether the same or different capillaries were perfused during each of the six observation periods. We found that the perfusion patterns were more reproducible than expected by chance alone indicating the existance of a stable, probably anatomic determinant of capillary opening pressures that controlled the order of capillary recruitment. Considerably more work is required, however, to elucidate the mechanisms that control capillary recruitment.

Key words: Capillarity, pulmonary arterial hypertension, hypoxia, gaseous exchange, pulmonary microcirculation, *in vivo* microscopy.

Resumen

Con el uso de microscopía *in vivo*, estudiamos la respuesta de la microcirculación pulmonar alta en perros sometidos a hipoxia pulmonar severa. Inesperadamente, encontramos que a mayores niveles de hipoxia, se observaba un mayor nivel de reclutamiento capilar. Se determinó a partir de una serie de estudios, que ni la constricción pulmonar venosa, ni el aumento de la presión auricular izquierda, ni el aumento del gasto cardíaco eran la causa del reclutamiento. Más bien, la hipertensión arterial pulmonar, resultado de la constricción precapilar era la causa de la redistribución del flujo sanguíneo desde el pulmón dependiente hasta la parte alta del pulmón donde se observaba el reclutamiento de capilares. Los capilares reclutados de novo incrementarían el área de superficie para el intercambio gaseoso. Se buscó luego, por medio de la microscopía por video, determinar si los patrones de abertura de los capilares reclutados eran estables o variables. Se aisló un lóbulo pulmonar de manera que la bomba perfundiera la mitad de los capilares. Seguidamente, se procedía a apagar la bomba, quedando cerrados todos los capilares. Luego de seis ciclos de encendido y apagado de la bomba era posible determinar si eran los mismos u otros los capilares perfundidos durante cada uno de los seis períodos de observación. Encontramos que los patrones de perfusión eran más reproducibles que lo esperado para una perfusión aleatoria, indicando la existencia de una determinante estable, probablemente anatómica, que controla las presiones capilares de apertura, esta a su vez comandaría la orden para el reclutamiento de capilares. Sin embargo, se requiere aún considerablemente más trabajo para explicar los mecanismos que controlan el reclutamiento capilar.

Palabras claves: Capilaridad pulmonar, hipertensión arterial pulmonar, hipoxia, intercambio gaseoso, microcirculación pulmonar, microscopía *in vivo*.

Résumé

Grâce à la microscopie *in vivo*, nous étudions la réponse de la forte micro circulation pulmonaire chez des chiens soumis à une hypoxie pulmonaire sévère. Nous nous sommes rendus compte, de façon inattendue, qu'à des niveaux d'hypoxie élevée correspondait un niveau supérieur de recrutement capillaire. On a déterminé, à partir d'une série d'études, que ce ne sont ni la constriction pulmonaire veineuse, ni l'augmentation de la pression auriculaire gauche ni celle du débit cardiaque, qui étaient la cause du recrutement. Ce serait plutôt l'hypertension artérielle pulmonaire, résultat de la constriction précapillaire, qui serait la cause de la redistribution du flux sanguin depuis la base du poumon jusqu'à la partie supérieure du poumon où l'on observe le recrutement des capillaires. Les capillaires recrutées de nouveau augmenteraient la superficie destinée à l'échange gazeux. On a ensuite essayé, à l'aide du microscope par vidéo, de déterminer si les modèles d'ouverture des capillaires recrutées étaient stables ou variables. On a procédé à l'isolement d'un lobe pulmonaire de façon à ce que la pompe perfuse la moitié des capillaires. On a ensuite éteint la pompe et les capillaires se sont fermés. Après avoir allumé et éteint six fois de suite la pompbe, il a été possible de déterminer si les capillaires perfusés au cours de chacune des périodes d'observation étaient les mêmes ou non. On s'est rendu compte que les modèles de perfusion se reproduisaient plus que ce que l'on attendait au cours d'une perfusion aléatoire, indiquant l'existence d'une déterminante stable, probablement anatomique, qui contrôle les pressions capillaires d'ouverture, qui, à son tour, donnerait l'ordre pour le recrutement des capillaires. Cependant, un travail considérable est encore nécessaire pour expliquer les mécanismes qui contrôlent le recrutement capillaire.

Mots clés : Capillarité pulmonaire, hypertension artérielle pulmonaire, hypoxie, échange gazeux, micro circulation pulmonaire, microscopie *in vivo*.

Recruitment of pulmonary capillaries is an important component of gas exchange reserve, because the newly perfused capillaries add directly to the surface area for gas uptake. This response helps meet the demand for increased oxygen uptake during stresses such as exercise or exposure to high altitude. Important gaps exist in our understanding of the way in which alterations of pulmonary hemodynamics, with the attendant redistribution of pulmonary blood flow, affect capillary recruitment. The major reason that many aspects of pulmonary microcirculatory function are poorly understood stems from the considerable technical difficulties involved in studying these vessels directly. The classical direct approach of in vivo microscopy is plagued by problems of tissue movement during the cardiorespiratory cycles. Nevertheless, important information has come from *in vivo* microscopy of the lung. There are three outstanding historical examples thath demonstrate the usefulness of this technique. First, Malpighi (6) in 1661 discovered the existence of capillaries using *in vivo* microscopy of the frog lung and solved the millennia long dilemma of how blood gets from the arteries to the veins. His observations also revealed the existence of red blood cells. Next, Hales in 1733 (5) published the first measurements of capillary transit times that are surprisingly accurate. In this century, Wearn and colleagues (14) demonstrated that gas exchange vessels could be recruited and concluded that considerable reserve existed in the pulmonary capillaries through this mechanism.

The directness of *in vivo* microscopy has continued to make the technique attractive, even though the subpleural capillary bed is somewhat less dense than interior capillary networks. In the early 1960s, Filley and Wagner began to study the pulmonary microcirculation using this technique. We had the good fortune of discovering a location on the surface of the lung under the second rib that moved only slightly with respiration (11). A transparent window was inserted into the chest wall over this area and the chest was closed to form an airtight seal. Later a suction manifold was added to the bottom of the window frame so that respiratory movement was completely arrested (10). This permitted us to make observations of the same field over many hours and thereby to use the same arterioles, capillaries, and venules as their own controls for hemodynamic studies. The animals had normal blood gases, cardiac output, blood pressures, and an undamaged microvasculature. We were able to make a number of studies of how the pulmonary capillaries responded to changes in pressure and flow. The majority of our observations have been made on the uppermost surface of the lung. This location is an interesting part of the pulmonary circulation, because that region is where much of the gas exchange reserve lies in terms of capillaries that can be recruited.

In our early studies, we noticed that red cells consistently perfused more capillaries when the animals inspired hypoxic gas mixtures (12). To quantify this recruitment, we made drawings of all the capillaries that were perfused by red blood cells in a given field during normoxia and hypoxia. By measuring the total lenght of the perfused capillaries per unit field area, we obtained an index of capillary recruitment. This capillary recruitment index consistently increased as oxygen tension fell to 40 Torr (Fig. 1).

These observations lead to a series of studies designed to determine what caused the capillary recruitment. The obvious extrapulmonary causes, increased left atrial pressure and cardiac output, were eliminated because left atrial pressure was unchanged by hipoxia and cardiac output fell in some instances of hypoxia when there was substantial recruitment (12,13).

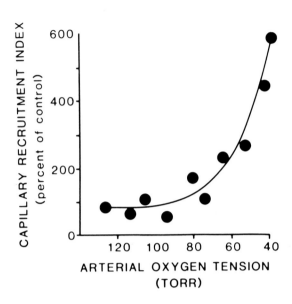

Fig. 1 - This curve represents the average effect of airway hypoxia on the level of capillary recruitment in the upper lung in a series of nine consecutive dogs (from 10).

In later work, we held output constant from control to hypoxia and found that recruitment occurred independently of total pulmonary blood flow (1,2). Thus an intrapulmonary mechanism seemed to be the likely cause of the recruitment. Venoconstriction could certainly cause a retrograde rise in capillary pressure that would lead to recruitment. The well known elevation of pulmonary arterial pressure during hypoxia might also account for the recruitment by redistributing blood flow upward to our upper lung observation site. To differentiate between these potential causes, we directly measured pressure in both small pulmonary veins and arteries, made the animal hypoxic, and measured capillary recruitment. Then, while maintaining the hypoxic challenge at a constant level, a vasodilator, prostaglandin E_1, was infused to relieve whatever vasoconstriction had occurred (2). The vasodilator caused a large reduction in the number of perfused capillaries. We could not measure any increase in pulmonary venous pressure during hypoxia, nor detect any effect of the vasodilator on vein pressure. Pulmonary artery pressure, however, fell to near control levels during vasodilator infusion. The plots of pressure versus recruitment (Fig. 2) showed no correlation with vein pressure but an impressive correlation with artery pressure. Therefore capillary recruitment during hypoxia did not correlate with cardiac output, pulmonary venous, or left atrial pressure, but did correlate with pulmonary arterial pressure.

That correlation lead to the following difficult question. If recruitment was caused by a rise in capillary pressure, which it certainly must be, then how could the pressure rise in the capillaries which are located downstream

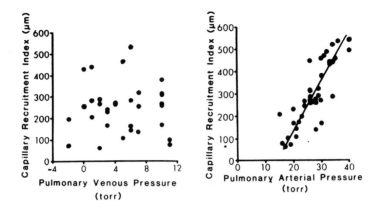

Fig. 2 - The correlation between capillary recruitment and pulmonary venous pressure was not significant (P=0.9), but was significantly correlated with pulmonary arterial pressure (P<0.001) for this group of 10 dogs (from 11).

of an upstream arterial constriction? It seemed more plausible that constriction of an artery feeding a capillary bed would have to be associated with reduced flow and derecruitment.

We were assisted in thinking abouth this dilemma by modeling the pressure, flow, and resistance relationships in the pulmonary circulation as an apartment building. When the demand for water was maximal in the morning, the lower floors would benefit from a rapid flow of water through a fully recruited shower head, analogous to the capillary bed in the lower lung. The upper floors would have very low flow and derecruited shower heads. To this point, the model reproduced the elegant hydrostatic zone model of the pulmonary circulation developed by Permutt et al. (8) and West (15) to describe the distribution of blood flow under normal conditions.

To extend the apartment house model to mimic hypoxia, suppose that all faucets were only partially opened. This condition would represent generalized pulmonary arterial vasoconstriction. With the higher resultant pressure, water would be redistributed to the upper floors and holes in the shower heads would be recruited. This model resolved the paradox of how capillaries could be recruited downstream from an upstream constriction, because more water was available to flow past the constriction in the control valves to the upper floors, whereas little water had been available to flow past the wide open control valve under control conditions.

The model predicted, that with conditions of steady total flow, analogous to a lack of cardiac output changes during hypoxia, and an evenly distributed constriction of all faucets, that there would be upward redistribution of flow which could result in an overall gain in the total number of holes in the shower heads via recruitment. Under these conditions, the extra flow to the upper shower heads must come from the lower floors. The lesser flow in the lower apartments, however, need not lead to local derecruitment; rather the extra water could come from a reduction in the velocity of the water passing through the lower shower heads, analogous to slower capillary transit times. If this reasoning was correct, then the model predicted that in the lung there should be an increase in total capillary volume during the increased pulmonary arterial pressure associated with airway hypoxia.

To test this prediction, it was necessary to determine the effect of hypoxia on total pulmonary capillary volume. To do this, we measured the diffusing capacity of the lung for carbon monoxide (1). A diffusing capacity increase during hypoxia, however, could reflect either increased capillary volume (recruitment), or less competition from oxygen for hemoglobin binding sites which would alter the reaction rate between carbon monoxide and hemoglobin (Ú), or some combination of the two. To determine the effect of recruitment alone, the vasodilator prostaglandin E_1 was infused while airway hypoxia was held at a constant level. The resultant decrease in pulmonary artery pressure caused, as expected from earlier work, capillary derecruitment (Fig. 3, left). Diffusing capacity also decreased (Fig. 3, right). By assuming no change in membrane diffusing capacity, and by having held Ú constant by keeping the level of hypoxia constant, the experiment showed that there was a net gain in capillary volume, almost certainly through capillary recruitment. Such an increase in gas exchange surface area would be advantageous during whole lung hypoxia.

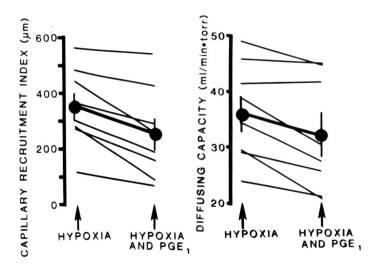

Fig. 3 - Capillary recruitment index and diffusing capacity of the lung for carbon monoxide are plotted for a group of eight dogs. The thin lines are data from individual dogs. The heavy lines are group means and standard errors. Under these conditions, hypoxia was held constant and recruitment was varied by infusing the vasodilator prostaglandin E_1. The derecruitment resulting from the vasodilator was associated with a fall in diffusing capacity (from 1).

The model predicted upward redistribution of flow with constriction and downward redistribution with dilation. There is evidence that hypoxia causes upward redistribution of pulmonary blood flow both acutely in anesthetized dogs (4) and in man native to high altitude (3). To determine what vasodilation did to blood flow distribution in our preparation, we injected radiolabelled 15 μm microspheres into the rifht atrium and measured the location of the wedged spheres in the lungs during hypoxia and hypoxia plus prostaglandin E_1. As expected, hypoxia caused microsphere distribution to be relatively even from top to bottom (Fig. 4). The vasodilator caused the curve to rotate (Fig. 4) indicating that blood flow diminished in the upper lung and returned to high levels in the lower lung. This seemed convincing evidence that upward redistribution of blood flow existed in our preparations and was a likely explanation for capillary recruitment in the upper lung during hypoxia.

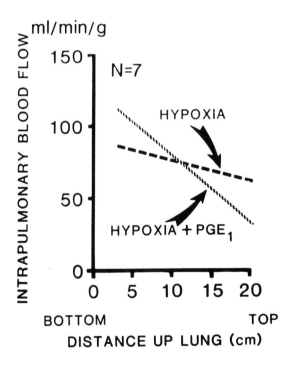

Fig. 4. The intrapulmonary distribution of blood flow determined by radiactive microsphere distribution per gram of dry lung tissue plotted against distance up from the bottom of the lung (n=7). During hypoxia, the blood flow is fairly even from bottom to top, but when the vasodilator prostaglandin E_1 is infused to relieve the pulmonary arterial constriction, the curve rotates causing the curve to be steeper, an indication that blood flow is redistributed toward the bottom of the lung. The slopes of the lines are different from each other (P<0.05) (from 2).

From these data, the response of the pulmonary circualtion to airway hypoxia can be summarized in the following way: hypoxia —> pulmonary arterial constriction —> increased pulmonary arterial pressure —> upward redistribution of blood flow —> capillary recruitment —> increased surface area for gas exchange. It is not certain how much improvement in arterial oxygen tension might occur from the increase in gas exchange surface area provided by the recruited capillaries. As best we can calculate, it might not exceed 5 Torr in a normal lung, although it could be substantially more in a heterogeneously diseased lung. In any case, whenever arterial oxygen tension in below 30 or 40 torr, any addition would be welcome.

One of the main conclusions that we draw from this series of studies has to do with control of the pulmonary circulation. This and other work suggests that capillary recruitment is a passive event resulting from increased pressure in the capillary bed. Presumably the pressure rise can be from any source. For example, a downstream increase in resistance causing a retrograde rise in capillary pressure would be expected to cause recruitment just as readily as an upward redistribution of blood flow causes recruitment in the case of whole lung hypoxia. Since, however, we found no evidence that venoconstriction played an active role in capillary recruitment, we believe that changes in pulmonary arterial pressure play the dominant role in controlling whole lung capillary recruitment.

Although these findings convey considerable information about the ways in which the pulmonary capillary bed responds to gross hemodynamic changes, these studies provide no information abouth the important area of how capillary blood flow is regulated within the capillary networks of single alveolar walls. As a first step in investigating this area, we studied the effects of one specific hemodynamic fluctuation on perfusion of a single capillary network. Consider a capillary network in a single alveolar wall located in the upper lung. Under typical perfusion conditions, perhaps half of the capillary segments in the wall would be perfused by red blood cells. We defined this network to be 50% recruited, regardless of whether the non-erythrocyte-perfused capillaries had a trickle of plasma or were not perfused at all. During bouts of exercise or positional changes with respect to gravity, capillary transmural pressure could increase sufficiently to open all of the capillaries. Later, when the network returned to the original baseline perfusion conditions, considerable information could be deduced about capillary structure and function by observing the resultant pattern of perfusion. For example, it would be interesting to know whether the level of capillary recruitment, *i.e.* the gas exchange surface area, was the same after each return to baseline, since that would indicate whether total network perfusion is stable.

It would be perhaps of greater interest to determine whether the same or different capillary segments would be perfused each time. If the perfusion pattern was consistent, in that a specific set of pathways through the network was perfused each time, the stability would imply that each segment has a consistent resistance and, further, that the resistance of each segment differs from the resistances of other segments. These characteristics would cause the flowing blood to seek repeatedly the same unique combination of segments with the least total pathway resistance. On the other hand, if the capillary perfusion pattern varied from one baseline period to the next, it would indicated either that individual segmental resistances altered over time or that the resistances of all segments were essentially equal, since equal resistances would allow perfusion to change randomly between segments. Thus the kind of pattern that predominated, whether stable or variable, had significant implications abouth the characteristics of the pulmonary capillary bed that influenced perfusion at the alveolar level.

To investigate these possibilities, we transiently inflated a balloon in the mitral orifice to raise capillary transmural pressure to a high enough level to open all capillary segments. Then the balloon was deflated and pulmonary hemodynamics returned to baseline conditions. The capillaries that remained perfused after reaching baseline were videotaped. The cycle of complete capillary opening and baseline observation was repeated three times. The videotapes were compared to determine the pattern of capillary perfusion. We found that the total number of capillary segments that were perfused at least once during the three observations periods averaged 48 segments. Of those segments, an average of 38 segments were always perfused during all observation periods. Thus, the *consistency of perfusion* was 79% (38/48), a strong indication that a reproducible combination of individual segmental resistances determined the predominant pattern of pulmonary capillary perfusion. In Fig. 5, the results from a typical alveolar wall are shown.

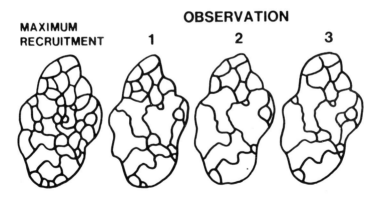

Fig. 5 - Drawing of a typical alveolar wall. In the left panel, maximal capillary recruitment has been elicited by inflating a left atrial balloon and raising capillary pressure to >25 Torr for 15 seconds, then the balloon was deflated and the perfused capillaries were videotaped. The cycle was repeated three times, shown in the three right panels. If all of the capillaries that were perfused during all three of these observations were identified, 79% of that group were perfused during each observation, indicating that a highly consistent pattern of perfusion (from 7).

This study provided the first evidence that resistances vary significantly among capillary segments in a single alveolar wall, and that the resistance of each segment tended to be stable, even after large changes in transmural pressure. We conclude that the distribution of segmental resistances is an important determinant of the pattern of capillary perfusion within alveolar capillary networks. Further, we can tentatively conclude that under these experimental conditions, the evidence does not support the idea that there is active regulation present in the capillary bed.

Recently, we began investigating the opening pressure characteristics of the pulmonary capillaries. This time we used video microscopy to study the isolated, pump perfused, canine lobe so that control of the circulation could be optimized (9). After having set pump flow to perfuse half of the capillaries, the pump was turned off and all of the capillaries closed. Turning the pump back on reopened the capillaries. The on-off cycle was repeated six times. If exactly the same capillaries were perfused each time the pump was on, it would demonstrate that there were significant, stable differences between individual capillary opening pressures causing consistent recruitment of those capillaries with the lowest opening pressures. Alternatively, variable perfusion patterns would result: if the differences in opening pressures between capillary segments were negligible, or if capillary opening pressures changed over time, or if trans-network pressure changed between cycles.

The average *consistency of perfusion* for any pair of consecutive cycles was 64± 3% which was greater than the *consistency of perfusion* expected by chance alone (Fig. 6).

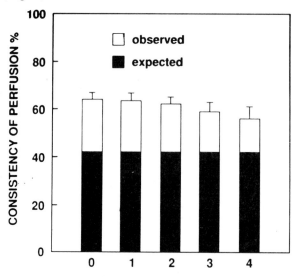

NUMBER OF INTERVENING OBSERVATIONS

Fig. 6. The *consistency of perfusion* for pairs of 1-min observation periods. When the 1-min observations were consecutive (0 intervening observation periods), the *consistency of perfusion* was 64± 3%. When 2 observation periods were separated in time by 4 other off-on pump cycles, the consistency of perfusion decreased (P=0.02) to 56± 4% (from 9).

This indicated that a stable, probably anatomic factor resulted in differences in opening pressure between segments. We also found that the consistency of perfusion decreased when we compared the perfusion pattern from cycles made farther apart in time (Fig. 6). In contrast to the previous study of the distribution of capillary resistances, this study suggested that some process changed capillary segmental opening pressure over time.

A this point we can conclude that the pulmonary arterial hypertension resulting from airway hypoxia causes pulmonary blood flow to be redistributed from the lower to the upper lung. The increased upper lung perfusion results in an increased total surface area for gas exchange. Thus far we have found the capillary network to be largely passive; capillary segmental resistances and, to a lesser extent, opening pressures are different between segments and stable over time. In the case of opening pressure, we also found evidence of active alteration of perfusion within single capillary networks. Much work, however, remains to be done to determine what factors control perfusion in individual capillary networks. For example we know little about how stable the patten of perfusion in an alveolar wall is over time in the absence of hemodynamic fluctuation, or what factors might be changing the distribution of opening pressures over time, or whether capillaries that are not perfused by red blood cells have a small amount of plasma flowing through them. Answers to these kinds of questions will provide much needed insight into the ways in which the pulmonary circulation increases its surface area for gas exchange during times of stress.

REFERENCES

1. CAPEN, R.L., LATHAM, L.P. & WAGNER, W.W. Jr. 1981. Diffusing capacity of the lung during hypoxia: the role of capillary recruitment. *J. Appl. Physiol.* 50: 165-171.

2. CAPEN, R.L. & WAGNER, W.W. Jr. 1982. Intrapulmonary blood flow redistribution during hypoxia increasse gas exchange surface area. *J. Appl. Physiol.* 52: 1575-1581.

3. DAWSON, A. & GROVER, R.R. 1974. Regional lung function in natives and longterm residents at 3,100 m altitude. *J. Appl. Physiol.* 36: 294-298.

4. DUGARD, A. & NAIMARK, A. 1967. Effect of hypoxia on distribution of pulmonary blood flow. *J. Appl. Physiol.* 23: 663-671.

5. HALES, S. 1987. *Containing Haemastaticks. 1773.* Birmingham AL: Graphon editions.

6. MALPIGHY, M. 1976. Epistle II. About the lungs. 1661. *In*: Comroe, J. H. Jr. (ed), *Pulmonary and respiratory physiology*. New York: Halsted Press.

7. OKADA, O., PRESSON, R.G. Jr., KIRK, K.R., GODBEY, P.S., CAPEN, R.L. & WAGNER, W.W. Jr. 1992. Capillary perfusion patterns in single alveolar walls. *J. Appl. Physiol.* 72: 1838-1884.

8. PERMUTT, S., BROMBERGER-BARNEA, B. & BANEA, H.N. 1965. Alveolar pressure, pulmonary venous pressure, and the vascular waterfall. *Med. Thorac* 22: 118-131.

9. PRESSON, R.G. Jr., GODBEY, P.S., OKADA, O., HANGER, C.C. HILLIER, S.C. & WAGNER, W.W. Jr. 1992. Distribution of segmental opening pressures in single alveolar walls. *FASEB J.* 6: 2047.

10. WAGNER, W.W. Jr. 1969. Pulmonary microcirculatory observations in vivo under physiological conditions. *J. Appl. Physiol.* 26: 375-377.

11. WAGNER, W.W. Jr. & FILLEY, G. G. 1965. Microscopic observation of the lung in vivo. *Vasc. Dis.* 2: 229-241.

12. WAGNER, W.W. Jr. & LATHAM, L.P. 1975. Airway hypoxia causes pulmonary capillary recruitment in the dog. *J. Appl. Physiol.* 39: 900-905.

13. WAGNER, W.W. Jr., LATHAM, L.P. & CAPEN, R.L. 1979. Capillary recruitment during airway hypoxia: the role of pulmonary artery pressure. *J. Appl. Physiol.* 47: 383-387.

14. WEARN, J.T., ERNSTENE, A.C., BROMER, A.W., BARR, J.S., GERMAN, W.J. & ZSCHIESCHE, L.J. 1934. The normal behavior of the pulmonary blood vessels with observations on the intermittence of the flow of blood in the arterioles and capillaries. *Am. J. Physiol.* 109: 236-256.

15. WEST, J.B. 1965. *Ventilation/blood flow and gas exchange.* Oxford: Blackwell.

REMODELLING OF THE HUMAN PULMONARY VASCULATURE AT HIGH ALTITUDE IN THE ANDES AND IN TIBET

Donald Heath

Abstract

Remodelling of the small pulmonary arteries and pulmonary arterioles occurs in response to the hypobaric hypoxia of high altitude. In naturally-acclimatized native Quechua and Aymara Indians of the Andes there is commonly muscularization of the pulmonary arterioles, an the development of intimal longitudinal muscle and inner muscular tubes in the small pulmonary arteries. In infants of Han origin ascending to live in Lhasa, Tibet, there may be inability to achieve initial acclimatization to high altitude, manifested by hipertrophy and constriction of small pulmonary arteries, muscularization of pulmonary arterioles and some migration of vascular smooth muscle cells from pulmonary arterioles. There are many data from animal species indigenous to mountains to support the concept of genetic adaptation to high altitude with lack of medial hypertrophy in small pulmonary arteries and lack of muscularization of pulmonary arterioles. Evidence of genetic adaptation to high altitude in native highlanders of the Himalaya is less convincing. Proliferation of vascular smooth muscle in response to the hypoxia of high altitude occurs in pulmonary veins and venules as well as in pulmonary arteries and arterioles.

Key words: High-altitude hypoxia, pulmonary vascular remodelling, acclimatized Quechuas, Aymaras, genetically adapted animals, Han infants, Tibet.

Resumen

La remodelación de las pequeñas arterias pulmonares y de las arteriolas pulmonares ocurre como respuesta a la hipoxia hipobárica de las grandes alturas. En nativos Quechuas y Aymaras de los Andes que están naturalmente aclimatizados, hay muscularización de las arteriolas pulmonares, y desarrollo del músculo longitudinal en la íntima así como de tubos musculares internos en las pequeñas arterias pulmonares. En niños de origen Han que ascienden a Lhasa, Tibet, para vivir, puede haber una incapacidad inicial para aclimatizarse a las grandes alturas que se manifiesta por hipertrofia y constricción de las pequeñas arterias pulmonares, muscularización de arteriolas pulmonares y alguna migración de células de músculo liso vascular desde las arteriolas pulmonares. Existen muchos datos provenientes des especies animales que viven en zonas de montañas altas que sustentan el concepto de adaptación genética a la altura mediante la ausencia de hipertrofia de la media en arterias pulmonares pequeñas y ausencia de muscularización de las arteriolas pulmonares.

La evidencia para una adaptación genética a la altura en nativos de los Himalayas es menos convincente. La proliferación del músculo vascular liso como respuesta a la hipoxia ocurre en venas y venulas pulmonares así como en arterias y arteriolas pulmonares.

Palabras claves: Hipoxia de altura, remodelación de vasculatura pulmonar, Quechuas, Aymaras, adaptación, niños Han, Tibet.

Résumé

La modification des petites artères pulmonaires et des artérioles pulmonaires constitue une réaction à l'hypoxie hypobarique à haute altitude. Chez les Quechua et les Aymara des Andes qui sont naturellement adaptés, on constate une musculation des artérioles pulmonaires et un développement du muscle longitudinal dans l'intima, ainsi que des tubes musculaires internes dans les petites artères pulmonaires. Chez les enfants Han qui vivent à Lhasa, au Tibet, on peut constater une incapacité initiale à l'acclimatation à la haute altitude qui se manifeste par de l'hypertrophie et la constriction des petites artères pulmonaires, la musculation des artérioles pulmonaires et un certain déplacement des cellules du muscle lisse vasculaire depuis les artérioles pulmonaires. Il existe beaucoup d'informations sur les espèces animales qui vivent en zones montagneuses qui soutiennent le concept d'adaptation génétique à l'altitude grâce à l'absence d'hypertrophie de la musculaire des petites artères pulmonaires et l'absence de musculation des artérioles pulmonaires. La preuve d'une adaptation génétique à l'altitude chez les habitants de l'Himalaya n'est pas aussi convaincante. La prolifération du muscle vasculaire lisse comme réaction à l'hypoxie se produit dans les veines et les veinules pulmonaires ainsi que dans les artères et les artérioles pulmonaires.

Mots clés : Hypoxie d'altitude, réseau vasculaire pulmonaire, adaptation, Quechua, Aymara, enfants Han, Tibet.

It has been known for over thirty years that the Quechuas highlanders living in and around Morococha (4550 m) in the Peruvian Andes have pulmonary hypertension. The pioneering studies of Peñaloza *et al.* (15) and Sime *et al.* (16) showed that in the adults the pulmonary hypertension was mild, the mean value in 38 adult Quechuas being 28 mmHg. In 7 children, 1-5 years of age, the elevation of pulmonary arterial pressure was greater the mean of the group being 45 mm Hg. From the outset a study by Arias-Stella and Saldaña (1) demonstrated that in these native highlanders remodelling of the pulmonary arterial tree took place in response to the hypobaric hypoxia of high altitude. They termed idiosyncratically the vessels they studied 'proximal and distal pulmonary arteries' which correspond to what most pathologists, using the classification of Brenner (2), would call 'muscular pulmonary arteries and pulmonary arterioles'. The significant remodelling was found to take the form of muscularization of pulmonary arterioles. These vessels are below 80 um in diameter and apart from their immediate origin from their parent arteries, normally have a wall consisting of a single elastic lamina (4). In the Quechuas they came to resemble small arteries with a coat of circularly-orientated smooth muscle sandwiched between inner and outer elastic laminae. Characteristically this muscularization occurred well out into the periphery of the pulmonary arterial tree, affecting vessels as small as pre-capillaries. It was consistent with providing an organic basis for the noted elevation of pulmonary arterial pressure and resistance in the highlander. In older subjects there was some degree of medial hypertrophy of parent pulmonary arteries, consistent with sustained mild or moderate pulmonary hypertension resulting from the increased pulmonary vascular resistance brought about by the muscularization of the pulmonary arterioles. The classic study by Arias-Stella and Saldaña (1) was a major contribution to high-altitude pathology but more recent work suggests that it is incomplete.

Our own studies of Mestizo and Aymara citizens of La Paz (3600 m), Bolivia, a decade apart (8, 12, 10) reveal that in addition to muscularization of pulmonary arterioles there is not infrequently the development of a layer of longitudinally-oriented smooth muscle in the intima. This is similar to what occurs in cases of pulmonary emphysema (13, 21) where sustained alveolar hypoxia is associated with hypercarbia in contrast to the hypobaric hypoxia of the native highlander. There is limited migration of mature-looking smooth muscle cells from the media into the intima through deficiencies in the inner elastic lamina. Electron-microscopic studies in cases of pulmonary emphysema have revealed the ultrastructure of this limited migration (17). This is in contrast to events in plexogenic pulmonary arteriopathy, as seen in primary pulmonary hypertension and congenital cardiac shunts, where the migrating vascular smooth muscle cells are electron-dense, dark, and elongated and show a smooth surface with loss of micropinocytotic activity (7). Such dark cells predominate in the inner media nad reach the intima by passing through the same gaps in the inner elastic lamina as in states of hypoxia. Here they become transformed into myofibroblasts which migrate freely and extensively into the vascular lumen. It was hitherto thought that the development of intimal longitudinal muscle in the pulmonary arteries in emphysema is the result of physical forces acting on the vessels as they are distorted around abnormal air spaces in the lung. Its occurrence in native highlanders as well as in patients with chronic obstructive lung disease suggest rather that it is more likely to be related to chronic alveolar hypoxia. Nevertheless, having intimal longitudinal muscle in the pulmonary arteries in emphysema is commoner and more pronounced than in native highlanders.

Another feature of the remodelling of the pulmonary arterial tree in native highlanders is the development of inner muscular tubes. These are far less common than muscularization of pulmonary arterioles or the development of intimal longitudinal muscle. Such inner muscular tubes are also found in chronic obstructive lung disease where they occur far more commonly than in native highlanders. Immediately beneath the endothelium of normal pulmonary arteries is a thin layer of circular muscle. With the development of intimal longitudinally oriented muscle this layer of circular muscle develops around itself inner and outer elastic laminae and forms a circular tube (17). In the investigation of 1990 in La Paz we studied 13 Aymara Indians who were born in the city and spent all their lives there. 3 of them showed muscularization of pulmonary arterioles, 4 the development of intimal longitudinal muscle and only one the formation of inner muscular tubes (Fig. 1, 2). In 12 Mestizos, 2 showed arteriolar muscularization, 5 the development of intimal longitudinal muscle but none the formation of inner muscular tubes. It is apparent that a characteristic triad of histological changes may contribute to the remodelling of the human pulmonary arterial tree of the native Quechua and Aymara Indians of the Andes but it is rarely complete.

When Arias-Stella and Saldaña (1) wrote their classic paper they entitled it 'The terminal portion of the pulmonary arterial tree in people native to high altitudes' implying that the peripheral muscularization that they reported in the lung was to be anticipated in all subjects born and living at great elevations. This is not so. In our initial study in La Paz (8) we studied necropsy material from the citizens of that city which include whites and Mestizos as well as Aymara Indians. In subjects beyond infancy we found muscularization of pulmonary arterioles in 5 of 7 Aymara Indians, in one of 4 Mestizos and in one of 5 Caucasians. This led us to the conclusion that the ethnic background of subjects at high altitude may influence the reaction of their pulmonary circulation to the hypobaric hypoxia.

At present there are no published data on the state of the pulmonary vasculature in native highlanders from the Himalaya. Gupta *et al.* (3) found no evidence of remodelling of the pulmonary arterial tree with no medial hypertrophy in small pulmonary arteries or muscularization of pulmonary arterioles in 7 adult native Ladakhi highlanders. This led them to consider whether the Himalayan highlander is genetically adapted to the hypobaric hypoxia of high altitude in contrast to the naturally acclimatized Quechua and Aymara highlanders of the Andes. One might query whether negative findings in 7 subjects living at only 3 300 m are significant enough to be taken as evidence of genetic adaptation.

In the Aymara muscularization develops in the pulmonary veins and venules as well as in the pulmonary arteries and arterioles. This suggests that the classic view of muscularization and constriction of the pulmonary arterioles in the native highlander is incomplete and likely to give rise to an incorrect concept of the method and extent of the effects of alveolar hypoxia on the pulmonary vasculature. It would seem more likely that sustained hypoxia induces a proliferation of vascular smooth muscle in blood vessels in the entire area adjacent to alveolar spaces. Thus the process affects pulmonary veins and venules as well as pulmonary arteries and arterioles. The proliferation of muscle in the intima of pulmonary veins has a different histological appearance from that in the intima of pulmonary arteries and arterioles (10). In the veins the smooth muscle cells are found largely individually with considerable amounts of collagen separating them, a difference that is probably related to the haemodynamic influences in the two classes of vessel. While

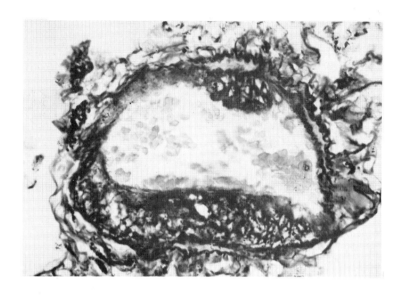

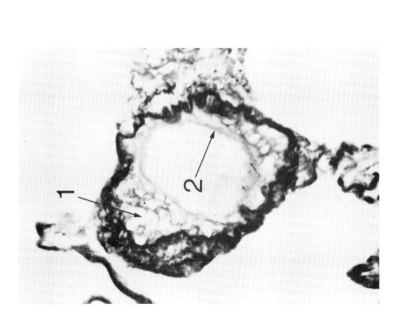

Fig. 1 - Transverse section of a pulmonary arteriole from a male Aymara Indian of 28 years who died from a cerebellar tumour. From outwards to the lumen its layers consist of the original thick elastic lamina, a layer of intimal longitudinal muscle (arrow 1) and an inner muscular tube (arrow 2) (EVG. x 745.).

Fig. 2 - Transverse section of small pulmonary artery from the same case showing collections of longitudinally-oriented smooth muscle cells in the intima separated by elastic tissue (EVG. x 475.).

alveolar hypoxia appears to be the prime stimulus in inducing proliferation of vascular smooth muscle cells, the arterial pulsation appears to ensure that initially they retain a compact, overtly muscular nature before becoming sclerotic. In contrast, in the veins where they are not subjected to a comparable pulsatile stimulus they are widely spaced and separated by much sclerotic tissue. Wagenvoort & Wagenvoort (20) found that the pulmonary veins, especially smaller ones, of healthy residents at high altitude had a significantly thicker media compared to those of lowlanders. There was a parallel increase in muscularity of pulmonary arteries and veins within the same lungs suggestive of a common aetiological factor such as hypoxia.

A different form of remodelling of the human pulmonary vasculature is to be found in Tibet where infants of Han origin are taken up by their Chinese parents to live in Lhasa (3 600 m), the capital city of that country. We have given an account of the vascular changes in the lung which occur in this new and often fatal condition at high altitude which is distinct from both acute and chronic mountain sickness and to which reference had been previously made only in the Chinese literature (14). We studied necropsy material from 15 infants and children (18). All were of Han origin except one who was Tibetan. Ten were male. Their ages ranged from 3 to 16 months of age, the average being 9 months. Thirteen had been born at low altitude and had been taken subsequently to live at Lhasa. The average survival at high altitude of those who had been born at low altitude was only 2.1 months. Most of the patients had been brought to hospital because of dyspnoea and cough. Other common symptoms were sleeplessness, cyanosis, oedema of the face, and oliguria. The salient features on clinical examination were tachypnoea, tachycardia, enlargement of the liver and rales in the lungs. The heart was often thought clinically to be enlarged and the chest radiograph characteristically showed cardiac enlargement. The haemoglobin and red cell count, where measured, were normal.

The pathological features of this disease suggests the presence of a severe degree of pulmonary hypertension. There is hypertrophy of both cardiac ventricles but particularly of the right. There is dilatation of the right atrium and pulmonary trunk. The right ventricular hypertrophy is secondary to remodelling of the pulmonary arterial tree which includes severe medial hypertrophy and fibrous thickening of the adventitia of the small pulmonary arteries but no intimal proliferation (Fig. 3, 4). There is arteriolar muscularization. In one case of subacute infantile mountain sickness we found that there was a proliferation of spindle-shaped cells from the intima of the pulmonary arterioles. Histological examination suggested that they were myofibroblasts but this was not subjected to confirmation by electron microscopy (18). There was also a prominent proliferation of similar cells from the intima of pulmonary veins (Fig. 5). Clusters of pulmonary endocrine cells were found in the terminal bronchioles. They were disorganised so that they did not resemble those seen in normal lowland infants. In addition to the greater size of the clusters they were found to be increased in number. Quantitative studies revealed per cm^2 of lung tissue section, some 98 cells immunoreactive for bombesin (gastrin-releasing peptide) and 31 for calcitonin (6).

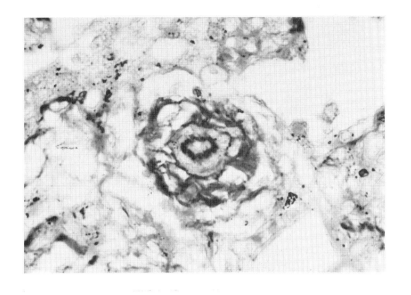

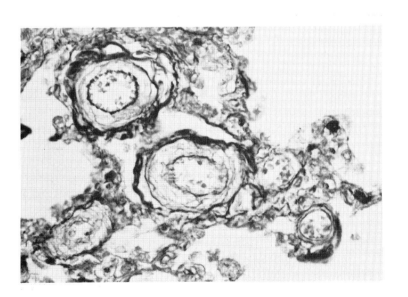

Fig. 3 - Transerve sections of small pulmonary arteries from an infant of Han origin aged 11 months who was taken by his parents to live in Lhasa (3 600 m) and who developed subacute infantile mountain sickness there. There is severe medial hypertrophy and fibrous thickening of the adventitia (EVG. x 600.).

Fig. 4 - Transverse section of muscularized pulmonary arteriole from the same case. There is a very thick muscular media sandwiched between the elastic laminae, the inner of which is particularly thick (EVG. x 1000.).

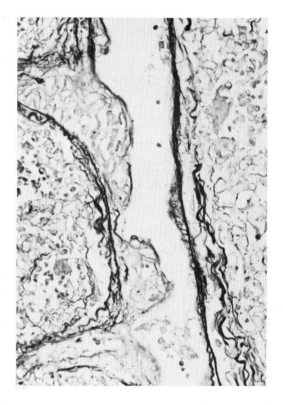

Fig. 5 - Longitudinal section of a pulmonary vein from an infant of Han origin who died of subacute infantile mountain sickness in Lhasa. There is a prominent proliferation of cells from the intima considered to be myofibroblasts.

This disease is easily distinguished from acute mountain sickness. It is also quite different from Monge's disease. The many differences are indicated in Table 1 which suggest that subacute infantile mountain sickness is the human counterpart of 'brisket disease' which afflicts cattle and particularly calves ascending into the Wasatch mountains around Salt Lake City for the spring grazing. Cattle are prone to brisket disease because they have a naturally muscular pulmonary vasculature which is peculiarly susceptible to hypobaric hypoxia even at low altitudes and genetic susceptibility in individual animals also seem to operate. In the same way the human infant would be prone to hypoxic pulmonary hypertension because it retains, at that stage, the muscular pulmonary arterial vessels of the fetus. Thus the pulmonary vascular remodelling in this disease of infants of Han origin appears to be a manifestation of failure to achieve initial acclimatization to high altitude.

It is clear that the remodelling of the pulmonary arterial tree that occurs in man is related to the status with regard to acclimatization in the class of subject concerned. The naturally acclimatized Quechua or Aymara

Table 1 - Criteria indicating that subacute infantile mountain sickness is akin to brisket disease but not to Monge's disease.

Criterion	Monge's disease	Brisket disease	Subacute infantile mountain sickness
Age of subject	Middle-aged men	Calves	Infants
Nature of exposure to high altitude	After prolonged exposure	On subacute exposure	On subacute exposure
Acclimatization status	Loss of established acclimatization	Failure of initial acclimatization	Failure of initial acclimatization
Basic mechanism	Alveolar hypoventilation	Hyper reactivity of muscular pulmonary arterial tree	Hyper reactivity of muscular pulmonary arterial tree
Form of syndrome	Respiratory	Cardiovascular	Cardiovascular
Unsaturation of systemic arterial blood	Pronounced	Slight	Slight
Hypercapnia	Pronounced	Absent	Absent
Haematocrit	Greatly raised	Normal	Normal
Polycythaemia	Pronounced	None	None
Pulmonary arterial hypertension	Moderate	Severe	Severe

highlander of the Andes manifests a hyperplasia of vascular smooth muscle into the distal extremities of the pulmonary arterial tree and a limited migration of longitudinal muscle into the intima of the pulmonary arteries; this remodelling is associated with a benign and mild pulmonary hypertension. The infant of Han origin ascending to high altitude in Tibet who fails to achieve initial acclimatization to hypobaric hypoxia manifests this in intense pulmonary vasoconstriction, muscularization of pulmonary arterioles and limited migration myofibroblasts in pulmonary arterioles and veins.

As noted above it has been suggested that native highlanders of the Himalaya show no remodelling of their pulmonary arterial tree and this has been considered to be a manifestation of genetic adaptation to high altitude. The evidence so far for involving this major biological principle in man is weak, being based on negative findings in a small number of highlanders. This is not the case in indigenous mountain species in which there is a wealth of data to support the concept that the lack of remodelling of their pulmonary arteries and arterioles is an expression of the fact that they have become genetically adapted to high altitude over countless millenia. Species in which we have found neither medial hypertrophy of small pulmonary arteries nor muscularization of pulmonary arterioles during our studies in the Andes and the Himalaya include the llama (*Lama glama*), the alpaca (*Lama pacos*), and the guanaco (*Lama guanicoe*) (5), the mountain-viscacha (*Lagidium peruanum*) (11), the yak (*Bos grunniens*) (9), and the Tibetan snow-pig (*Marmota himalayana*) (19).

REFERENCES

1. ARIAS-STELLA, J. & SALDAÑA, M. 1963. The terminal portion of the pulmonary arterial tree in people native to high altitudes. *Circulation* 28: 915-925.

2. BRENNER, O. 1935. Pathology of the vessels of the pulmonary circulation. *Arch Inter Med* 56: 211-237.

3. GUPTA, M. L., RAO, K. S., ANAND, I. S., BANERJEE, A. K. & BOPARAI, M. S. 1992. Lack of smooth muscle in the small pulmonary arteries of the native Ladakhi - Is the Himalayan highlander adapted? *Amer Rev Resp Dis.* Submitted.

4. HARRIS, P. & HEATH, D. 1986. The structure of the normal pulmonary blood vessels after infancy. *In: The Human Pulmonary Circulation.* Edinburgh: Churchill-Livingstone: 30-47.

5. HARRIS, P., HEATH, D., SMITH, P., WILLIAMS, D.R., RAMÍREZ, A., KRÜGER, H. & JONES, D.M. 1982. Pulmonary circulation of the llama at high and low altitudes. *Thorax* 37: 38-45.

6. HEATH, D., HARRIS, P., SUI, G. J., LIU, Y. H., GOSNEY, J., HARRIS, E. & ANAND, I. S. 1989. Pulmonary blood vessels and endocrine cells in subacute infantile mountain sickness. *Resp Med* 83: 77-81.

7. HEATH, D., SMITH, P. & GOSNEY, J. 1988. Ultrastructure of early plexogenic pulmonary arteriopathy. *Histopathol* 12: 41-52.

8. HEATH, D., SMITH, P., RIOS-DALENZ, J., WILLIAMS, D. & HARRIS, P. 1981. Small pulmonary arteries in some natives of La Paz, Bolivia. *Thorax* 36: 599-604.

9. HEATH, D., WILLIAMS, D. & DICKINSON, J. 1984. The pulmonary arteries of the yak. *Cardiovasc Res* 18: 133-139.

10. HEATH, D. & WILLIAMS, D. 1991. Pulmonary vascular remodelling in a high-altitude Aymara Indian. *Int J Biometeorol.* In Pres.

11. HEATH, D., WILLIAMS, D., HARRIS, P., SMITH, P., KRUGER, H. & RAMIREZ, H. 1981. The pulmonary vasculature of the mountain viscacha (Lagidium peruanum). The concept of adapted and acclimatized vascular smooth muscle. *J Comp Pathol* 91: 243-301.

12. HEATH, D., WILLIAMS, D., RIOS-DALENZ, J., CALDERON, M. & GOSNEY, J. 1990. Small pulmonary arterial vessels of Aymara Indians from the Bolivian Andes. *Histopathol* 16: 565-571.

13. HICKEN, P., HEATH, D., BREWER, D. B. & WHITAKER, W. 1965. The small pulmonary arteries in emphysema. *J Pathol and Bacteriol* 90: 107-114.

14. LI, J. B. 1983. *In: High altitude medicine. People's hospital of tibetan autonomous region.* Lhasa: Tibetan people's: 288-304.

15. PEÑALOZA, D., SIME, F., BANCHERO, N. & GAMBOA, R. 1962. Pulmonary hypertension in healthy man born and living at high altitudes. *Medician Thoracalis* 19: 449-460.

16. SIME, F., BANCHERO, N., PEÑALOZA, D., GAMBOA, R., CRUZ, J. & MARTICORENA, E. 1963. Pulmonary hypertension in children born and living at high altitudes. *Amer J Cardiol* 11: 143-157.

17. SMITH, P., RODGERS, B., HEATH, D. & YACOUB, M. 1992. The ultrastructure of pulmonary arteries and arterioles in emphysema. *J Pathol.* In Press.

18. SUI, G. J., LIU, Y. H., CHENG, X. S., ANAND, I. S., HARRIS, E., HARRIS, P. & HEATH, D. 1988. Subacute infantile mountain sickness. *J Pathol.* 155: 161-170.

19. SUN, S. F., SUI, G. J., LIU, Y. H., CHENG, X. S., ANAND, I. S., HARRIS, P. & HEATH, D., 1989. The pulmonary circulation of the tibetan snow pig (marmota hymalayana). *J Zool (London)* 217: 85-91.

20. WAGENWOORT, C. A. & WAGENVOORT, N. 1982. Pulmonary veins in high altitude residents. A morphometric study. *Thorax* 37: 931-935.

21. WILKINSON, M., LANGHORNE, C. A., HEATH, D., BARER, G. R. & HOWARD, P. 1988. A pathophysiological study of 10 cases of hypoxic cor pulmonale. *Quart J Med* (New Series) 66(249): 65-85.

THE INTERACTIVE STRESSES OF HYPOXIA AND COLD AT HIGH ALTITUDE

Denise Chauca, John Bligh

Abstract

Although most changes in bodily functions observed at high altitude have been attributed to the effect of hipoxia, there exists the possibility that the effect of other climatic factor such as cold, could add to that of low oxygen pressure and affect with more intensity these functions.

To test this hypothesis we studied the effect of cold and the interaction of cold and hypoxia on pulmonary arterial pressure (PAP). The rise in PAP observed in shorn sheep during cold exposure was similar to that produced by hypoxia. The pulmonary arterial hypertension due to cold exposure is produced by the stimulation of the peripheral cold sensors and the activation of a nervous pathway from the cold sensors to the pulmonar vasculature via the central nervous system. The simultaneous exposure to cold and hypoxia produced an increase of PAP higher than the addition of th₂ effects of cold and hypoxia *per se*. These results indicate that at high altitude the effect of cold on PAP could induce the development of high mountain sickness.

We recommend the need to take note of all the different environmental variables when studying the effects of altitude upon organisms.

Key words: Hypoxia, cold, pulmonary arterial pressure.

Resumen

A pesar que la mayoría de las alteraciones observadas en un organismo expuesto a la altura han sido atribuidas a la hipoxia, existe la posibilidad de que otro factor climático como el frío se sume al de la baja presión de oxígeno y afecte con mayor intensidad las diferentes funciones del mismo.

Para probar esta hipótesis, se estudió el efecto del frío y el de la interacción de la hipoxia y el frío sobre la presión arterial pulmonar (PAP) en carneros esquilados. La hipertensión arterial pulmonar observada durante la exposición al frío fue similar a la producida por la exposición a la hipoxia y se debería a la estimulación de los sensores periféricos de frío, y una activación de una vía nerviosa desde los sensores de frío hasta los vasos sanguíneos pulmonares. La exposición simultánea al frío y a la hipoxia produjo una elevación de la PAP mayor a la suma de las producidas por estos dos factores en forma individual. Estos resultados indicarían que, en la altura, el efecto del frío sobre la PAP podría precipitar el desarrollo del mal de altura.

Se recomienda la necesidad de que los estudios llevados a cabo en la altura tengan en cuenta los diferentes factores ambientales.

Palabras claves: Hipoxia, frío, presión arterial pulmonar.

Résumé

Bien que la plupart des altérations observées sur un organisme exposé à l'altitude aient été attribuées à l'hypoxie, il est possible qu'un autre facteur climatique comme le froid, s'ajoute à celui de la basse pression de l'oxygène et affecte de façon plus intense les fonctions de cet organisme.

Afin de prouver cette hypothèse, des études ont été faites sur les effets du froid et ceux de l'interaction de l'hypoxie et du froid sur la pression artérielle plumonaire (PAP) des moutons tondus. L'hypertension artérielle pulmonaire observée durant l'exposition au froid se révéla similaire à celle produite par l'exposition à l'hypoxie et serait due à la stimulation des récepteurs périphériques du froid et l'activation d'une voie nerveuse depuis les récepteurs du froid jusqu'aux vaisseaux sanguins pulmonaires.

L'exposition simultanée au froid et à l'hypoxie produisit une élévation de la PAP supérieure à la somme de celles produites par ces 2 facteurs de façon individuelle. Ces résultats indiqueraient que, en altitude, l'effet du froid sur la PAP pourrait accélerer le développement du mal d'altitude.

Il est donc nécéssaire que les études menées en altitude prennent en compte les différents facteurs du mimieu ambiant.

Mots clés : Hypoxie, froid, pression artérielle pulmonaire.

INTRODUCTION

Studies of the pathophysiological effects of altitude have been concentrated mostly upon those due to the reduction in the partial pressure of atmospheric oxygen. The possibility that other environmental stresses, such as may occur at any altitude, could add to those of low atmospheric pressure and exacerbate the resultant biological strain has received scant attention. Indeed, it has often been considered unnecessary to record standard meteorological data during high altitude studies. Consequently no retrospective data analyses can now be made to inquire whether any correlations exist between such environmental variables as air temperature, wind speed and precipitation and the pathophysiological consequences of temporary or permanent residence at high altitudes.

Here we discuss our own studies of the interaction of the effects of hypoxia and cold exposure upon sheep, and draw attention to the possible implications of our findings with regard to other species including man, and to the need to take note of all the many other environmental variables when studying the effects of altitude upon organisms.

COLD-INDUCED AND HYPOXIA-INDUCED PULMONARY ARTERIAL HYPERTENSION

During a study of the effects of sustained cold exposure on the conscious shorn sheep, Chauca (8) found that pulmonary arterial pressure (PAP) at an ambient temperature (Ta) of 3°C was substantially above that at thermoneutrality (24°C Ta). Since some degree of pulmonary arterial hypertension occurs during altitude hypoxia in most if not in all the several mammalian species in which PAP has been measured in this circumstance, it seemed possible that in the sheep, at least, the effects of cold-exposure and of hypoxia upon PAP could be additive and that any pathological effects of high altitude hypoxia could thus be aggravated by concurrent cold stress.

To test the hypothesis that the effects of hypoxia -and cold- stress upon PAP could be additive, Chauca & Bligh (9) extended the study of the PAP of shorn sheep to include the effect of breathing an air mixture containing only 12% oxygen (which is equivalent to a partial pressure of O_2 of 90 mm Hg). When breathing this hypoxic air at 25°C Ta, the rise in PAP above that when breathing normal air at 25°C Ta was of the same order as that when the shorn sheep was exposed to 3°C Ta while breathing normal air: there was a 24% increase in PAP during cold exposure, and a 27% increase in PAP in response to the hypoxia. When shorn sheep were then concurrently subjected to 3°C Ta and the hypoxic atmosphere, the mean increase in PAP was 62%, which was marginally greater that the effects of the two stresses when applied separately. This additive effect of hypoxia and cold exposure on the PAP of sheep has been confirmed by Sakai *et al.* (20), and Bligh & Chauca (4, 5) have shown that there is the same additive effect of hypoxia and cold exposure on the shorn sheep when the hypoxia is the consequence of breathing normal air but at a simulated altitude of 3355 m in a hypobaric chamber.

Whether there could be pathological consequences of the additional effect of cold-exposure on the pulmonary arterial hypertension at high altitude in natural circumstances might depend upon whether the rise in PAP during cold exposure is a transitory one or is sustained for so long as the cold stress persists. Kasprzak & Bligh (14) found that a 28% rise in PAP was sustained during exposure of the shorn sheep to 5°C Ta over a period of 4-months. This finding increased the possibility that the effect of cold upon PAP at high altitude could aggravate the pathophysiological consequences of high-altitude hypoxia and could sometimes be the precipitating factor in the development of high mountain sickness (HMS).

THE DIFFERING ETIOLOGIES OF HYPOXIA-INDUCED AND COLD-INDUCED PULMONARY HYPERTENSION

While earlier studies on open-chested anaesthetized dogs indicated the involvement of sympathetic efferent pathways in the effect of hypoxia upon the pulmonary vasculature, other studies have indicated that this reflexive effect diminishes with maturity (13). Tucker (22) concluded that in the dog the pulmonary vascular resistance is under little sympathetic influence and that the pulmonary vasoconstriction resulting from hypoxia is not mediated by the sympathetic nervous system. Allowing for possible species differences, and the continuing degree of uncertainty in the experimental evidence, it is possible that the effect of hypoxia upon PAP in the sheep could be either indirect or direct, or both. It is unlikely, however, that the effect of cold exposure upon the pulmonary vasculature is a direct one. This is both because the inspired air of mammals is thermally conditioned well before it reaches the alveoli (16, 11); and because we found no cold-induced rise in PAP when unshorn sheep were exposed to 3°C Ta, while Sakai *et al.* (19) found that the inhalation of cold air by the sheep caused no rise in PAP. Thus our supposition was that the primary effect of cold-exposure in the shorn sheep is upon exposed peripheral cold-sensors, and that the effect upon PAP involves afferent pathways from the cold sensors to the central nervous system (CNS) and efferent pathways from the CNS to the pulmonary vasculature. If this is so, then the reflexive response of the pulmonary vasculature to cold exposure probably involves the same afferent and, perhaps, the same central neural pathways as those involved in thermoregulatory responses to cold exposure.

In the sheep there is evidently a cholinergic synapse on the cold-sensor to heat production effector pathway through the CNS, the blockade of which by an intracerebroventricular (ICV) injection of atropine greatly attenuates the thermoregulatory responses to cold exposure (6, 1). Thus we conjectured that an ICV injection of atropine might likewise attenuate the effect of cold exposure upon PAP. Bligh & Chauca (2) found this to be so.

Since an ICV injection of norepinephrine (NE) also attenuates a cold-induced increase in heat production by shivering (6), probably by mimicking a natural adrenergic inhibitory influence, it also seemed likely that an ICV injection of NE might attenuate the effect of cold exposure upon PAP. This, too, was found by Bligh & Chauca (2) to be so. These experimental findings sustain the proposition that the effect of cold exposure upon PAP is a reflexive one involving peripheral cold sensors and the CNS.

If, by constrast, the hypoxia-induced rise in PAP is due entirely to a direct effect upon the pulmonary vasculature then an ICV injection of NE should be without effect upon it. Even at thermoneutrality, however, when it may be presumed that there was no activating drive from the cold sensors, an ICV injection of NE had some attenuating influence upon the PAP elevated by hypoxia. Since this attenuation also occurred in the absence of hypoxia it has interpreted as evidence of a tonal central influence upon PAP, which was being interrupted by centrally-administered NE. Even so, it remains possible that there is a reflexive component to the effect of hypoxia upon PAP.

PULMONARY ARTERIAL HYPERTENSION IN SHEEP DURING FEVER

In sheep, as with some other mammals, the fever induced by a single intravenous (IV) injection of a bacterial endotoxin (BE) is biphasic, with each phasic rise in body temperature (Tb) being due to an increase in the rate of heat production and/or a decrease in the rate of heat loss. Since the increase in heat production caused by cold-stress is accompanied by a rise in PAP it seemed possible that the increase in heat production during fever might also be accompanied by an elevated PAP. Bligh & Chauca (3) found that PAP rose from 16 mm Hg to 37 mm Hg with the onset of the fever induced by a single IV injection of a BE. This rise, however, occurred only during to the first phase of the biphasic elevation in Tb. These two phases of a BE-induced fever probably relate to the successive release and central action of two different endogenous terminal pyrogens. Evidently one of these terminal pyrogens is a prostaglandin E (PGE), derived from the metabolism of arachidonic acid, and which gives rise to the second and longer-lasting rise in Tb. The antipyretic effect of aspirin and aspirin-like drugs is attributed to the blockade of the synthesis of the PGEs. If, however, a PGE is involved only in the second phase of the febrile response to the injected BE, then it might be expected that a fever induced by an injection of a PGE into a lateral cerebral ventricle would be unaccompanied by a rise in PAP. Bligh & Chauca (unpublished observation) found that to be so in the sheep. Thus the first phase of fever induced by a single injection of a BE, and the accompanying rise in PAP is presumably due to the release of anothern terminal pyrogen, the identity of which remains uncertain.

In a later study Kasprzak & Bligh (14) observed some unintended spontaneous fevers while making measurements of PAP-in sheep, and noted that the accompanying rise in PAP then lasted throughout the febrile period. A probable explanation for this is that a spontaneous fever resulting from an infection is not biphasic. This could be because the terminal pyrogens responsible for the first and second elevations of Tb following a single injection of a bacterial pyrogen are then being produced and released together and continuously.

Since there is a largely common etiology of fever in mammals, these observations on fever and PAP with sheep indicate that in other mammalian species also the occurrence of fever at a high altitude might cause a further rise in the hypoxia-induced pulmonary arterial hypertension, which could take PAP above the threshold at which HMS begins to develop. If the rise in PAP is not caused by the action of a PGE but by another terminal pyrogen, then it would not be expected that the administration of aspirin or aspirin-like antipyretic substances would lower the effect of fever upon PAP and stem the development of HMS.

SHEEP, BOVINE CALVES AND BROILER CHICKENS AT HIGH ALTITUDE WITH AND WITHOUT COLD STRESS

Upon learning of our observations of the additive effects of hypoxia and cold on sheep, which are not know to suffer from HMS, McMurtry *et. al.* (17) and Talavera (21) made similar observations in cattle and broiler chickens which are known to develop a form of HMS known in cattle as brisket disease. To examine further the possibility that the aditive effects of cold exposure upon PAP could be a contributory factor in the occurrence of HMS in sheep and cattle, Chauca (8) studied the effects of transporting 4 Criollo sheep and 6 Holstein calves from an altitude of 150 m. above sea level (near Lima, Peru) to an altitude of 3300 m in the Andes near to Huancayo. There the animals were divided into two groups, one being kept indoors at 20°C and the other being kept outdoors where the temperature was 10°C, but which varied between -8.5 and +20°C.

Sheep

The transport from low to high altitude had little effect on the PAP of the 4 sheep, the mean rise being from 12.5 mm Hg to 15 mm Hg. After 50 days at high altitude the PAP of the indoor sheep varied between 16 and 17.5 mm Hg while that of the outdoor sheep was substantially higher (21.5 to 22.5 mm Hg). By the 80th day, however, the PAP of one of the outdoor sheep had risen to 39.5 mm Hg. The locations of the two pairs of sheep were then reversed, and there was a fall in the PAP in both of the sheep moved from outdoors to indoors, and a rise in the PAP of the sheep moved from indoors to outdoors.

Cattle

The transport from low to high altitude caused PAP to rise from a mean of 22.6 mm Hg to 40.5 mm Hg. After 28 days at the high altitude environments, the mean PAP of the indoor group (62.6 mm Hg) was lower than that of the outdoor group (78.8 mm Hg). Surprisingly, after 50 day the mean PAP of two of the outdoor calves was the same as that of the 3 indoor calves (50 mm Hg). On the 40th day, however, one of the oudoor calves was obviously ill, with symptoms of imminent right heart failure typical of brisket disease. It was immediately transferred to indoors at 20°C where recovery occurred with no additional treatment. When the other 2 outdoor calves were moved indoors on the 80th day, the mean PAP declined from 55 mm Hg to 46 mm Hg, while that of the group moved outdoors rose from 55 mm Hg to 61 mm Hg.

With both the shorn sheep and the bovine calves the small numbers of animals used in this study, and the uncontrollable fluctuations in external ambient temperatures disallow any firm conclusions. It seems unlikely that unshorn sheep would have been at risk, but one of the shorn sheep may have been adversely affected by cold exposure at altitude. Thus it is possible that young lambs and adult sheep immediately after shearing could be at risk at high altitude if also exposed to cold. Even adult cattle are not immune from the risk of HMS, and the one suspected incident of brisket disease in a calf exposed to both altitude and a low ambient temperature was a likely occurrence. The point of particular interest is that the condition was reversed when the animal was removed from the cold-stress situation. Cattle are often removed to a lower altitude in an effort to arrest developing symptoms of brisket disease, and if relief can be achieved at the high altitude by the provision of a warm environment, this could be a more economic form of treatment as well as being more readily applicable.

Broiler chickens

Talavera (21) studied 60 broiler chickens hatched at sea level and taken to high altitude (3320 m) at one day of age. These animals were divided into two groups, the control one kept at an ambient temperature of 22 ± 2°C and the other kept at a cold ambient temperature (15 ± 2°C) for six weeks. He found a larger right heart hypertrophy, which indicates a higher pulmonary arterial hypertension, in the animals exposed simultaneously to hypoxia and cold. At the same time he only found mortality due to HMS in this group of animals.

A tentative indication derived from these studies was that the provision of shelter from cold *per se*, and from wind and precipitation which increase the degree of cold stress, could minimise the occurrence of HMS in animals when they are transferred from low to high altitudes. This hypothesis was put to test by Chauca, Cueva & Ayon (10) who, by management procedures designed to ameliorate cold exposure following the transfer, achieved a much lower incidence of brisket disease, and consequent mortality, than was to be expected on the basis of previous experiences of such movements of bovine calves. Also De La Cruz (12), working in a commercial farm with a large number of broiler chickens, found that the animals exposed to hypoxia (1990 m of altitude) but protected against cold stress had a smaller right heart hypertrophy and a lower mortality due to HMS than the animals exposed to cold stress.

CAN COLD EXPOSURE ALSO BE A FACTOR IN THE DEVELOPMENT OF HMS IN HUMANS?

It has long been known that HMS in humans is accompanied by an elevation in PAP (18). The causation of HMS in humans is attributable to the effects of the low partial pressure of atmospheric oxygen, since breathing pure oxygen affords some degree of temporary relief, and descent to sea level effects the complete loss of symptoms. If the onset of HMS in humans can be precipitated by an environmental stress additional to that of hypoxia, it could be supposed that this would have been noted, and followed up by studies of the relationship between hypoxia and the added stress in the causation of HMS. The apparent absence of such observations and studies would seem to counter the notion that the stress of cold exposure adds to that of hypoxia at high altitudes. Perhaps, however, the emphasis on the low partial pressure of oxygen as the causation of human distress at high altitudes has caused other components of the environment to be overlooked. In future studies of humans permanently resident at or visiting high altitudes it is now clear that attention should be paid to the possible additive effects of cold and hypoxia upon PAP and other circulatory parameters, and upon pathological conditions associated with altitude. Unfortunately PAP cannot measured by non-invasive means, and it would now be considered unethical to cannulate the pulmonary artery of a human subject to satisfy a curiosity about the environmental factors which may exert influences upon PAP and other circulatory parameters. Burns *et al.* (7) were able make some observations on hospitalized patients with pulmonary arterial cannulation for clinical purposes to test the hypothesis that exposure of the nasal vestibules and the upper lip of the human subject to coldness causes a reflexive increase in PAP. When a stream of cold area was directed onto upper-lip and nasal region of the face PAP increased from a mean of 35.7 to 39.7 mm Hg. Burns *et al.* suggested that the observed increase in PAP together with an increase in pulmonary arterial resistance and a decrease in pulmonary wedge pressure may contribute to the development of high altitude pulmonary oedema. There is, then, at least the possibility that in humans also, cold exposure may cause a rise in PAP which adds to that caused by altitude hypoxia.

TENTATIVE CONCLUSIONS

i) In sheep both cold exposure and the occurrence of fever cause rises in PAP which at high altitudes may add to that caused by the inhalation of oxygen-deficient air and thus contribute to the causation of HMS.

ii) Both cold-induced and fever-induced rises in PAP are evidently due to the stimulation of peripheral cold sensors, and the activation of a nervous pathway from the cold sensors, and through the CNS, to the pulmonary vasculature. The rise in PAP during fever is apparently not due to the release of an endogenous Prostaglandin E, and therefore antipyretic drugs which block the production of prostaglandins are unlikely to alleviate the effect of a fever upon PAP

iii) It is now evident that in cattle, and in calves particularly, exposure to cold can contribute to the development of HMS which may be relieved by a warm environment at the same altitude. Only lambs and recently shorn sheep are likely to develop any degree of HMS when exposed to cold at high altitudes.

iv) In humans also cold-exposure and fever may give rise to increases in PAP which, superimposed upon that due to hypoxia could likewise trigger or exacerbate the condition of HMS. This possibility needs to be investigated further. It is also possible that those pulmonary and circulatory conditions that appear to be particularly troublesome to humans during very cold winter weather even at low altitudes might also be precipitated or aggravated by the effect of cold upon PAP (5, 15). This also needs to be investigated.

v) While the evidence that cold exposure and fever might add to that of hypoxia on PAP and trigger symptoms of HMS is noteworthy, an even more noteworthy point is that at high altitudes as well as low ones many components of the total environment change periodically and circumstantially. In the study of the consequences of any one recognized environmental stress such as that of hypoxia at high altitudes, it is imperative, therefore, that other environmental circumstances are also monitored so that any interactions between environmental stresses can be detected by analyses of these variables.

REFERENCES

1. BLIGH, J. 1979. The central neurology of mammalian thermo-regulation. *Neuroscience* 4: 1213-1236.

2. BLIGH, J. & CHAUCA, D. 1978. The effects of intracerebro ventricular injections of carbachol and noradrenaline on cold induced pulmonary artery hypertension in sheep. *J Physiol* 284: 53.

3. BLIGH, J. & CHAUCA, D. 1981. The effect of a bacterial pyrogen on the pulmonary artery pressure of the sheep. *Fed Proc* 40: 439.

4. BLIGH, J. & CHAUCA, D. 1982. Cold-induced and altitude-induced pulmonary arterial hypertension in the sheep. *J Physiol* 332: 41-42.

5. BLIGH, J. & CHAUCA, D. 1982. Effects of hypoxia, cold exposure and fever on pulmonary artery pressure, and their significance for arctic residents. *In*: B. Harvald & J. P. Hart Hansen (eds), *Circumpolar health 81* (Proc. 5th Intl. Symp. on Circumpolar Health. Nordic council for arctic medical research report series 33.

6. BLIGH, J., COTTLE, W.H. & MASKREY, M. 1971. Influences of ambient temperature on the thermoregulatory responses to 5-hydroxytryptamine, noradrenaline and acetylcholine injected into the lateral cerebral ventricles of sheep, goats and rabbits. *J Physiol* 212: 377-392.

7. BURNS, B., GELBLUM, J., McCAULEY, M., CHODOFF, P. & STENE, J. 1983. Elevation of pulmonary arterial pressure and resistance following brief exposure of the naso-maxillary region to cold air (-50°C) in humans. *In*: J. R. Sutton, C. S. Houston & N. L. Jones (eds), Hypoxia, exercise and altitude. New York: Liss: 453.

8. CHAUCA, D. 1978. Physiological adaptation of farm animals to natural environments. Ph. D. thesis, University of Cambridge, England.

9. CHAUCA, D. & BLIGH, J. 1976. The additive effect of cold exposure and hypoxia on pulmonary artery pressure in sheep. *Res Vet Sc* 21: 123-124.

10. CHAUCA, D., CUEVA, S. & AYÓN, M. 1980. Indicencia de mal de altura según el tipo de hemoglobina en vaquillas Brown Swiss importadas. Reporte anual del Instituto Veterinario de Investigaciones Tropicales y de Altura. Lima, Perú.

11. COLE, P. 1954. Recordings of respiratory air temperature. *J Laryngol* 68: 295-307.

12. DE LA CRUZ, W. 1991. Efecto aditivo de la temperatura ambiental y la hipoxia sobre la incidencia de mal de altura en pollos machos y hembras. Tesis Fac. Med. Vet. UNMSM. Lima, Perú.

13. FISHMAN, A. P. 1980. Vasomotor regulation of the pulmonary circulation. *Canadian J Physiol and Pharmacol* 63: 131-135.

14. KASPRZAK, H. & BLIGH, J. 1983. Effects of sustained cold exposure on pulmonary arterial pressure in sheep. *In*: *34th Alaska Science Conference* Abstracts; 80.

15. LLOYD, E.LL. 1985. Environmental cold may be a major factor in some respiratory disorders. *In*: R. Fortune (ed), *Circumpolar Health 84*. Seattle: University of Washington Press: 66-69.

16. MATHER, G. W., NAHAS, G. G. & HEMINGWAY, A. 1953. Temperature changes of pulmonary blood during exposure to cold. *Am J Physiol* 173: 390-392.

17. McMURTRY, I.F.J., REEVES, J.T., WILL, D.H. & GROVER, R.F. 1975. Hemodynamic and ventilatory effects of skin-cooling in cattle. *Experientia* 31: 1303-1304.

18. MONGE, C. 1928. La enfermedad de los Andes: síndromes eritrémicos. *Anales de la Facultad de Medicina* 11: 314-319.

19. SAKAI, A., UEDA, G., KOBAYASHI, T., KUBO, K., FUKUSHIMA, M. & SHIBAMOTO, T. 1984. Cold exposure on pulmonary circulation in conscious sheep. *In*: *Abstracts 10th International Congress of Biometeorology*: 225.

20. SAKAY, A., UEDA, G., KOBAYASHI, T., SHIBAMOTO, T., YOSHIMURA, K., FUKUSHIMA, M. & KUBO, K. 1983. Potentiated effects of cold and low-pressure in sheep pulmonary hemodynamics. *In*: J. R. Sutton, C. S. Houston & N. L. Jones (eds), *Hypoxia, exercise and altitude*. New York: Liss: 471.

21. TALAVERA, H. 1984. Efecto de la hipoxia y el frío sobre el ventrículo derecho, la mortalidad por mal de altura y la productividad en pollos parrilleros. Tesis Fac. Med. Vet. UNMSM. Lima, Perú.

22. TUCKER, A. 1979. Pulmonary and systemic vascular responses to hypoxia after chemical sympathectomy. *Cardiovasc Res* 13: 469-476.

GENETIC BASES OF OXYGEN TRANSPORT AT HIGH ALTITUDE: TRADITIONAL AND NEW APPROACHES

Cynthia M. Beall

Abstract

The purpose of this paper is to review the types of evidence for genetic influences on several widely studied physiological links in the chain of oxygen transport in Andean and Himalayan high altitude populations. The interest in this topic derives from the desire to test the hypothesis that natural selection has modified the gene pools of long established high populations and increased the frequency of alleles for adaptive traits. Traditional natural experimental approaches using cross-population and migrant studies provide circumstantial evidence supporting the hypothesis that natural selection has acted on different oxygen transport characteristics in the two populations with the result that Himalayan highlanders have a unique gene pool for preserving hypoxic ventilatory response and modestly elevating hemoglobin concentration while Andean highlanders have a unique gene pool for large FVC. A new statistical genetic approach to the question reveals the presence of a major gene with a dominant allele frequency of 0.466 influencing % oxygen saturation of arterial hemoglobin in a Himalayan population. With this approach, it is feasible to compare populations on the basis of the presence or absence of such major genes, their allele frequencies and the mean phenotypic values of genotypes.

Key words: Andes, Himalayas, high altitude, HVR, FVC, hemoglobin concentration, SaO_2, statistical genetics, natural selection.

Resumen

Este artículo tiene como objetivo revisar las evidencias de una influencia genética en las diferentes variables involucradas en la cadena de eventos del transporte de oxígeno en poblaciones de altura (Andes e Himalayas). El interés en este tema deriva del deseo de probar la hipótesis de que la selección natural ha modificado las reservas genéticas y aumentado la frecuencia de alelos para las características adaptativas de las poblaciones con una larga historia de residencia en la altura. Las aproximaciones experimentales naturales tradicionales, basadas en estudios poblacionales transversales y de migrantes, proveen evidencias circunstanciales que apoyan la hipótesis de que la selección natural habría actuado en las diferentes características del transporte de oxígeno en las dos poblaciones. En la de los Himalayas, preservando una reserva genética única para la conservación de la respuesta ventilatoria a la hipoxia y para una moderada elevación de la concentración de hemoglobina, mientras que en las poblaciones Andinas, para una mayor capacidad vital forzada. Una nueva aproximación genética de tipo estadístico, revela la presencia de un gen mayor, cuyos alelos presentan una frecuencia de 0.466, con influencia en la saturación arterial de oxígeno en las poblaciones de los Himalayas. Con esta aproximación es posible comparar poblaciones, en base a la presencia o ausencia de estos genes mayores, a la frecuencia de sus alelos y a la media de los valores fenotípicos de los genotipos.

Palabras claves: Andes, Himalayas, altura, respuesta ventilatoria a la hipoxia, capacidad vital forzada, concentración de hemoglobina, saturación de oxígeno, estadística genética, selección natural.

Résumé

Cet article passe en revue les arguments en faveur d'une influence génétique dans les différentes variables impliquées dans la chaîne d'événements du transport de l'oxygène chez des populations d'altitude (Andes et Himalayas). L'intérêt de ce thème vient du désir de prouver l'hypothèse suivant laquelle la sélection naturelle a modifié les réserves génétiques et augmenté la fréquence des allèles pour les caractéristiques d'adaptation des populations qui ont une longue tradition de résidence en altitude. Les approximations expérimentales naturelles traditionnelles, basées sur des études de populations transversales et de migrants, fournissent des évidences circonstancielles qui appuient l'hypothèse selon laquelle la sélection naturelle aurait agi sur les différentes caractéristiques du transport de l'oxygène chez les deux populations: chez les Himalayens, en préservant une réserve génétique unique pour la conservation de la réponse ventilatoire à l'hypoxie et pour une élévation modérée de la concentration d'hémoglobine, tandis que pour les populations andines, cela signifiait une plus grande capacité vitale forcée. Une nouvelle approximation génétique de type statistique révèle la présence d'un gène plus important, dont les allèles présentent une fréquence de 0.466, avec une influence sur la saturation artérielle d'oxygène chez les populations de l'Himalaya. Cette approximation permet de comparer des populations, en se basant sur la présence ou l'absence de ces gènes importants, sur la fréquence de ses allèles et à la moyenne des valeurs phénotypiques des génotypes.

Mots clés : Andes, Himalayas, altitude, réponse ventilatoire à l'hypoxie, capacité vitale forcée, concentration d'hémoglobine, saturation d'oxygène, statistique génétique, sélection naturelle.

«It can be definitely stated that the Man of the Andes possesses biological characteristics distinct from those of sea-level man.» due to «genetic factors of both hereditary and acquired type» (30).

More than forty years later, scientists continue to design studies to identify the genetic factors discussed by Monge-M. The enduring interest in genetic factors is explained by the desire to test the hypothesis that natural selection has modified the gene pools of long established high altitude populations in the direction of a relatively high frequency of alleles for adaptive traits. However, the goal of detecting natural selection in indigenous high altitude human populations has been elusive. One reason is that the likely adaptive traits are quantitative, continuously varying phenotypes with unknown correspondence to genotypes rather than discrete phenotypes corresponding to specific genotypes. It has been difficult to a) demonstrate that such quantitative functional traits are under genetic control and b) to determine whether population differences in mean values of a physiological trait reflect differences in their gene pools or in environmental influences on the same array of genes. At the same time, however, there is substantial circumstantial evidence for genetic adaptation in Himalayan and Andean high altitude natives, two populations with long histories of high altitude residence and opportunity for natural selection. The purpose of this paper is to review the types of evidence for genetic influences on several widely studied physiological links in the chain of oxygen transport of these two high altitude populations. It does not exhaustively review the evidence, but, instead illustrates the traditional approach and presents a new one deriving from recent developments in statistical genetics.

Traditionally, scientists have relied upon natural experiments to evaluate the hypothesis that various distinctive biological characteristics of high altitude populations are largely genetically determined and, by inference, the result of natural selection. These natural experiments have used two general research designs: cross-population studies and migrant studies.

There are two types of cross-population studies. One compares geographically distant, long-established, successful highland populations, usually Andean and Himalayan. If these two populations share biological characteristics that are different from sea level populations, this would imply that the severe stress of high altitude hypoxia selected for the same characteristics although these populations that have been evolving separately for thousands of years. Alternatively, if these two populations differ, this would imply genetic differences between them and raise the possibility that natural selection has acted differently in the two geographic areas.

A second type of cross-population study helps analyze the latter situation. It compares recently arrived highland populations, usually of European descent with 1-2 generations of high altitude residence, that are assumed to have no genetic adaptations to high altitude, with the long established highland populations who might have genetic adaptations. If the new arrivals were similar to one, but, not both, long established high altitude populations, this would imply that natural selection has acted on the trait in the divergent population.

Migrant studies give additional insight by comparing «experimental samples» of people born at one altitude and measured at another with «control samples» of people born and remaining at sea level and/or high altitude. For example, if migrants from sea level to high altitude and high altitude natives had similar mean values for an adaptive trait, this would be evidence that basic human homeostatic mechanisms can account for the findings and that natural selection has not acted on the high altitude gene pool for that trait. If upward migrants were similar to one, but not both, long established high altitude population, this would imply that natural selection has acted on the trait in the divergent population.

The first example of these traditional approaches illustrates the cross-population study design applied to the control of breathing, an early link in the chain of oxygen transport. Although sea level natives acutely exposed to experimental hypoxia at sea level or to environmental hypoxia at high altitude exhibit a marked increase in ventilation, Andean high altitude natives exhibit only a small increase in ventilation following a reduction in arterial pO_2. For example, Andean highlanders in one study had just one-quarter the ventilatory increase of lowlanders (42). This is described as a «blunted» hypoxic ventilatory response (HVR). Five studies of approximately 30 Andean adult males and 21 non-pregnant adult females are consistent in reporting a small or absent HVR (42, 23, 32, 41). This is not present at birth, but, develops through childhood and adolescence as demonstrated by cross-sectional study of 161 Andean native highlanders age newborn to 25 years (33, 24). The age-specific prevalence of «blunted» HVR increased from 0% at birth, to 5% at 2-12 years, to 17% at 13-20 years, and to 100% at 22-25 years. This has been interpreted as indicating initial development of normal HVR followed by its depression after prolonged exposure (24).

Cross-population comparison with samples of Himalayan high altitude natives finds normal HVR. Four studies of approximately 80 men report a «well-preserved» HVR (43, 16, 27, 17). Just one contradictory study of 3 mountaineers temporarily at 4800 m reports a blunted HVR (29). Overall, these data indicate that Himalayan highlanders do not develop a blunted HVR and suggest that there are population differences in genes influencing this initial step of oxygen transport.

Cross-population comparison with samples of European descent native to high altitude in the Rocky Mountains finds that children have normal HVR at age 9-10 while adults have blunted HVR (7, 13, 47). Upward migrant studies of adolescents and adults of European descent confirm that HVR is gradually depressed over a decade of high altitude residence (13, 47). This European population with no history of selection for high altitude adaptation and the Andean population both appear to develop blunted HVR during adolescence and adulthood. The similarity implies that these two populations exemplify the normal homeostatic response to prolonged high altitude exposure. All three populations appear to develop normal HVR during childhood, but this is maintained throughout life only in the Himalayan population.

The main environmental factor causing blunted HVR at sea level is endurance training (e.g. 40). It is unlikely that the Andean and Rocky Mountain adolescents and adults reported in the literature are markedly better physically trained than the Himalayan study subjects, over half of whom were elite mountaineers.

If this initial step in the chain of processes transporting oxygen from the ambient air to the tissue differs among these populations, it is likely that subsequent steps also differ in order to compensate. Pulmonary function in conveying ambient air to the alveoli is one of these. It has been widely assessed at high altitude by measuring Forced Vital Capacity (the volume of air expelled on full expiration following a full inspiration). Andean highland adults and children consistently have large FVC for their body size compared with sea level populations. Figure 1 summarizes 23 Andean samples (16 of adults and 7 of children 10-12 years, total n=1231) on the basis of reported FVC as a percent of that predicted on the basis of age, sex and stature using sea level prediction equations (6). The value is 105% or more in 18 of the 23 samples. The three with values below 100% are from one study that nevertheless did find higher FVC at high altitude than sea level (35, 36).

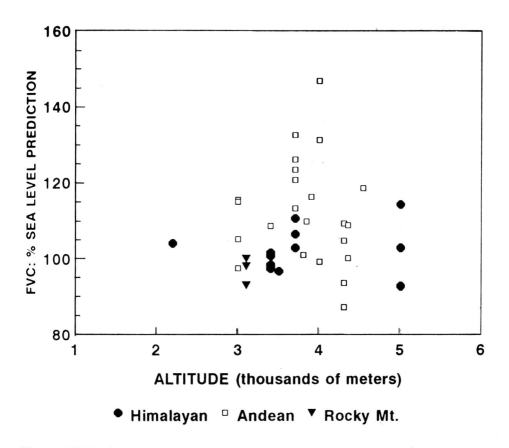

Fig. 1 - FVC of 23 Andean and 13 Himalayan samples of high altitude native children age 9-10 and adults expressed as a percent of sea level prediction based on sex, age and height. Sources for the Andean data are 36; Greksa, personal communication re sample from 3700 m, 1992; 4; 14; 18; 5; 15; 10; 15; 28; 46; 49; Beall, unpublished data from 3700 m. Sources for the Himalayan data are Beall and Reichsman unpublished data from 3400 m; 26; 12; 45; 49; Beall and Goldstein, unpublished data from 5000 m; 16. Sources for the Rocky Mountain data are 13 and 11 (recalculated with sexes separate).

Cross-population comparison with 12 Himalayan samples (8 adult, 5 children 10-12 years, total n=276) reveals that all but two have FVCs within 5% of the predicted sea level values (Fig. 1). Between 3000 and 4000 m, the average % FVC for 8 Himalayan samples is 102% compared with 116% for 16 Andean samples. Similarly, three samples of young adults from the Rocky Mountains (total n=22) have FVC that are 93-100% of the predicted sea level values. Another Rocky Mountain sample had FVC that «differed little» from sea level predictions, although actual values were not reported (22).

These data suggest that the Himalayan and European populations represent populations that have not been subject to natural selection for this phenotypic trait while the Andean population represents the results of natural selection for large FVC at high altitude.

Upward migrant studies of individuals of Andean descent born at low altitude and migrating to high altitude reveal that the Andean genotype responds to hypoxic stress with development of large FVC only if high altitude exposure occurs before adolescence (14). Thus a critical period of high altitude exposure appears necessary for the expression of this distinctive Andean phenotypic characteristic.

The normal sized FVC of Rocky Mountain and Himalayan highlanders is probably not due to environmental factors preventing achievement of a large, Andean sized FVC. The Rocky Mountain samples were healthy and the Himalayan samples between 3000 and 4000 m were healthy and medically screened. Information on smoking history for the samples at 3400 m and 5000 m reveals no correlation with FVC.

Another frequently reported link in the chain of oxygen transport of high altitude populations is hemoglobin concentration, a measure of oxygen carrying capacity. Hemoglobin concentration is generally greater at high altitudes than at sea level, but, the amount of increase is not uniform. Cross-population studies reveal that the hemoglobin concentration of Himalayan highlanders is generally lower than that of Andean highlanders at the same altitude (Fig. 2) (2). Between 3400 and 4000 m altitude, rural Himalayan highlanders average 1.4 gm/dl lower mean hemoglobin concentration than their Andean counterparts. A sample from the Rocky Mountain population at 3100 m (37) has a mean hemoglobin concentration similar to the rural Andean mean at 3800 m in Figure 2. This suggests the possibility that Andean and European highlanders represent the basic human homeostatic response to prolonged high altitude hypoxia and the Himalayan highlanders represent a population selection for a smaller response.

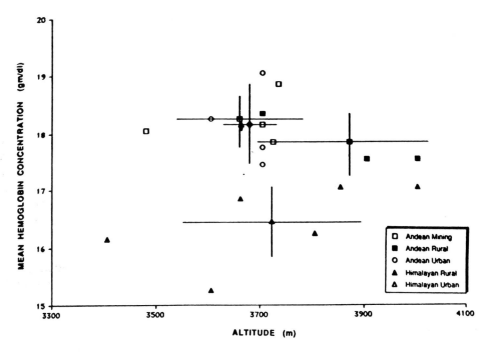

Fig. 2 - Hemoglobin concentration of 10 Andean and 8 Himalayan samples of high altitude native men (reprinted from 2, with author's permission).

Systematic methodological, nutrition, lifestyle and disease differences do not appear to lower hemoglobin concentration in the Himalayas or raise it in the Andes (2, 49). There may be a functional link between HVR and hemoglobin concentration. Individuals within one Himalayan population with greater HVR had lower hematocrits (49). The Himalayan higher HVR and the lower hemoglobin reviewed above suggests the hypothesis that this relationship may hold across populations as well.

In summary, cross-population studies indicate that Himalayan highlanders maintain sea level values of HVR throughout life, sea level values of FVC and slightly elevated hemoglobin concentration. They also indicate that Andean highlanders develop blunted HVR during adolescence and young adulthood, larger FVC if exposure occurs prior to adolescence and relatively more elevated hemoglobin concentration.

A parsimonious interpretation of similar responses in a high altitude population with a long history of exposure and one with just 1-2 generations of exposure is that the populations have the same alleles in the same frequencies for that trait. Thus the Himalayan and Rocky Mountain populations' similarity in FVC, could be interpreted as evidence of genetic similarity and the absence of natural selection on genes controlling size of FVC in the Himalayan population. Similarly, the Andean and Rocky Mountain similarity in depressed HVR and relatively more elevated hemoglobin concentration could be interpreted evidence for similarity in genes controlling these traits and the absence of natural selection.

Furthermore, a parsimonious interpretation of the pattern whereby one population of long high altitude ancestry differs from both another population of long high altitude ancestry and one of short high altitude exposure suggests that the divergent high altitude population differs genetically from the latter two in alleles influencing that particular trait, either due to natural selection or to random genetic drift. Using this logic to interpret the information reviewed above leads to the inference that the Andean and Himalayan high altitude populations have both been subject to natural selection, yet natural selection has acted on different oxygen transport characteristics in the two populations. The hypothesis is that Himalayan highlanders have a unique gene pool for preserving HVR and modestly elevating hemoglobin concentration while Andean highlanders have a unique gene pool for large FVC.

For natural selection to operate on a trait, it must have heritable, genetically based variation. This is analyzed using the similarities and differences in the values of these traits among relatives. Familial patterning of each of the traits discussed above provides evidence that genes influence an individual's position in the normal range of variation.

For example, HVR varies widely among sea level residents. Twin studies (9; 20; 19) and family studies (20, 31, 39) show familial patterning consistent with the hypothesis that genes influence the magnitude of HVR in healthy individuals.

Evidence that genes influence FVC relative to stature have been identified in twin studies at sea level (21, 38). Another type of genetic analysis calculates the heritability, h^2, which is the proportion of interindividual phenotypic variation due to additive genetic effects. A significant heritability of FVC was found in a Himalayan population (1). In contrast, an Andean study found no significant heritability; that is evidence for pronounced environmentally caused variation in FVC (34). This is consistent with the finding that FVC of Andean highlanders is sensitive to the altitude of residence during growth. These contrasting findings may reflect a fundamental population difference resulting from natural selection for greater environmental responsiveness in the Andes.

Evidence for genetic determinants of interindividual variation in hemoglobin concentration and hematocrit come from twin studies at sea level (48), family studies in the Andes (8) and in the Himalayas (1).

While each of these traits has a demonstrated genetic basis and it seems plausible to exclude various environmental explanations for the population differences, the genetic adaptation argument is incomplete. It remains to identify a specific gene, mode of inheritance, and allele frequency. Such analysis is undertaken using statistical genetics techniques for detecting major loci influencing quantitative, physiological traits.

This new approach to studying the genetic bases of high altitude adaptation is illustrated by a statistical genetic analysis of % oxygen saturation of arterial hemoglobin (SaO_2). This measure reflects the ability of the lungs to oxygenate the blood and together with hemoglobin concentration determines the arterial O_2 content. Although reliable cross-population information on SaO_2 is not available due to use of different measurement techniques, intrapopulation analysis of family data in a Himalayan population at 5000 m has detected evidence for a major gene influencing SaO_2 (1).

Applying standard quantitative genetic analysis revealed a significant genetic component to variation in SaO_2 ($h^2=.41$). This finding justified the use of complex segregation analysis, a statistical technique to determine if a segregating autosomal locus could explain all or part of the genetic variation in SaO_2. It permits evaluating a series of potential genetic transmission models: no major gene, a Mendelian major gene, a polygenic model with no major gene and a sporadic model in which there is no familial patterning to the trait (25).

A Mendelian model represented the best fitting most parsimonious model for transmission of quantitative SaO_2 levels in the Himalayan population. Figure 3 presents a histogram of the observed data and the theoretical genotypic distributions obtained from the parameters of the best fitting model. The Mendelian model exhibits two distributions of SaO_2. Individuals in the lower one are comprised of AA homozygotes and have a mean SaO_2 of 78.1%, while Aa heterozygotes and aa homozygotes exhibit a mean of 84.0%. The estimated allele frequency for the dominant allele a for higher SaO_2 is 0.466. The major locus accounts for 39% of the total phenotypic variation in SaO_2 in this population while polygenes account for an additional 15% of the variance (1). The finding suggests the hypothesis that individuals with the dominant allele a are at a selective advantage in the hypoxic high altitude environment.

This statistical genetic evidence of a major locus influencing normal quantitative variation in an oxygen transport variable illustrates the feasibility of explicitly testing the hypothesis that a major gene influences a physiological character measuring high altitude adaptation. Investigation of other Himalayan and Andean populations using this new approach will enable testing hypotheses regarding population genetic similarities and differences in high altitude

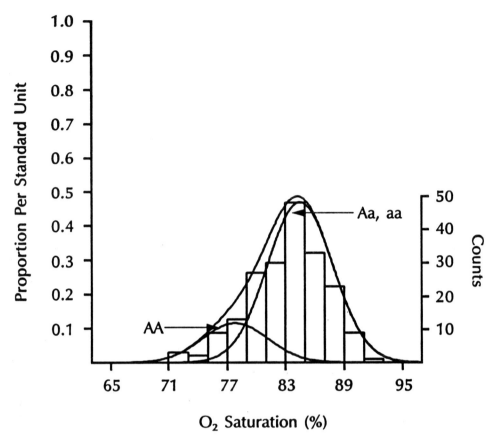

Fig. 3 - Observed SaO$_2$ distribution in a high altitude Himalayan population and theoretical genotypic distributions calculated using statistical genetic techniques (1).

adaptation by directly comparing populations on the basis of the presence or absence of major genes, their allele frequencies, and the mean values of genotypes.

The traditional and the new approaches work well together. The traditional approach aids in developing hypotheses about the particular traits to study and about similarities and differences. The new approach enables explicit testing of these hypotheses.

References

1. BEALL, C.M., BLANGERO, J., WILLIAMS-BLANGERO, S. & GOLDSTEIN, M. C. A major gene for % oxygen saturation of arterial hemoglobin in Tibetan highlanders (submitted).

2. BEALL, C.M., BRITTENHAM, G.M., MACUAGA, F. & BARRAGAN, M. 1990. Variation in Hemoglobin Concentration Among Samples of High-Altitude Natives in the Andes and the Himalayas. *Amer J Human Biol* 2: 639-651.

3. BEALL, C.M. & GOLDSTEIN, M. C. 1990. Hemoglobin Concentration, Percent Oxygen Saturation and Arterial Oxygen Content of Tibetan Nomads at 4,850 to 5,450 M. *In*: J. R. Sutton, G. Coates & J. E. Remmers (eds.), *Hypoxia: The Adaptations*. Toronto: B.C. Decker, Inc.: 59-65

4. BOYCE, A.J., HAIGHT, J.S.J., RIMMER, D.B. & HARRISON, G.A. 1974. Respiratory Function in Peruvian Quechua Indians. *Annals Human Biol* 1: 137-148.

5. BRODY, J.S., LAHIRI, S., SIMPSER, M., MOTOYAMA, E.K. & VELÁSQUEZ, T. 1977. Lung Elasticity and Airway Dynamics in Peruvian Natives to High Altitude. *J Appl Physiol* 42: 245-251.

6. BURROWS, B., CLINE, MG., KNUDSON, R.J., TAUSSIG, L.M. & LEBOWITZ, M.D. 1983. A Descriptive Analysis of the Growth and Decline of the FVC and FEV1. *Chest* 83: 717-724.

7. BYRNE-QUINN, E., SODAL, I.E. & WEIL, J.V. 1972. Hypoxic and hypercapnic ventilatory drives in children native to high altitude. *J Appl Physiol* 32: 44-46.

8. CHAKRABORTY, R., CLENCH, J., FERRELL, R.E., BARTON, S.A. & SCHULL, W. J. 1983. Genetic components of variation of red cell glycolytic intermediates at two altitudes among the South American Aymara. *Annals Human Biol* 10: 174-184.

9. COLLINS, D.D., SCOGGIN, C.H., ZWILLICH, C.W. & WEIL, J.V. 1978. Hereditary Aspects of Decreased Hypoxic Response. *J Clin Invest* 62, 105-110.

10. CRUZ, J.C. 1973. Mechanics of Breathing in High Altitude and Sea Level Subjects. *Respir Physiol* 17: 146-161.

11. DE GRAFF, A.C., GROVER, R.F., JOHNSON, R.L., HAMMOND, J.W. & MILLER, J. M. 1970. Diffusing capacity of the lung in Caucasians native to 3,100m. *J Appl Physiol* 29: 71-76.

12. DROMA, T., MCCULLOUGH, R.S., MCCULLOUGH, R.E., ZHUAN, J., CYMERMAN, A., SUN, S., SUTTON, J.R. & MOORE, L.G. 1991. Increased vital and total lung capacities in Tibetan compared to Han residents of Lhasa 3,658m. *Amer J Phys Anthropol* 86: 341-352.

13. FORSTER, H.V., DEMPSEY, J.A., BIRNBAUM, M.L., REDDAN, W.G., THODEN, J., GROVER, R.F. & RANKIN, J. 1971. Effect of Chronic Exposure to Hypoxia on Ventilatroy Response to CO2 and Hypoxia. *J Appl Physiol* 31: 586-592.

14. FRISANCHO, A.R. 1969. Human Growth and Pulmonary Function of a High Altitude Peruvian Quechua Population. *Human Biol* 41: 365-379.

15. FRISANCHO, A.R., VELÁSQUEZ, T. & SÁNCHEZ, R. 1973. Influence of Developmental Adaptation on Lung Function at High Altitude. *Human Biol* 45: 583-594.

16. HACKETT, P.H., REEVES, J.T., REEVES, C.D., GROVER, R.F. & RENNIE, D. 1980. Control of Breathing in Sherpas at Low and High Altitude. *J Appl Physiol* 49: 374-379.

17. HUANG, Z.R., ZHU, S.C., BA, Z.F. & HU, X.C. 1981. Ventilatory control in Tibetan highlanders. *In*: D. S. Liu Ed., *Geological and ecological studies of Qinghai-Xizang Plateau* vol. II. Environment and ecology of Qinghai-Xizang Plateau. New York: Gordon and Beach: 1363-1369.

18. HURTADO, A. 1932. Respiratory Adaptation in the Indian Natives of the Peruvian Andes. Studies at High Altitude. *American J Phys Anthropol* 17: 137-165.

19. KAWAKAMI, Y., YAMAMOTO, H., YOSHIKAWA, T. & SHIDA, A. 1985. Age-related Variation of Respiratory Chemosensitivity *In*: Monozygotic Twins. *Amer Rev Respir Dis* 132: 89-92.

20. KAWAKAMI, Y., YOSHIKAWA, T., SHIDA, A. & ASANUMA, Y. 1981. Relationships Between Hypoxic and Hypercapnic Ventilatory Responses in Man. *Japan J Physiol* 31: 357-368.

21. KLISSOURAS, V. 1977. Twin Studies on Functional Capacity. *In*: J. S. Weiner Ed., *Physiological Variation and its Genetic Basis*. London: Taylor and Francis, Ltd.: 43-56.

22. KRYGER, M., ALDRICH, F., REEVES, J.T. & GROVER, R.F. 1978. Diagnosis of Airflow Obstruction at High Altitude. *Amer Rev Respir Dis* 117: 1055-1058.

23. LAHIRI, S., KAO, F.F., VELÁSQUEZ, T., MARTÍNEZ, C. & PEZZIA, W. 1969. Irreversible Blunted Respiratory Sensitivity to Hypoxia in High Altitude Natives. *Respir Physiol* 6: 360-374.

24. LAHIRI, S., DELANEY, R.G., BRODY, J.S., VELÁSQUEZ, T., MOTOYAMA, E.K. & POLGAR, C. 1976. Relative role of environmental and genetic factors in respiratory adaptation to high altitude. *Nature* 261: 133-135.

25. LALOUEL, J.M., RAO, D.C., MORTON, N. E. & ELSTON, R.C. 1983. A unified model for complex segregation analysis. *Amer J Human Genet* 35: 816-826.

26. MALIK, S.I. & SINGH, I.P. 1979. Ventilatory Capacity among Highland Bods: a Possible Adaptive Mechanism at High Altitude. *Annals Human Biol* 6: 471-476.

27. MASUYAMA, S., KOJIMA, A., HONDA, Y. & KURIYAMA, T. 1990. Do Nepalese Sherpas maintain high hypoxic ventilatory drive? Studies at 5140m and 6500m in Mt. Everest Expedition 1988. *In*: J. R. Sutton, G. Coates & J. E. Remmers Ed., *Hypoxia. The Adaptations*. Toronto: B. C. Decker, Inc.: 292.

28. MAZESS, R.B. 1969. Exercise Performance of Indian and White High Altitude Residents. *Human Biol* 41: 494-518.

29. MILLEDGE, J.S. & LAHIRI, S. 1967. Respiratory Control in Lowlanders and Sherpa Highlanders at Altitude. *Respir Physiol* 2: 310-322.

30. MONGE-M, C. 1978. *Acclimatization in the Andes* reissue of 1948 edition Baltimore: The Johns Hopkins Press: pp. i-130.

31. MOORE, G.C., ZWILLICH, C.W., BATTAGLIA, J.D., COTTON, E.K. & WEIL, J. V. 1976. Respiratory Failure Associated with Familial Depression of Ventilatory Response to Hypoxia and Hypercapnia. *New Eng J Med* 295: 861-865.

32. MOORE, L.G., BRODEUR, P., CHUMBE, O., D'BROT, J., HOFMEISTER, S. & MONGE-C, C. 1986. Maternal hypoxic Ventilatory Response, Ventilation, and Infant Birth Weight at 4,300m. *J Appl Physiol* 60: 1401-1406.

33. MORTOLA, J.P., REZZONICO, R., FISHER, J.T., VILLENA-CABRERA, N., VARGAS, E., GONZÁLES, R. & PENA, F. 1990. Compliance of the Respiratory System in Infants Born at High Altitude. *Amer Rev Respir Dis* 142: 43-48.

34. MUELLER, W.H., CHAKRABORTY, R., BARTON, S.A., ROTHHAMMER, F. & SCHULL, W.J. 1980. Genes and epidemiology in anthropological adaptation studies: familial correlations in lung function in populations residing at different altitudes in Chile. *Medical Anthropol* 3: 367-384.

35. MUELLER, W.H., YEN, F., ROTHHAMMER, F. & SCHULL, W.J. 1978. A Multinational Andean Genetic and Health Program: VI. Physiological Measurements of Lung Function in an Hypoxic Environment. *Human Biol* 50: 489-513.

36. MUELLER, W.H., YEN, F., SOTO, P., SCHULL, V.N., ROTHHAMMER, F. & SCHULL, W.J. 1979. A Multinational Andean Genetic and Health Program: VIII. Lung Function Changes with Migration between Altitudes. *Amer J Phys Anthropol* 51: 183-196.

37. OKIN, J.T., TREGER, A., OVERY, H.R., WEIL, J.V. & GROVER, R.F. 1966. Hematologic Response to Medium Altitude. *Rocky Mountain Med J* 63: 44-47.

38. REDLINE, S., TISHLER, PV., ROSNER, B., LEWITTER, F.I., VANDENBURGH, M., WEISS, S.T. & SPEIZER, F.E. 1989. Genotypic and Phenotypic Similarities in Pulmonary Function Among Family Members of Adult Monozygotic and Dizygotic Twins. *Amer J Epidemiol* 129: 827-36.

39. SAUNDERS, M.A., LEEDER, S.R. & REBUCK, A.S. 1976. Ventilatory response to carbon dioxide in young athletes: a family study. *Amer Rev Respir Dis* 113: 497-502.

40. SCHOENE, R.B. 1982. Control of Ventilation in Climbers to Extreme Altitude. *J Appl Physiol* 53: 886-890.

41. SCHOENE, R.B., ROACH, R.C., LAHIRI, S., PETERS, R.M., HACKETT, P.H. & SANTOLAYA, R. 1990. Increased diffusion capacity maintains arterial saturation during exercise in the Quechua Indians of Chilean altiplano. *Amer J Human Biol* 2: 663-668.

42. SEVERINGHAUS, J.W., BAINTON, C.R. & CARCELEN, A. 1966. Respiratory Insensitivity to Hypoxia in Chronically Hypoxic Man. *Respir Physiol* 1: 308-334.

43. SUN, S., ZHANG, J.G., ZHOMA, T., HUANG, S.Y., MCCULLOUGH, R.E., MCCULLOUGH, R.S., REEVES, C.S., REEVES, J.T. & MOORE, L.G. 1988a. Higher Ventilatory Drives in Tibetan than male residents residents of Lhasa (3658m). *Amer Rev Respir Dis* 188 137: 410.

44. SUN, S., ZHANG, J.G., ZHOMA, T., HUANG, S.Y., MCCULLOUGH, R.E., MCCULLOUGH, R.G., REEVES, C.S., REEVES, J.T. & MOORE, L.G. 1988b. Higher Exercise Capacities in Tibetan than Han Male Residents of Lhasa 3658 m. *FASEB Journal* 2: A1281.

45. SUN, S.F., DROMA, T.S., ZHANG, J.G., TAO, J.X., HUANG, S.Y., MCCULLOUGH, R.G., MCCULLOUGH, R.E., REEVES, C.S., REEVES, J.R. & MOORE, L.G. 1990. Greater maximal O_2 uptakes and vital capacities in Tibetan than Han residents of Lhasa. *Respir Physiol* 79: 151-162.

46. VELÁSQUEZ, T. 1972. *Análisis de la Función Respiratoria en la Adaptación a la Altitud,* Tesis de Doctorado. Lima, Perú: Universidad Nacional Mayor de San Marcos. pp. 1-205.

47. WEIL, J.V., BYRNE-QUINN, E., SODAL, I.E., FILLEY, G.F. & GROVER, R.F. 1971. Acquired Attenuation of Chemoreceptor Function in Chronically Hypoxic Man at High Altitude. *J Clin Invest* 50: 186-195.

48. WHITFIELD, J.B. & MARTIN, N.G. 1985. Genetic and Environmental Influences on the Size and Number of Cells in the Blood. *Genetic Epidemiol* 2: 133-144.

49. WINSLOW, R.M., CHAPMAN, K.W. & MONGE-C., M. 1990. Ventilation and the control of erythropoiesis in high-altitude natives of Chile and Nepal. *Amer J Human Biol* 2: 653-662.

II.

TRANSPORTE DE
OXÍGENO
EN HIPOXIA

MAXIMAL OXYGEN UPTAKE RATE AT HIGH ALTITUDE: A GRAPHICAL ANALYSIS

S. Marsh Tenney

Abstract

Graphical analyses are employed to elucidate the combined convective and diffusive processes which determine the upper limits of oxygen uptake rate at sea level (normoxia) and at high altitude (the case of hypoxia at about 5450 m is selected) under acute and chronic (acclimatized) conditions. Comparison of equivalent oxygen transport rates, on the one hand, set by high blood flow and low oxygen saturation, and on the other, by low blood flow and normal oxygen saturation, lead to different effects on tissue oxygenation and hence, on metabolic rate. Venous oxygen pressure is the final determinant. Finally, the effect of increasing red cell mass on venous oxygen, and of increasing tissue diffusing capacity on oxygen extraction ratio are examined. The principle of optimal response is emphasized throughout.

Key words: Tissue oxygenation, coefficient of oxygen delivery, critical Po_2, oxygen extraction ratio, oxygen transport, tissue diffusing capacity, polycythemia, convective transport.

Resumen

Mediante análisis gráficos se elucidan los procesos combinados de convección y difusión que determinan la tasa máxima de consumo de oxígeno a nivel del mar (normoxia) y en la altura (se selecciona una altura correspondiente a 5450 m) en condiciones agudas y crónicas (aclimatación). La comparación de tasas de transporte de oxígeno equivalentes, por un lado, determinadas por un alto flujo sanguíneo y una baja saturación de oxígeno, y, por otro lado, por bajo flujo de oxígeno y saturación normal, conducen a efectos diferentes en la oxigenación tisular y, por lo tanto, en la tasa metabólica. La determinante final es la presión venosa de oxígeno. Finalmente se examina el efecto de incrementar la masa de glóbulos rojos sobre el oxígeno venoso, y el efecto de incrementar la capacidad de difusión tisular sobre la tasa de extracción de oxígeno. Se enfatiza a lo largo del trabajo el principio de la respuesta óptima.

Palabras claves: Oxigenación tisular, coeficiente de liberación de oxígeno, PO_2 crítico, tasa de extracción de oxígeno, transporte de oxígeno, capacidad de difusión tisular, policitemia, transporte convectivo.

Résumé

Grâce à des analyses graphiques, on élucide les processus combinés de convection et de diffusion qui déterminent la consommation maximale d'oxygène au niveau de la mer (normoxie) et en altitude (on sélectionne une hypoxie correspondant à

5450 m) en conditions aiguës et chroniques (acclimatation). La comparaison entre des taux de transport d'oxygène équivalents, d'un côté, déterminés par un flux sanguin important et une saturation d'oxygène basse, et d'un autre côté, un flux sanguin lent et une saturation normale, ont des effets différents pour l'oxygénation des tissus et donc pour le métabolisme. Finalement, c'est la pression veineuse d'oxygène qui est l'élément déterminant. On examine enfin l'augmentation de la masse de globules rouges sur l'oxygène veineux et l'accroissement de la capacité de diffusion des tissus sur le taux d'extraction de l'oxygène. Tout au long de ce travail, l'accent est mis sur le principe de la réponse optimum.

Mots clés : Oxygénation des tissues, quotient de la liberation de l'oxygène, PO_2 critique, taux d'extraction de l'oxygene, transport d'oxygène, capacité de diffusion des tissus, polycythémie, transport par convection.

It has been said that exercise reveals the essence of the machine; a corollary could well be added to emphasize how the limits of exercise performance are exposed at high altitude. Fueling the machine is handicapped at high altitude, and it is a classic observation that maximal oxygen uptake rates are decreased. Identification of the point in the supply line that limits the flow of oxygen from mouth to mitochondria has been a subject of debate for many years, but analysis of the problem has been obscured by the tendency to argue the case for a particular failure when, in fact, although the transport processes can be treated as a linear sequence of discrete events, there are inter-relationships which cannot be ignored in constructing an integrated scheme. Bulk flow of oxygen by convection must deliver a quantity of molecules in amount sufficient to meet metabolic demand, but they must be at a partial pressure high enough to drive the oxygen from the capillary to cell interior by diffusion. Convection and diffusion are thus linked, and when oxygen capacity of the blood is increased, as in acclimatization to high altitude, the transport system is affected in ways that may be counter-intuitive and which also lead to consideration of qoptimal responses. These problems have been examined by Wagner (14) and by Tenney & Mithoefer (12) to reach similar conclusions, but they employed different graphical analyses and, to some extent, each considered different physiological factors. The purpose of this communication will be to treat the approaches of Wagner and of Tenney and Mithoefer together to develop further the insights they provide, and to extend the analysis, on those grounds, to other aspects of gas exchange and maximal oxygen consumption rates of acclimatized man at high altitude.

WAGNER'S GRAPHICAL ANALYSIS

Starting with the mass balance equation of Fick,

$$\dot{V}o_2 = \dot{Q}\,(Cao_2 - Cvo_2) \quad 1)$$

where $\dot{V}o_2$ is oxygen uptake rate, $\dot{Q}$ is cardiac output, Cao_2 is arterial oxygen content; and Cvo_2 is venous oxygen content, and next writing the equation for diffusive flow of oxygen (Fick's first law),

$$\dot{V}o_2 = Do_2 \, \Delta Po_2 \qquad\qquad 2)$$

where Do_2 is "tissue diffusing capacity" for oxygen and ΔPo_2 is oxygen partial pressure difference between "source" (capillary blood) and "sink" (mitochondria), the two equations define conditions that must be satisfied simultaneously for a steady state. The problem is simplified if the following assumptions are made: Po_2 in the region of mitochondria is close to zero, which must be true at $\dot{V}o_2$ (max); Pvo_2 approximates mean capillary Po_2 (the source); since exchange in hypoxic conditions is over the linear portion of the oxyhemoglobin dissociation curve (OHDC), Po_2 is proportional to Cvo_2. Then Eq. (2) becomes,

$$\dot{V}o_2 = Do_2 \cdot Pvo_2 \approx Do_2 \cdot Cvo_2 \qquad 3)$$

and a plot of $\dot{V}o_2$ as a function of Cvo_2 (Fig. 1) illustrates the dependence of $\dot{V}o_2$ on both convective and diffusive transport. The lines sloping down and to the right describe convective transport, and their points of intersection with ordinate and abscissa define values of interest. Remembering that oxygen transport (OT) is defined as,

$$OT = \dot{Q} \cdot Cao_2 \qquad\qquad 4)$$

the point of intersection with the ordinate ($Cvo_2 = 0$) must be OT, and the point of intersection with the abscissa ($\dot{V}o_2 = 0$) is Cao_2.

The lines running up and to the right describe diffusive transport. Their slope is Do_2, and their point of intersection with the convective transport line defines the particular rates of the two transport processes which determine $\dot{V}o_2$. In a steady state it is only at that point that both convective and diffusive requirements are satisfied simultaneously.

With this graphical display the explanation of the reduction of $\dot{V}o_2$ (max) at high altitude becomes clear. Hypoxia will reduce Cao_2, and if $\dot{Q}$ is unchanged, OT will be reduced in proportion to the decrease of Cao_2, a new line of convective transport will run parallel to the sea level line but will be displaced toward the origin. If the conditions describing diffusive flow of oxygen remain unchanged at high altitude, the point of intersection of the lines for convective and diffusive transport will be found to lie below the sea level point and will indicate a decreased $\dot{V}o_2$ (max). Now, it could be at high altitude, that $\dot{Q}$ would be stimulated to increase in amount that would match the decrease of Cao_2, in which case OT would be returned to normal, but, clearly, the aforementioned point of intersection although improved would still show a low $\dot{V}o_2$ (max). Therefore, the cause of the decreased $\dot{V}o_2$ (max) cannot, in this instance, be ascribed to a low OT. Further, it can be seen that the combination of a low $\dot{Q}$ and normal Cao_2 leads to a higher $\dot{V}o_2$ (max) than does a normal $\dot{Q}$ and low Cao_2, although each combination can be arranged to give the same OT. The fact is that each example delivers the same number of molecules to the tissue, but that fact alone is not enough to maintain the same $\dot{V}o_2$ in each: in one, due to greater arterial unsaturation, the capillary O_2 pressure head for diffusion is more severely compromised, and $\dot{V}o_2$ is depressed accordingly.

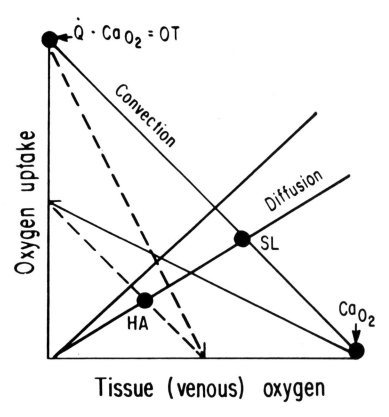

Tissue (venous) oxygen

Fig. 1 - Integrated processes in oxygen delivery and the determination of maximal oxygen uptake rate as developed by Wagner (14). Convective and diffusive transport conditions are indicated, and the points of intersection define V_{O_2} (max) in the steady state. SL and HA indicate status at sea level and at acute high altitude, respectively. For further explanation see text.

Somewhere along the C_{VO_2} axis there will be a "critical" value below which oxygen consumption cannot be sustained, because the driving pressure head for diffusion of oxygen would be insufficient to keep P_{O_2} in the region of mitochondria above zero. This will create regions of anoxia. Maintenance of an adequate P_{O_2} for diffusion is dependent on convective transport, but what is "adequate" is also dependent on the "diffusing capacity" of the tissue D_{O_2}. If D_{O_2} increases (for example, by increasing capillary density and thus shortening the diffusion path) the diffusion line steepens and will cut any given convection line at a point to indicate a higher V_{O_2} (max). Such a change would be an important aspect of acclimatization to high altitude (10)

It is important at this point to clarify the interpretation of "critical" P_{O_2} (or C_{VO_2} in Fig. 1, or S_{VO_2} in Fig. 2). First, the "critical" value in the graphs can be regarded as regional and applicable to a particular tissue, or it may be mixed venous, in which case it is a weighted average and is more conceptual than specifically determinant (11). Second, mitochondrial O_2 uptake is independent of regional oxygen concentration (zero order kinetics) down to a very low value, but below that -the "critical" value- it becomes dependent and follows (approximately) first order kinetics. The tissue in this latter state is hypoxic, $\dot{V}o_2$ of the tissue, and of the whole body, will be reduced; at the limit (zero concentration) the tissue is anoxic, and there is no oxygen uptake.

The feature of acclimatized man that is most apparent is the increase of red cell mass and hence, of the oxygen carrying capacity of the blood. This important change cannot be treated reliably with the graph of Fig. 1, because the shift in position of OHDC makes Cvo_2 a misleading guide for estimating Pvo_2. Neglecting for the moment, changes in hemoglobin affinity for oxygen, it is oxygen saturation (So_2) that is required for accuracy in dealing with the problem introduced by polycythemia.

OT AND O_2 PRESSURE HEAD FOR DIFFUSION WITH CHANGING O_2 CAPACITY

Tenney & Mithoefer had concluded, as has Wagner, that the effect of OT on venous oxygen depends on which component of the product ($\dot{Q} \cdot Cao_2$) is reduced. That problem takes on special significance with changing oxygen capacity, and to clarify this effect the graph shown in Fig. 2 was introduced. When O_2 content and O_2 capacity are plotted on ordinate and abscissa, respectively, a family of O_2 saturation isopleths radiate from the origin. Arterial and venous oxygen content values can be located, and the vertical distance separating them is (from Eq. 1.) the inverse of $\dot{Q}/\dot{V}o_2$. Note first, representation of the case of acute hypoxic exposure of a degree severe enough to reduce Sao_2 to 75%. If (Cao_2-Cvo_2) is unchanged, the new venous point is located by a vertical drop from the new Cao_2 of the same length as control (normoxia), and a new Svo_2 is identified which will certainly be below control. If Svo_2 falls enough to reach a "critical" value at 40% (assumed) this defines the limiting (a-v) difference before $\dot{V}o_2$ in some region becomes supply limited. Clearly, narrowing (Cao_2-Cvo_2), i.e., increasing $\dot{Q}/\dot{V}o_2$, would be the expedient, acute regulatory response to lift Svo_2 out of the "critical" range. The increase of cardiac output early in acute hypoxic exposure is, in fact, what is commonly observed.

However, after a few days at high altitude a hematopoietic response begins to elevate O_2 capacity of the blood, and if Sao_2 remains unchanged (the slight increase of Sao_2 that occurs with "ventilatory acclimatization" is ignored here) Cao_2 may return to normal (which is the case; in fact, Cao_2 often rises above normal). Once again, at this new state characterized by an elevated red cell mass, sustained arterial unsaturation, and an arterial oxygen content restored to normal, if the (Cao_2-Cvo_2) difference remains the same (cardiac output at high altitude is observed to return to normal as the hematocrit rises) OT will once again be normal, the venous saturation will have increased about 8%, but it is still far below normal. Combining Eq. 1 and 4, we can write

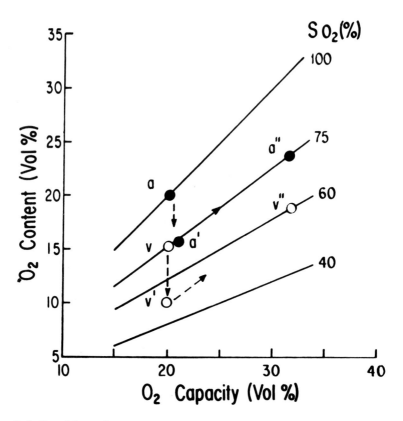

Fig. 2 - Relationships of oxygen contents under conditions of changing oxygen capacity of the blood. Arterial (a) and venous (v) points at sea level, acute (primed) and acclimatized (double primed) state at high altitude (5450 m.) are shown. Iso-saturation lines are drawn, and oxygen delivery can be inferred (see text).

$$\frac{OT}{\dot{V}o_2} = \frac{Cao_2}{Cao_2 - Cvo_2} \qquad 5)$$

or, by rearrangement,

$$\dot{V}o_2 = OT \cdot \frac{Cao_2 - Cvo_2}{Cao_2} \qquad 6)$$

These two forms of the same equation are useful in emphasizing the relationship of two frequently discussed parameters used to explain a common process. $OT/\dot{V}o_2$ in Eq. 5 is defined as the "coefficient of O_2 delivery" (COD), and it is graphically explicit in Fig. 2. Eq. 6 connects oxygen transport and the oxygen extraction ratio (OER), a parameter that has become a topic of much discussion in the recent gas exchange literature. It is obvious that for the same OT, it is OER that determines $\dot{V}o_2$, but what is not often appreciated is the fact that the particular OER which brings Svo_2 to the "critical" value depends on Cao_2 and O_2 capacity (see Fig. 2). For the moment, discussion of adaptive responses that may reduce the "critical" Svo_2 are postponed.

OXYGEN EXTRACTION RATIO AND "CRITICAL" SVO_2

Taking Svo_2 = 40% as the lowest value capable of sustaining oxygen consumption, the maximum (Cao_2-Cvo_2) that can be afforded will depend on Sao_2 and O_2 capacity, as shown in Fig. 3. The isopleths of this figure are calculated from relationships shown in Fig. 2. When Sao_2 = 100%, an OER = 60% will reach Svo_2 = 40% at all values of O_2 capacity. Note that (Cao_2-Cvo_2) narrows as Cao_2 falls. Hence, $\dot{Q}/\dot{V}o_2$ increases. When Sao_2 = 75%, the OER that will reach Svo_2 = 40% is reduced to 50%. Therefore, with arterial unsaturation, even if O_2 capacity increases, the OER to reach a "critical" Svo_2 will be decreased.

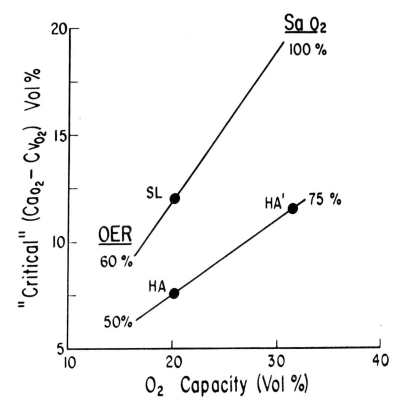

Fig. 3 - The arterio-venous oxygen content difference that would reach a "critical" venous oxygen saturation (assumed to be 40%) is shown as a function of oxygen capacity of the blood. Isopleths for arterial oxygen saturation at sea level (100%) and high altitude (5450 m.; 75%) are drawn, and the applicable oxygen extraction ratios (OER) are indicated.

Acclimatization, however, may introduce a change in the tissues which has the effect of reversing the depressed OER. This would come about if the change were such that the "critical" Svo_2 could be lowered. This, in fact, would be the consequence of increasing the tissue diffusing capacity, an effect that would follow from an increase of capillarity density. In the graphical portrayal of Fig. 2 a lower "critical" Svo_2 line would be drawn, a wider permissable (Cao_2-Cvo_2) would be apparent, and in the OER formula the numerator would increase, but the denomination is unchanged. A new, higher OER line in Fig. 3 would follow.

RELATIONSHIP OF $\dot{V}O_2$ TO OT AT DIFFERENT OER, AS DETERMINED BY SAO_2

Fig. 4 returns the argument to the message of Fig. 1. Fig. 4 illustrates an intuitively obvious deduction, viz., $\dot{V}o_2$ at the same OT will be lower if OER is decreased, but that the decrease becomes necessary when Sao_2 is

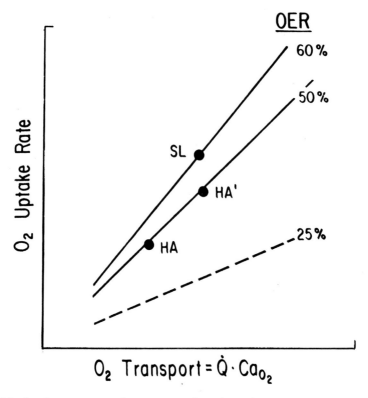

Fig. 4 - Maximal oxygen uptake rate as a function of convective oxygen transport is defined by isopleths of oxygen extraction ratio (OER). Relationships graphed in Figs. 2 and 3 show clearly that the same values of convective oxygen transport lead to a lower Vo_2 (max) at high altitude. Sea level (SL), acute high altitude (HA) and acclimatized high altitude (HA´) are shown.

decreased is only implicit. The sea level condition (O_2 capacity = 0.2 ml/ml; Cao_2 = 0.2 ml/ml; Sao_2 = 100%) is described by the line labelled OER = 60%. It is that value shown in Fig. 3 which reduces Svo_2 to 40% (Cvo_2 = 0.08 ml/ml), the limit below which (it is assumed) oxidative metabolism cannot be sustained. On acute exposure to high altitude (O_2 capacity = 0.2 ml/ml; Cao_2 = 0.15 ml/ml; Sao_2 = 75%), it is the OER = 50% line that is applicable. If cardiac output did not change, OT would be reduced in proportion to the decrease of Cao_2, and $\dot{V}o_2$ (max) would be much reduced. If $\dot{Q}$ increased in proportion to the decreased Cao_2 in the acute exposure period at high altitude, OT would return to sea level value, but $\dot{V}o_2$ would still be well below that observed at sea level. Only by further increase of $\dot{Q}$ could the necessary increment of $\dot{V}o_2$ be achieved to reach sea level value, but since it is $\dot{V}o_2$ (max) that is under consideration, $\dot{Q}$ must be assumed to be already at the maximum. With a little time at high altitude the hematopoietic response will elevate Cao_2, often above sea level values (O_2 capacity = 0.3 ml/ml; Cao_2 = 0.225 ml/ml; Sao_2 = 75%), and if $\dot{Q}$ has returned to sea level value, OT will be slightly above normal, but $\dot{V}o_2$ (max) will still be reduced. The determinant factor is ultimately the partial pressure of O_2 at the tissue level (11; 13). It could be envisioned that the hematopoietic response would proceed to elevate the hematocrit enough to raise OT sufficiently, by increasing Cao_2, to restore $\dot{V}o_2$ to the sea level value. However, that hypothetical response would introduce a new set of problems that are developed below.

OXYGEN TRANSPORT AND OPTIMAL HEMATOPOIETIC RESPONSE

As the red cell mass increases two significant changes in oxygen transport and tissue oxygenation occur: (1) oxygen capacity of the blood increases, and for the same arterial saturation the oxygen content increases, but there is a limit beyond which this is no longer true; (2) viscosity of the blood increases, and this will act, generally, to reduce cardiac output. Taking these effects in order:

In order to examine the relationship of oxygen capacity (O_2 cap.) to arterial oxygen saturation, Husson & Otis (5) derived, on the basis of data from the literature, the following equation:

$$O_2 \text{ cap} = -0.476 \ Sao_2 + 67.1 \qquad 7)$$

With Eq. 7 in hand the arterial point on each of the isosaturation lines of Fig. 2 can be located. See Fig. 5. The reference point is the abscissa on that figure, and although the ordinate value can be read directly, the behavior of Cao_2 over a full range of the Sao_2: O_2 ċap relationships emerges by multiplying Eq. 7 by Sao_2, in which case,

$$Cao_2 = -0.476 \ Sao_2 + 67.1 \ Sao_2 \qquad 8)$$

Differentiating with respect to Sao_2, and setting $\dfrac{dCao_2}{dSao_2} = 0,$

a maximum is reached when Sao_2 is about 70%, which can be identified in graphic form on Fig. 5. This deduction was first made by Husson & Otis, but the conclusion can also be anticipated in Fig. 2 from the mere fact that the isosaturation lines rise less steeply as the saturation decreases. In other words, the hematopoietic response is not likely to be of a magnitude to elevate Cao_2 in the low Sao_2 range in amounts at all comparable to the effect at higher Sao_2. In fact, the situation soon becomes impossible, since, when Sao_2 approaches zero, no amount of hemoglobin could result in a significant Cao_2. It is an interesting observation that Cao_2 reaches a maximum at the Sao_2 associated with an altitude of 18,000 ft. (5450 m.), and that is the maximum altitude at which humans can make permanent residence.

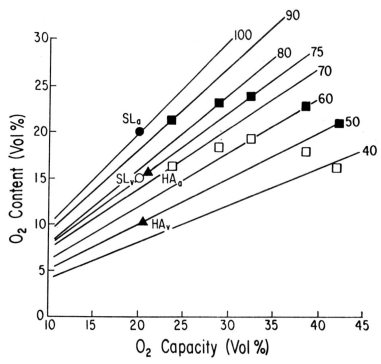

Fig. 5 - This graph follows the conventions of Fig. 2 but adds points to show O_2 content and O_2 capacity values applicable for different arterial oxygen saturations (or altitudes) as given by Eq. 7. Cao_2 passes through a maximum at $Sao_2 = 75\%$. Control sea level arterial value (SLa, solid circle) and sea level venous (SĹv, open circle); acute high altitude arterial (HAe, solid triangle) and venous (HAv, open triangle) are indicated. The contour of closed squares show the arterial values that are a consequence of the hematopoietic response of an acclimatized individual at different altitudes (or Sao_2) and the open squares are the respective mixed venous values assuming a constant cardiac output throughout.

The problem posed for the cardiovascular system as the blood becomes' progressively more viscous has been the subject of considerable experimental study. Simple hemoconcentration leads to substantial decreases of cardiac output (9), but if the blood volume is not allowed to decrease, or if it increases, as is the case in fully acclimatized man and animals, (8), the effect remains, but it is less drastic (7). The decrease it cardiac output would decrease oxygen transport, but the approximate solution is that the increase of arterial oxygen content just about matches the decrease of cardiac output, and oxygen transport is normal. There remains an unsolved problem of energy optimum. We have already seen that regulation of OT by increasing O_2 cap, in the face of continued arterial unsaturation, is a less satisfactory solution for tissue oxygenation than would be the case if the same OT were achieved by increasing Q. The explanation usually given is that the added cost of cardiac work in the long term would be prohibitive. Maintenance of the increase of red cell mass and expanded blood volume is considered to be the less expensive solution, but when the maintenance costs of those functions are calculated they are not trivial (6). Still, an expanded blood volume serves the dual purposes of alleviating the tendency of polycythemia to reduce the cardiac output by increasing the pre-load (Starling effect) and of expanding the capillary bed in the tissues. The "best" solution to be found in nature avoids polycythemia and increases hemoglobin oxygen affinity instead.

BLOOD AND MICROCIRCULATORY FACTORS IN ACCLIMATIZATION

Animals normally resident in high altitude environments characteristically (3; 1) have an increased hemoglobin affinity for oxygen (low P_{50}), an important influence aiding oxygen loading in the lung. In normoxia oxygen unloading in the tissues is compromised by this effect, but in hypoxia it is not, so it constitutes an important adaptation. However, in man the increase of P50, which is brought about by an increase in intraerythrocytic DPG, is an acute event at high altitude, and in the chronic state, the OHDC of man at high altitude is not appreciably shifted. For this reason it is neglected in this analysis.

A decrease in inter-capillary distance, whether by an increase in the number of capillaries per unit volume of tissue, or by a shrinking of fiber size, would shorten diffusion paths and lead to an increase of tissue oxygen diffusing capacity (10). The effect of this change is to lower the "critical" capillary Po_2 and thus to permit a widening of the (Cao_2-Cvo_2). Graphically, this is manifest as a steepening of the diffusion line of Fig. 1 and to raise $\dot{V}o_2$ (max) at high altitude. It remains an open question which of the several possible diffusion barriers in that stage is most significant. Red cell membrane? Blood plasma? Capillary wall? Cell wall and interior? It has been traditional to disregard the first three and to treat the last as a homogeneous tissue with an assignable diffusion coefficient, but recent evidence ascribes a highly important role to myoglobin which, by facilitating oxygen diffusion intracellularly (2; 4) nearly eliminates intracellular oxygen gradients.

The emphasis is thereby shifted back to the other barriers. One consequence of such a shift in emphasis is to minimize the importance of geometric factors in tissue diffusion, a change in the traditional way of thinking about this aspect of high altitude acclimatization that requires a radical re-orientation of concept and process.

CONCLUSION

Convection and diffusion are necessarily linked in the maintenance of tissue oxygenation, and their adequacy determines the limits of oxygen uptake rate. Convection, expressed as oxygen transport, is effective to different extents, depending on whether hypoxemia exists. Even when there has been hematopoietic response at high altitude, sufficient to return arterial oxygen content to normal in the face of continued arterial unsaturation, venous and tissue oxygen are compromised, and maximal oxygen uptake will remain low. Further, increased oxygen capacity, though helpful, even if not restorative, is effective only within limits that depend on the quantitative nature of the hematopoietic response and the effect of increased viscosity on cardiac output.

Arterial unsaturation necessitates a decrease in the oxygen extraction ratio, and since oxygen uptake rate is the product of oxygen transport and the extraction ratio, oxygen consumption will be reduced at high altitude. The adaptive change that would alleviate this problem is to increase tissue diffusing capacity (increase capillary density) which would have the effect of reducing the "critical" Po_2 and thus permitting a wider arterio-venous oxygen difference (thereby elevating the extraction ratio).

The ultimate determinant of oxygenation of the tissue is the partial pressure of capillary oxygen.

REFERENCES

1. BLACK, C.P. & TENNEY, S.M. 1980. Oxygen transport during progressive hypoxemia in high altitude and sea level water fowl. *Respir. Physiol.* 39: 217-239.
2. GAYESKI, T. & HONIG, C.R. 1978. Myoglobin saturation and calculated PO_2 in single cells of resting gracilis muscles. *Adv. Exp. Biol. Med.* 94: 77-84.
3. HALL, F.G., DILL, D.B. & GUZMÁN-BARRÓN, E.S. 1936. Comparative physiology in high altitudes. *J. Cell. Comp. Physiol.* 8: 301-313.
4. HONIG, C.R., GAYESKI, T.E.J., FEDERSPIED, W., *et al.* 1984. Muscle oxygen gradients from hemoglobin to cytochrome: New concepts, new complexities. *In*: Lubbers, D.W., H. Acker, E. Leniger-Follert, et al., (eds), *Oxygen Transport to Tissue.* Vol. 5: 23-28.
5. HUSSON, G. & OTIS, A.B. 1957. Adaptive value of respiratory adjustments to shunt hypoxia and altitude hypoxia. *J. Clin. Invest.* 36: 270-278.
6. MURRAY, C.D. 1926. The physiological principle of minimum work. The vascular system and the cost of blood volume. *Proc. Nat. Acad. Sci.* 12: 207-214.

7. MURRAY, J.F., GOLD, P. & LAMAR, B. 1962. Systemic oxygen transport and induced normovolemic anemia and polycythemia. *Am. J. Physiol.* 203: 720-724.

8. OU, L.C., CAI, Y.N. & TENNEY, S.M. 1985. Responses of blood volume and red cell mass in two strains of rats acclimatized to high altitude. *Respir. Physiol.* 62: 85-94.

9. RICHARDSON, T.Q. & GUYTON, A.C. 1959. Effects of polycythemia and anemia on cardiac output and other circulatory factors. *Am. J. Physiol.* 197: 1167-1170.

10. TENNEY, S.M. & OU, L.C. 1970. Physiological evidence for increase of tissue capillarity in animals acclimatized to high altitude. *Respir. Physiol.* 8: 137-150.

11. TENNEY, S.M. 1974. A theoretical analysis of the relationship of venous to average tissue oxygen pressure. *Respir. Physiol.* 20: 283-296.

12. TENNEY, S.M. & MITHOEFER, J.C. 1982. The relationship of mixed venous oxygenation to oxygen transport: with special reference to adaptations to high altitude and pulmonary disease. *Am. Rev. Resp. Dis.* 125: 474-479.

13. TENNEY, S.M. 1987. Tissue oxygenation. *In:* D.H. Simmons (ed) *Current Pulmonology* Yearbook Publishers, Inc. Chicago, London, Boca Raton, Chap. 11: 299-328.

14. WAGNER, P.D. 1988. An integrated view of the determinants of maximum oxygen uptake. *In:* N.C. Gonzalez and M.R. Fedde (eds), *Oxygen Transfer from Atmosphere to Tissues.* Plenum, New York.

COMPUTER MODEL ANALYSIS OF MYOCARDIAL TISSUE OXYGENATION: A COMPARISON OF HIGH ALTITUDE GUINEA PIG AND RAT

Zdenek Turek, Karel Rakusan

Abstract

A model of myocardial tissue oxygenation that simulates the naturally occuring heterogeneity in capillary spacing was developed at our laboratories. With this model the oxygen pressure (PO_2) histograms can be computed, and a radial PO_2 profile as well as the O_2 consumption can be calculated. Two flow arragements (homogeneous, blood flow per volume of tissue always the same, and heterogeneous, same absolute flow in each capillary) were considered. It was assumed that the tissue was anoxic when PO_2 was lower than 0.005 mm Hg. The facilitation of O_2 difussion by myoglobin was included. We applied this model for computing myocardial PO_2 histograms in guinea pig and rat born at natural or simulated high altitude. It was found that at rest the high altitude-born guinea pig and rat have similar myocardial PO_2 histograms. In the guinea pig, however, this is achieved with a substantially smaller polycythemia than in the case of the rat. When physical exercise is simulated, the oxygenation of the guinea pig myocardium becomes clearly better than that of the rat. Thus, a combination of high O_2 affinity and lower hemoglobin concentration in the high altitude guinea pig is not disadvantageous for myocardial oxygenation when compared with the results of high altitude simulation in the rat.

Key words: Guinea pig, hypoxia, myocardial oxygenation, O_2 affinity, PO_2 histograms, simulated high altitude.

Resumen

Se presenta un modelo computarizado de oxigenación tisular miocárdica desarrollado en nuestros laboratorios, que simula la natural heterogeneidad de la disposición capilar miocárdica. Este modelo permite realizar histogramas de presiones parciales de oxígeno (PO_2), así como calcular el perfil radial de las PO_2 y el consumo de O_2. En términos de flujo sanguíneo, se consideran dos posibilidades: homogéneo, flujo sanguíneo por volumen de tejido constante; y heterogéneo, el mismo flujo absoluto por capilar. Se asume anoxia tisular cuando la PO_2 es menor que 0.005 mm de Hg. El rol de la mioglobina en la difusión del O_2 es también tomado en cuenta. Con este modelo se determinaron los histogramas de PO_2 miocárdicas en cobayos nacidos en la altura y en ratas nacidas en altura simulada. Se encontró histogramas de PO_2 similares tanto para los cobayos de altura como para las ratas, ambos en condiciones naturales, no obstante la sustancialmente menor policitemia del cobayo. Cuando en el modelo se simulaban condiciones de ejercicio, la oxigenación del cobayo era claramente mejor que la de la rata. Se postula, en base al modelo, que una alta afinidad de la hemoglobina por el O_2 y una menor concentración de hemoglobina, características del cobayo, no resultan desventajosas para la oxigenación miocárdica cuando se compara con una rata en condiciones de altura simulada.

Palabras claves: Cobayo, hipoxia, oxigenación miocárdica, afinidad de la hemoglobina por el O_2, histogramas de PO_2, altura simulada.

Resumé

L'article présente un modèle informatique de l'oxygénation du tissu miocardiaque développé dans nos laboratoires qui simule l'hétérogénéité naturelle de la disposition capillaire miocardiaque. Ce modèle permet de réaliser des histogrammes de pressions partielles d'oxygène (PO_2), ainsi que de calculer le perfil radial des PO_2 et la consommation de O_2. En termes de flux sanguin, il y a deux possibilités : homogène, flux sanguin par volume de tissu constant, et éthérogène, le même flux absolu par capillaire. On dit qu'il y a anoxie tissulaire quand la PO_2 est inférieure 'a 0.005 mm de Hg. Le rôle de la myoglobine dans la diffusion de O_2 est également prise en compte. A l'aide de ce modèle, on a déterminé les histogrammes de PO_2 myocardiaque chez des cobayes nés en altitude et des rats nés en altitude simulée. On a trouvé des histogrammes similaires chez les cobayes d'altitude et chez les rats, les deux étudiés en condition naturelle, malgré une polycythémie très inférieure chez le cobaye. Quand on simulait des exercices au cours du modèle, l'oxygénation du cobaye était clairement meilleure que celle du rat. On postule, sur la base du modèle, qu'une grande affinité de l'hémoglobine par le O_2 et une concentration moins importante d'hémoglobine, caractéristiques du cobaye ne représentent aucun désavantage pour l'oxygénation myocardiaque quand celui-ci se compare avec un rat en conditions d'altitude simulée.

Mots clés : Cobaye, hypoxie, oxygénation myocardiaque, qffinité de l'hémoglobine pour le O_2, histogrammes de PO_2, altitude simulée.

Many high altitude animals possess blood O_2 transport characteristics that differ from man adapted to high altitude, *e.g.* a leftward shift of the blood O_2 dissociation curve, indicating higher blood O_2 affinity, lower hemoglobin concentration and lower values of hematocrit (for review see 5; 16). The guinea pig is a common laboratory animal and it is not always realized that it originates from high altitude regions. In the Andes the guinea pig is still bred for food and lives in semi-captivity. The guinea pig has a left-shifted O_2 dissociation curve, when compared to laboratory rat. Furthermore, guinea pig adapts to chronic hypoxic exposure with only moderate polycythemia while the reactive polycythemia in the rat is considerable. The difference in the polycythemic response between these two species is most evident when animals born at hypoxic conditions are compared. Guinea pigs native to high altitude in Peru have hematocrit of about 47 percent and P_{50} (= PO_2 corresponding to 50 percents of saturation on the standard dissociation curve) of about 31 mm Hg (15). On the other hand, rats born in the low pressure chamber have hematocrit of about 60 percents and P_{50} close to 39 mm Hg (9). It has been speculated that a combination of high O_2 affinity and low hematocrit, characteristic for genotypically high altitude-adapted mammals and birds does not favor the release of O_2 to tissues and might result in a low venous and probably tissue PO_2. It has been suggested that these animals must resort to tissue and/or biochemical adaptation to hypoxia in order to keep a normal O_2 consumption despite the low concentration of O_2 at cellular level (see 5). Our previous theoretical work suggested that this may not always be necessary. When arterial PO_2 is very low, a shift of the blood O_2 dissociation curve to the left may result in a higher end-capillary PO_2 than that obtained with a curve situated to the right. This advantage of a high blood O_2 affinity at profound hypoxia becomes further strengthened when arterio-venous O_2 difference is large and blood O_2 capacity is increased (11). This has been reported in cardiac muscle (10), using the classical Krogh model which implicitly assumes a uniform capillary spacing in the tissue. However, it has been demonstrated repeatedly that capillary spacing in cardiac muscle is not uniform but heterogeneous. Furthermore this heterogeneity may have an important effect on tissue PO_2 values (12; 6; 13).

Recently a model of myocardial tissue oxygenation that simulates the naturally occurring heterogeneity in capillary spacing was developed at our laboratories. With this model the PO_2 histograms can be computed. For the present communication we applied this model for computing myocardial PO_2 histograms in guinea pig and rat born at natural or simulated high altitude. It was found that at rest the high altitude-born guinea pig and rat have similar myocardial PO_2 histograms. In the guinea pig, however, this is achieved with a substantially smaller polycythemia than is the case in the rat. When physical exercise is simulated, the oxygenation of the guinea pig myocardium becomes clearly better than that of the rat. Thus the high blood O_2 affinity does not obstruct the myocardial oxygenation of the guinea pig at high altitude.

MATERIAL AND METHODS MODEL

The computer model has been described in detail elsewhere (13). In brief, the model consists of parallel tissue cylinders with log-normally distributed radius size. At the beginning of each cylinder, O_2 and CO_2 contents were calculated from the arterial PO_2, PCO_2, pH and O_2 capacity using a combination of O_2 and CO_2 dissociation curves. Each cylinder was divided into one hundred slabs. In each slab a radial PO_2 profile was calculated, as well as O_2 consumption. In this communication O_2 consumption was assumed to follow zero-order kinetics. An iterative procedure was used in order to calculate the radial PO_2 profiles. It was assumed that the tissue was anoxic when PO_2 was lower than 0.005 mm Hg. The facilitation of O_2 diffusion by myoglobin was included in the model.

Using this procedure, a radial PO_2 profile, as well as the actual O_2 consumption in each slab, was calculated. Assuming that RQ of the cardiac muscle is 0.8, CO_2 production could also be obtained. This allowed us to calculate O_2 and CO_2 contents in the capillary blood at the beginning of the following slab using values of blood flow and hematocrit. PO_2, PCO_2 and pH were then derived from these contents using a combination of the respective dissociation curves and acid-base equations, assuming no change in Base Excess.

Two flow arrangements were considered. Flow type A ("homogeneous flow") assumed that blood flow per volume of tissue was always the same. Thus, flow in the capillaries supplying thick cylinders had to be proportionally higher than in thin cylinders. Flow type B ("heterogeneous flow") assumed that the absolute flow in each capillary was the same, *i.e.* the flow per volume tissue was smaller in thick and larger in thin cylinders. Flow type A can be expected when blood flow through capillaries is perfectly regulated with respect to O_2 consumption of the tissue, while flow type B would result when the hydrostatic pressure and resistance in each capillary were identical. Because of the lack of experimental data on local flow with respect to O_2 consumption, we have arbitrarily chosen these two flow types, expecting the actual flow pattern somewhere between these limits. In this model, it is also assumed that flow does not change with cardiac cycle and therefore, average steady-state PO_2 histograms are calculated.

INPUT DATA

Blood gas value of guinea pigs native to Peruvian high altitude (15), were used as basic data for the calculation of PO_2 histograms in guinea pig and also in rat. The blood oxygen dissociation curve was calculated using Adair constants of rat blood (11) and P_{50} and hematocrit (Hct) as observed in guinea pig (15) and rat (9) native to chronic hypoxic hypoxia. The coronary blood flow and the myocardial O_2 consumption of guinea pig is not known. Therefore, in both cases, we used values published for the rat (12). In addition, we also used values representing a 3-fold increase of both parameters. These values simulated the increased O_2 consumption and accompanying proportional increase of blood flow as might be expected during exercise. The radius of the mean Kroghian tissue cylinder was calculated from our values of capillary density observed in guinea pig (7) and rat (2) born at high altitude. It was found that there was no difference in heterogeneity in ·capillary spacing between guinea pig and rat and, therefore, the same average value for log SD was used for both species (13). Myoglobin facilitated O_2 transport is dependent on myoglobin concentration as well as the diffusion coefficient of myoglobin and on O_2 permeability, and is expressed quantitatively by a facilitation pressure Pf (for details, see 13). Left ventricular myocardial concentration of myoglobin in hypoxia adapted guinea pigs and rats is similar, and in the left ventricle, there is no difference between high altitude-adapted and control sea-level animals in myoglobin concentration (1; 14). Therefore we employed the same value of facilitation pressure (13) for both species. All other input data were identical to those used in our previous publication (13). The most relevant input data are summarized in Table 1.

Variable	Value	
	Guinea pig	Rat
Arterial blood gases		
$\quad$ PO$_2$ (mm Hg)	43.0	43.0
$\quad$ PCO$_2$ (mm Hg)	30.3	30.3
$\quad$ pH	7.52	7.52
$\quad$ O$_2$ capacity (Vol%)	16.42	26.22
$\quad$ P$_{50}$ (standard)	31.00	39.70
Circulatory data		
$\quad$ blood flow (ml/min.g)		
$\quad$ at rest	4.00	4.00
$\quad$ exercise	12.00	12.00
$\quad$ hematocrit	47.0	59.0
Morphometric data		
$\quad$ average R (æm)	9.59	11.20
$\quad$ Log SD	0.086	0.086
$\quad$ capillary radius(æm)	2.40	2.40
Tissue		
$\quad$ O$_2$ permeability *108 (ml/s.cm.mm Hg)	2.1	2.1
$\quad$ O$_2$ consumption (ml/min.g)		
$\quad$ at rest	0.4	0.4
$\quad$ exercise	1.2	1.2
$\quad$ Pf (mm Hg)	14.0	14.0
$\quad$ Mb conc. (mg/g w.w.)	4.4	4.4
$\quad$ temperature (°C)	37.0	37.0

R= radius of the Kroghian tissue cylinder; Pf= facilitation pressure; Mb= myoglobin; w.w.= wet weight.

Table 1 - Input data.

RESULTS

The myocardial PO$_2$ histograms calculated for the guinea pig (upper panel) and rat (lower panel) for a hypoxic situation corresponding to high altitude of about 4 500 m (arterial PO$_2$= 43 mm Hg) are shown in Fig. 1 and 2, respectively. The left columns of the histograms indicate the percentage of tissue with low PO$_2$. There is no striking difference between the histograms of both species, even though the oxygenation of the guinea pig myocardium seems to be slightly better. This is most apparent when the percentage of tissue with anoxic tissue and that of PO$_2$ lower than 5 mm Hg are compared. It is so, when the homogeneous flow is assumed (flow type A) and also in the case of flow heterogeneity (flow type B). The program also calculates

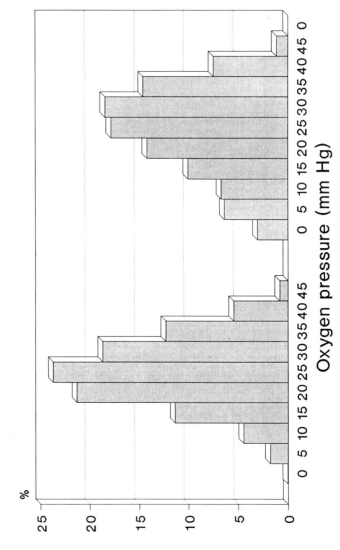

Fig. 1 - Myocardial PO$_2$ histograms in the high altitude guinea pig. Flow type A., identical specific flow in all capillaries ("homogeneous flow"); flow type B., identical absolute flow in all capillaries ("heterogeneous flow"). Numbers on the abscissa indicate the top value of the particular interval, e.g. number 5 designates tissue with PO$_2$ between 0.005 and 5 mm Hg and number 10 that with PO$_2$ between 5.005 and 10 mm Hg. Number 0 indicates portion of tissue with PO$_2$ between 0 and 0.005 mm Hg.

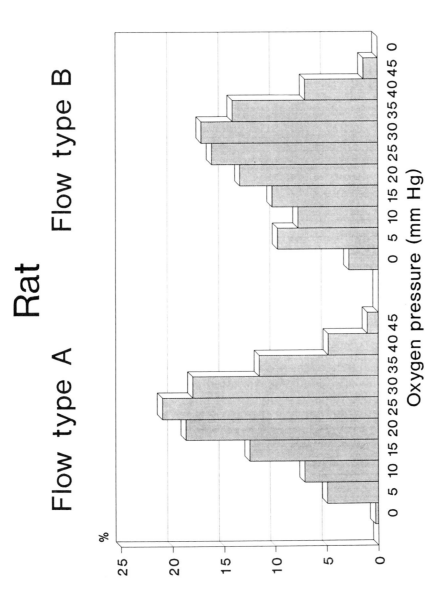

Fig. 2 - Myocardial PO$_2$ histograms in the high altitude rat. Flow type A., identical specific flow in all capillaries ("homogeneous flow"); flow type B., identical absolute flow in all capillaries ("heterogeneous flow"). Otherwise the same as Fig. 1.

values of venous blood gases. The venous PO_2 is lower in the guinea pig than in the rat (20.4 *vs.* 24.0 mm Hg in flow type A, and 21.0 *vs.*24.5 mm Hg in flow type B) and O_2 saturation is higher in the guinea pig (30.7 *vs* 26.$_2$ and 32.1 *vs.* 27.2, respectively). The venous blood O_2 content is lower in the guinea pig (6.5 *vs.* 6.9 and 6.8 *vs.* 7.2, in ml O_2 per 100 ml blood) but the difference is rather small.

Fig. 3 depicts PO_2 histograms calculated when large values of oxygen consumption and blood flow were used. The purpose was to simulate physical exercise. Here, a distinctly better tissue oxygenation was obtained in the guinea pig when compared to the rat. Values of venous blood gases were similar to what was found at rest. Thus, also here, a lower venous PO_2, a higher saturation and a lower O_2 content were observed in the guinea pig. In Fig. 2 only flow type A of the flow arrangement was presented. However, when PO_2 histograms at flow type B were calculated, the difference between guinea and rat remained similar.

DISCUSSION

The computations indicate a better myocardial oxygenation in high altitude guinea pig when compared to rat. Of course, the results of a computer model of tissue oxygenation must be interpreted with caution. It has been demonstrated that the same computer program can yield very different data, depending on the input data (13). The outcome always depends on many necessary assumptions, including the values of the input data. However, we believe that even though the computed of PO_2 values may not be numerically correct, at least the trend will be indicative.

The results in both species at rest show a small but distinct percentage of anoxic tissue. During exercise simulation this percentage becomes more pronounced. This is the result of the assumed zero-order kinetics of O_2 consumption and we do not expect that anoxic parts of really occur within the tissue. It has been demonstrated that when tissue PO_2 is lowered below a critical value, myocardial tissue reacts with a local decrease of O_2 consumption, thus maintaining an adequate tissue PO_2 (3). When a model that includes a PO_2-dependent O_2 consumption is used, the percentage of anoxic tissue disappears (13). However, such a model requires many additional time consuming calculations and, in the present situation, does not add important additional information. Therefore the calculated percentage of anoxic tissue should be considered as indicative of potential anoxic danger and serves here as a sensitive index of tissue oxygenation (12).

The computation originates in both species at the same arterial PO_2 but due to higher blood O_2 affinity saturation is higher in guinea pig than in rat (78 *vs.* 64 percents). However, in spite of this, due to the much higher Hct in rat, blood O_2 content tends to be larger in rat than in guinea pig (16.9 *vs.* 16.4 ml O_2 per 100 ml blood). Still, when the resting situation is compared, there is only a negligible difference between guinea pig and rat

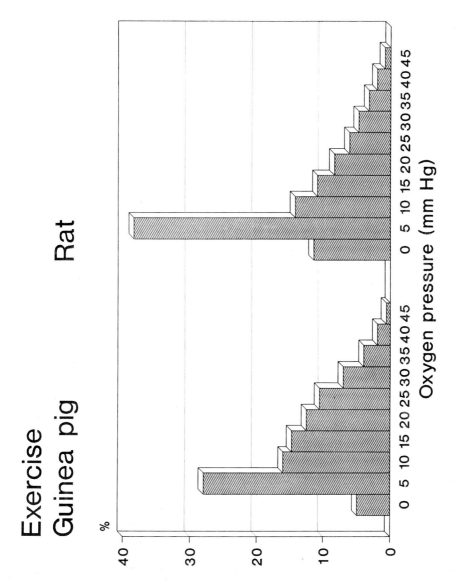

Fig. 3 - Myocardial PO$_2$ histograms in the high altitude guinea pig (left) and rat (right). Only flow type A is shown, here ("homogeneous flow"). Otherwise the same as Fig. 1.

as reflected by the PO_2 histograms. Thus the slightly higher capillary density in the guinea pig fully compensates for the lower arterial O_2 content. During exercise the myocardial oxygenation of the guinea pig is clearly better than that of the rat. It must be kept in mind that the guinea pig achieves this with a lower hematocrit and thus probably also a lower blood viscosity and peripheral resistance. Thus any increase of blood flow might be achieved more easily in the guinea pig than in rat.

The finding that the PO_2 histograms indicated a better myocardial oxygenation in the high altitude guinea pig, when compared to rat may at first seem surprising. The guinea pig has a left-shifted blood O_2 dissociation curve and a substantially lower hematocrit than rat born in the low pressure chamber. Traditionally, an increase of hematocrit and a O_2 dissociation curve situated to the right are considered to be the most effective adaptive mechanisms, probably because this is the situation in high altitude man. The relation between the position of the O_2 dissociation curve and life at high altitude is complex as the position of the curve also depends on body mass. Schmidt-Nielsen & Larimer (8) found a good linear correlation between P_{50} in mammals and their body weight in a double logarithmic plot. This plot was modified by Monge & Whittembury (4), who demonstrated that two parallel straight lines can, in fact, be drawn. One line pertaining to animals living in sea-level environments and, below it, another line for animals adapted to a hypoxic environment. Interestingly enough, the point corresponding to our value of P_{50} and body weight in guinea pig falls almost exactly on the line of hypoxia-adapted animals. Points corresponding to P_{50} of the rat and, notably, also of high altitude man lie close to the line of sea-level inhabitants. Based on this, it would seem that a high O_2 affinity may not be a bad start to life at high altitude.

There is another way to look at the differences between the O_2 dissociation curves of guinea pig and rat. When the dissociation curve is plotted in the traditional fashion, i.e. O_2 saturation against PO_2 (Fig. 4, left panel) than, indeed, saturation within the operating PO_2 range (between 44 to about 20 mm Hg) is always higher in guinea pig than in rat. However, when the more physiological plot of O_2 content against PO_2 is used (Fig. 4, right panel), than the difference between the curves below arterial PO_2 becomes much smaller. Thus, the combination of high O_2 affinity and lower hemoglobin concentration in the high altitude guinea pig results in a relationship between PO_2 and O_2 content that is similar to the combination of low O_2 affinity and high hemoglobin concentration in the rat adapted to high altitude. The situation in the high altitude rat has the disadvantage of a higher hematocrit with the potential danger of an increased blood viscosity. Thus there is no reason why high O_2 affinity, i.e. the blood O_2 dissociation curve situated to the left, should be a priori disadvantage for life at high altitude. It is also intuitively difficult to accept the fact that so many animals native to high altitude with a combination of low hematocrit and high blood O_2 affinity would suffer from impaired tissue oxygenation.

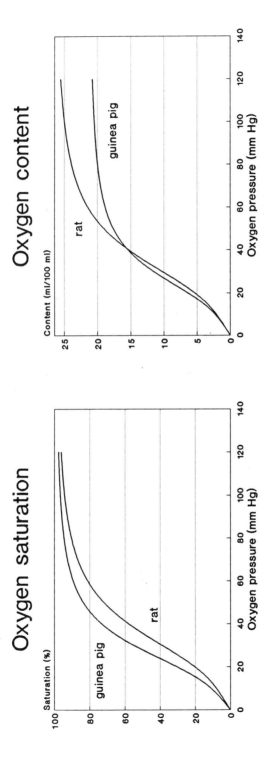

Fig. 4 - Blood O_2 dissociation curve of the guinea pig and rat plotted as saturation against PO_2 (let panel) or as blood O_2 content against PO_2 (right panel).

In conclusion, our theoretical model of tissue oxygenation indicates that a combination of a high O_2 affinity and lower hemoglobin concentration in the high altitude guinea pig is not disadvantageous for myocardial oxygenation when compared with the results of high altitude simulation in the rat. On the contrary, our computations indicate an improved myocardial oxygenation in the guinea pig, particularly during exercise.

REFERENCES

1. BUI, M.V. & BANCHERO, N. 1980. Effects of chronic exposure to cold or hypoxia on ventricular weights and ventricular myoglobin concentrations in guinea pigs during growth. *Pflügers Arch.* 385: 155-160.

2. GRANDTNER, M., TUREK, Z. & KREUZER, F. 1974. Cardiac hypertrophy in the first generation of rats native to simulated high altitude. *Pflügers Arch.* 350: 241-248.

3. KESSLER, M., & HOPER, J. 1985. Signaloxidasen, Signalketten in Leber, Niere und Myocard. *In*: R. Kinne, H. Acker & E. Leniger-Follert (eds.), *Festschrift aus Anlass der Emeritierung von Prof. Dr. med. D.W. Lübbers*, Dortmund: Max-Planck-Institut für Physiologie: 121-155.

4. MONGE, C., & WHITTEMBURY, J. 1976. High altitude adaptations in the whole animal. *In*: Bligh, J., J.L. Cloudsley-Thompson, and A.G. MacDonald (eds.), *Environmental Physiology of Animals*. New York: Wiley: 289-308.

5. MONGE, C., & LEON-VELARDE, F. 1991. Physiological adaptation to high altitude: oxygen transport in mammals and birds. *Physiol. Reviews* 71: 1135-1172.

6. RAKUSAN, K., HOOFD, L. & TUREK, Z. 1984. The effect of cell size and capillary spacing on myocardial oxygen supply. *In*: D. Bruley, H.I. Bicher & D. Reneau (eds.), *Oxygen Transport to Tissue- VI*. London and New York: Plenum Publishing Corporation: 463-475.

7. RAKUSAN, K., TUREK, Z., & KREUZER., F. 1981. Myocardial capillaries in guinea pigs native to high altitude (Junin, Peru, 4,105 m). *Pflügers Arch.* 391: 22-24.

8. SCHMIDT-NIELSEN, K. & LARIMER, J.L. 1958. Oxygen dissociation curves of mammalian blood in relation to body size. *Am. J. Physiol.* 195: 424-428.

9. TUREK, Z., GRANDTNER, M., RINGNALDA, B.E.M. & KREUZER, F. 1973. Hypoxic pulmonary steady-state diffusing capacity for CO and cardiac output in rats born at a simulated altitude of 3 500 m. *Pflügers Arch.* 340: 11-18.

10. TUREK, Z. & KREUZER, F. 1976. Effect of a shift of the oxygen dissociation curve on myocardial oxygenation at hypoxia. *In*: J. Grote, D. Reneau & G. Thews (eds.), *Oxygen Transport to Tissue- II*. New York and London: Plenum Press: 657-662.

11. TUREK, Z., KREUZER, F. & HOOFD, L. 1973. Advantage or disadvantage of a decrease of blood oxygen affinity for tissue oxygen supply at hypoxia. *Pflügers Arch.* 342: 185-197.

12. TUREK, Z. & RAKUSAN, K. 1981. Lognormal distribution of intercapillary distances in normal and hypertrophic rat heart as estimated by the method of concentric circles. *Pflügers Arch.* 391: 17-21.

13. TUREK, Z., RAKUSAN, K., OLDERS, J., HOOFD, L. & KREUZER, F. 1991. Computed myocardial PO_2 histograms: effects of various geometrical and functional conditions. *J. Appl. Physiol.* 70: 1845-1853.

14. TUREK, Z., RINGNALDA, B.E.M., GRANDTNER, M. & KREUZER, F. 1973. Myoglobin distribution in the heart of growing rats exposed to a simulated altitude of 3 500 m in their youth or born in the low pressure chamber. *Pflügers Arch.* 340: 1-10.

15. TUREK, Z., RINGNALDA, B.E.M., MORAN, O. & KREUZER, F. 1980. Oxygen transport in guinea pigs native to high altitude (Junin, Peru, 4,105 m). *Pflügers Arch.* 384: 109-111.

16. WEST, J.B. 1991. High altitude. *In:* R.G. Crystal, J.B. West, P.J. Barnes & N.S. Cherniak (eds.), *The Lung: Scientific Foundations.* New York: Raven Press: 2093-2107.

ENIGMAS EN EL MECANISMO DE CONTROL DE LA SECRECIÓN DE ERITROPOYETINA

Carlos E. Bozzini

Resumen

El eritrón circulante o masa roja circulante (MRC) provee la mayor parte del oxígeno al líquido intersticial; este último deberá contener oxígeno en una concentración tal que satisfaga la demanda celular que a su vez depende de su metabolismo energético. El volumen de la MRC es mantenido por la eritropoyesis, un proceso con alta capacidad de adaptación a diversas situaciones fisiológicas o patológicas. La magnitud de la eritropoyesis es dirigida por la hormona eritropoyetina (EPO), cuya principal acción es inducir la última etapa de diferenciación que ocurre en el proceso que conduce desde la célula basal hematopoyética multipotencial (stem cell) hasta el eritrocito maduro, actuando sobre "células progenitoras eritrocíticas" que, mediante procesos de amplificación y maduración, dan lugar al ingreso al eritrón de 16 eritrocitos/ unidad eritropoyética en el humano. Diversas observaciones experimentales y clínicas sugieren que la relación oferta/demanda de oxígeno constituye el principal factor que controla la producción de EPO. Sin embargo, existen observaciones que no pueden ser explicadas por esta teoría, que permanecen como enigmas en el mecanismo de control de la secreción de la hormona. Tales enigmas son: 1) la disminucíon de la síntesis de EPO que ocurre durante la exposición continua hipobaria, antes que la MRC haya incrementado su volumen lo suficiente como para satisfacer la demanda de oxígeno tisular, 2) el mecanismo mediante el cual la policitemia post-transfusional disminuye la producción de EPO en respuesta a hipoxemia, y 3) la diferente secreción de EPO en ratones con policitemia endógena o exógena como respuesta a hipoxemia.

Palabras claves: Eritropoyetina, policitemia, hipoxia.

Résumé

L'érythron circulant ou masse rouge circulante (MRC) fournit la majeure partie de l'oxygène au liquide interstitiel; celui-ci devra avoir une concentration d'oxygène suffisante pour satisfaire la demande cellulaire qui, à son tour, dépend de son métabolisme énergétique. Le volume de la MRC est maintenu grâce à l'érythropoïèse, processus de grande capacité d'adaptation à diverses situations physiologiques ou pathologiques. L'ampleur de l'érythropoïèse dépend de l'hormone érythropoïétine (EPO) dont l'action principale est d'induire la dernière étape de différentiation au cours du processus qui va de la cellule de base hématopoïétique multipotentielle (stem cell) à l'érythrocite mur, agissant sur les "cellules progénitrices érythropoïétiques" qui, grâce à des procesus d'amplification et de maturation, permettent la rentrée dans l'érythron de 16 érythrocites /unité érythropoïétique chez l'humain. Diverses observations expérimentales et cliniques suggèrent que la relation offre/demande de l'oxygène constitue le principal facteur qui contrô le la production de EPO. Cependant, certaines observations ne peuvent être expliquées par cette théorie, et des énigmes demeurent en ce qui concerne la compréhension du mécanisme de contrôle de la sécrétion de l'hormone. Ces énigmes sont : 1) la diminution de la synthèse de l'EPO qui se produit au cours de l'exposition hypobarique continue, avant que la MRC augmente suffisamment son volume pour satisfaire la demande d'oxygène tissulaire, 2) le mécanisme par lequel la polycythémie post-transfusion diminue la production d'EPO en réponse à l'hypoxie, et 3) la différente sécrétion d'EPO chez les souris avec polycythémie endogène ou exogène en réponse à l'hypoxie.

Mots clés : Erythropoïétine, polycythémie, hypoxie.

Abstract

The circulating erythron or circulating red mass (CRM) provides oxygen to interstitial fluids. The latter requires an oxygen concentration that can satisfy the cellular demands which in turn depend on its energy metabolism. The CRM volume depends on erythropoiesis, a highly adaptive process to diverse physiologic and pathologic situations. The magnitude of erythropoiesis is controlled by erythropoietin (EPO) whose main effect is to induce the last step of the differentiation of the mature erythrocyte (which starts with the stem cell) by acting on precursor erythrocyte cells. This process, which includes amplification and maturation, delivers 16 erythrocytes/ erythropoietic unit to the CRM in man. Several experimental and clinical observations suggest that the ratio supply/demand of oxygen is the main factor controlling the production of EPO. However, many observations cannot be explained by this theory and remain as enigmas in the mechanisms which control EPO secretion. These are: 1) the reduction in EPO synthesis seen during continuous hypobaric exposure and before the CRM volume has increased to satisfy the oxygen demand of tissues, 2) the mechanism by which post-transfusional polycythemia shuts off the production of EPO induced by hypoxemia, and 3) the differential secretion of EPO in mice with endogenous or exogenous polycythemia responding to hypoxemia.

Key words: Erythropoietin, polycythemia, hypoxia.

Más del 99% del oxígeno (O_2) transportado por la sangre arterial de un humano a nivel del mar se encuentra en el interior de células anucleadas ricas en hemoglobina (Hb), los eritrocitos, que presentan dos propiedades destacables desde el punto de vista fisiológico: poseen una vida media limitada y carecen de la capacidad de auto-renovación.

Por la primera, desaparecen diariamente de la circulación humana en una proporción equivalente a 1/120 de su número total; por la segunda, su reemplazo depende de eventos de diferenciación, proliferación y maduración de células progenitoras y precursoras que constituyen un proceso contínuo durante toda la vida de un individuo normal, llamado "eritropoyesis".

El conjunto de eritrocitos circulantes forma así un órgano, que ha sido denominado "eritrón circulante" o "masa roja circulante" (MRC). Su principal función es proveer de O_2 al líquido intersticial, que deberá contener el gas en una concentración tal que permita satisfacer la demanda celular en dependencia con su metabolismo energético. El volumen del órgano (MRC) dependerá de la relación entre las tasas de neoformación (eritropoyesis) y de desaparición (eritrocateresis) de los eritrocitos. La pérdida de la relación determinará atrofia del eritrón (anemia) o hipertrofia (policitemia). En condiciones normales, sin embargo, la sobrevida eritrocitaria no constituye una variable, por lo que, en general, el volumen de la MRC es una función directa de la eritropoyesis. Cuando la sobrevida eritrocitaria disminuye, aparece el "estado hemítico", que puede ser "compensado" por el incremento de la eritropoyesis, no instalándose anemia; ésta estará presente siempre que el estado hemolítico sea "no compensado".

La eritropoyesis constituye, por lo tanto, un proceso con alta capacidad de adaptación a diversas situaciones fisiológicas o patológicas. Así, su intensidad disminuirá hasta alcanzar valores mínimos o nulos si la MRC es artificialmente incrementada, como se observa en animales de laboratorios sometidos a transfusiones de eritrocitos homólogos, o fisiológicamente incrementada mediante exposición de animales a condiciones de hipobaria crónica, con regreso de los mismos a condiciones de normobaria. Por el contrario, se observará hypereritropoyesis en condiciones de hipoxia, definida, en general, como un descenso de la capacidad de transporte de O_2 por la sangre (anemia), una disminución de la pO_2 arterial (hipoxemia) o por un incremento de la afinidad de la Hb por el O_2 (en normobaria).

La magnitud de la eritropoyesis en las diversas condiciones señaladas es dirigida por una hormona de origen renal (y en mucha menor proporción hepático) llamada "eritropoyetina" (EPO), cuya principal acción es inducir la última etapa de diferenciación que ocurre en el proceso que conduce desde la célula basal hemopoyética multipotencial (*stem cell*) hasta el eritrocito maduro, actuando sobre "células progenitoras eritrocíticas" que generan así "unidades eritropoyéticas" que, mediante procesos de amplificación y de maduración, dan lugar al ingreso al eritrón de 16 eritrocitos/unidad eritropoyética en el humano.

La producción de EPO *in vivo* es influenciada por una variedad de parámetros fisiológicos que, en general, operan a través del aporte de O_2 a los tejidos y de la demanda del gas por los mismos. El aporte de O_2 está principalmente determinado por el volumen minuto circulatorio, la capacidad de transporte de O_2 de la sangre, la pO_2 arterial y la afinidad de la Hb por el O_2 (Fig. 1). La capacidad de transporte de O_2 es medida normalmente por la concentración de Hb. Una disminución de la misma está asociada con un incremento exponencial en la producción de EPO, mientras que su aumento determina menor producción de la hormona.

Si la capacidad de transporte de O_2 por la sangre es normal, el aporte de O_2 a los tejidos está determinado por la saturación con O_2 de la sangre arterial, que a su vez depende, principalmente, de la pO_2 del aire alveolar. Por lo tanto, la producción de EPO es inversamente proporcional a la pO_2 alveolar y arterial. El hecho que la estimulación de la producción de EPO en respuesta a hipoxemia pueda ser neutralizada por policitemia sugiere que ni la capacidad de transporte de O_2 ni la pO_2 de la sangre arterial constituyen, por sí solas, el principal determinante de la formación de EPO. El producto de ambos factores, o contenido arterial de O_2 sería el determinante más importante.

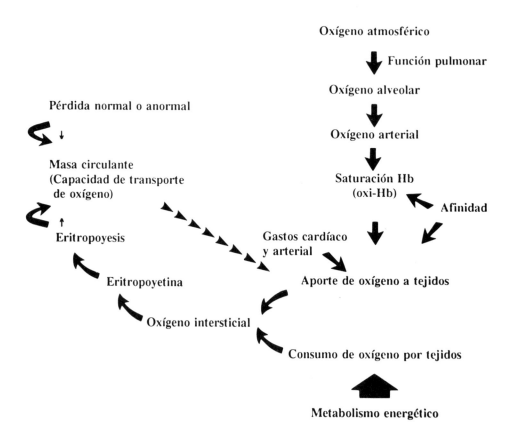

Fig. 1 - Representación esquemática del sistema de control de la eritropoyesis.

Si el contenido arterial de O_2 es normal, el aporte de O_2 a los tejidos es determinado por la afinidad de la Hb por el gas. Un incremento de la misma (desplazamiento hacia la izquierda de la curva de disociación) disminuye la magnitud de conversión de oxi - en deoxi-Hb para una pO_2 intersticial determinada, reduciéndose el aporte de O_2. Debido a la forma de la curva de disociación, esta disminución del aporte de O_2 es sólo parcialmente balanceada por el aumento de la saturación de la Hb de la sangre arterial, lo que determina producción aumentada de EPO.

A partir de estas observaciones se ha sugerido que el aporte de O_2 a los tejidos constituye el principal factor fisiológico que controla la producción de EPO. Frente a un consumo de O_2 más o menos constante por los tejidos, midificaciones en el aporte de O_2 inducen cambios en la pO_2 del líquido intersticial, por lo que parece razonable pensar que la pO_2 del líquido intersticial constituye la señal primaria para la secreción de EPO a través de un sensor de la misma (sensor de O_2).

Una enorme cantidad de datos experimentales y clínicos demuestran lo correcto de esta teoría sobre el control de la secreción de EPO, originalmente propuesta por Fried *et al.* (14) hace más de 30 años.

Sin embargo, otras evidencias no pueden ser fácilmente explicadas por ella, permaneciendo como enigmas, cuyo análisis somero constituye la esencia de esta comunicación.

Enigma 1. Disminución de la síntesis de eritropoyetina durante exposición contínua a hipobaria.

Durante la exposición aguda a hipobaria (hipoxia hipóxica) se ha observado incremento del contenido renal de mRNA-EPO dentro de 1 hora de iniciada la exposición (24) mientras que la concentración plasmática de EPO lo hace dentro de 1-5 horas. Los niveles de EPO circulante alcanzan valores máximos en 6-24 horas en roedores (1; 9) y dentro de las 48 horas en humanos (22), descendiendo luego pese a la persistencia de la hipoxia. Esta disminución de la EPO circulante ocurre antes de que la MRC y, por lo tanto, el contenido de O_2 de la sangre, hayan aumentado en forma significativa.

Los mecanismos involucrados en esta rápida caída de la EPO plasmática no han sido clarificados, habiéndose propuesto hipótesis diversas. Como el nivel de EPO en plasma depende del balance entre la producción de la hormona y su vida media en el compartimiento plasmático, alteraciones en ambos deben ser tenidas en cuenta. Un concepto expuesto hace bastante tiempo (26) sugiere que el consumo de EPO por el tejido eritropoyético en expansión estaría aumentado.

Esta posición ha sido avalada por algunos estudios de *clearance* (17; 23) mientras que otros demostraron la ausencia de diferencia en el *clearance* de EPO en animales con hipo o hiperactividad medular o durante (18; 6) o posterior a hipoxia (12). Alternativamente, el eritrón expandido podría ejercer un control inhibitorio retroalimentado sobre la producción de EPO que sería independiente del volumen de la MRC y del contenido arterial de O_2. Apoyan este concepto observaciones que indican que los niveles de EPO en plasma son mayores en pacientes con hipoplasia medular que en aquellos con grado de anemia similar pero con hiperplasia medular (10; 25). Otros factores que han sido considerados como induciendo reducción de la producción de EPO incluyen la disminución de la afinidad de la hemoglobina por el O_2 durante hipoxia prolongada debido a acidosis (16) y a malnutrición que ocurre durante el stress hipóxico contínuo (3). Observaciones recientes (11) sugieren que la reducción de la producción de EPO que ocurre durante hipoxia contínua no es el resultado de una inhibición *feed-back* ejercida por la hormona circulante sobre sus células productoras. La disminución de la producción tampoco parece debida a agotamiento de la capacidad productora, dado que la declinación de la síntesis de EPO ocurre en forma independiente de la cantidad de EPO producida (11).

Los resultados presentados indican que la secreción elevada de EPO en respuesta a hipoxemia contínua es breve; tal disminución ocurre antes que el volumen de la MRC haya aumentado significativamente. Este tipo de respuesta, pese a los estudios efectuados, permanece como un enigma.

Enigma 2. Mecanismo mediante el cual la policitemia post-transfusional disminuye la producción de eritropoyetina en respuesta a hipoxemia.

De acuerdo con la hipótesis sobre el control de la secreción de EPO que establece que la misma depende de la relación entre la demanda y la oferta de O_2, la policitemia inducida por transfusión resultaría en disminución de la secreción de eritropoyetina, y consecuentemente de la eritropoyesis, en virtud de su capacidad de incrementar el aporte de O_2 a los tejidos.

Sin embargo, resultados de varios estudios indican que otros factores además de la relación demanda/oferta de O_2 jugarían un importante rol en la regulación de la eritropoyesis en animales con policitemia severa.

En este sentido, merecen citarse brevemente los siguientes estudios y sus conclusiones más importantes: a) Kilbridge, Fried & Heller (15) obtienen eritrocitos incapaces de transportar O_2 por exposición de células humanas deficientes en metahemoglobina reductasa a nitrito. El efecto de la transfusión de esas células y de otras normales sobre la secreción de EPO fue comparada en ratones mantenidos en hipobaria (hipoxia hipoxémica) durante 4-5 horas. Los animales con hematocritos superiores a 0,60 mostraron una reducción de aproximadamente un 85% en relación con la observada en ratones normocitémicos similarmente expuestos, independientemente del tipo de eritrocito utilizado en la transfusión (metaHb o oxiHb); b) Bozzini, Alippi & Martínez, en 1971 (8), arriban a conclusiones similares al efectuar estudios en ratas en las cuales se logra una condición transitoria de policitemia hipovolémica (incremento del hematocrito por disminución del volumen plasmático o policitemia relativa) mediante inyección intraperitoneal de dextrán. Ratas así tratadas mostraron una significativa reducción de la secreción de EPO en respuesta a hipoxemia al ser comparadas con controles normocitémicos; c) Necas, Zivny & Neuwirt, en 1972 (19), determinan la pO_2 "tisular" en "bolsillos de gas" peritoneales después de un tiempo suficiente para su equilibrio en ratas normo- y policitémicas con hipoxemia. Observaron que las ratas policitémicas secretan menos EPO que las normocitémicas a pesar de mostrar ambas el mismo nivel de hipoxia tisular.

Los resultados presentados sugieren que los eritrocitos, además de incrementar la PO_2 tisular mediante transporte del gas, también disminuyen la secreción de EPO mediante un mecanismo que no depende de esa capacidad de transporte. Tal mecanismo permanece como un enigma.

Enigma 3. Diferente secreción de eritropoyetina en ratones con policitemia endógena o exógena en respuesta a hipoxemia.

El estado policitémico puede ser inducido en el ratón mediante administración intraperitoneal o endovenosa de eritrocitos homólogos (policitemia exógena) o mediante exposición contínua o discontínua (15-18 h/día) crónica a hipoxia normo o hipobárica. En ambos modelos experimentales (ratón transfundido = HT; ratón post-hipóxico = PH) la eritropoyesis es prácticamente nula a partir del cuarto día post-transfusión o post-exposición a hipobaria cuando el hematocrito supera 0.55. La capacidad de ambos animales de responder a EPO exógena con un incremento de la eritropoyesis ha posibilitado su uso como modelos para el bioensayo de la hormona.

Estudios realizados en nuestro laboratorio durante los últimos 10 años han mostrado algunas importantes diferencias entre ambos modelos animales, cuya explicación no ha sido debidamente aclarado. Las principales observaciones han sido (2-7).

1) La respuesta eritropoyética de ratones HT a periodos crecientes de exposición a hipobaria muestra relación inversa con el grado de policitemia alcanzado por los animales en respuesta al volumen de eritrocitos transfundido;

2) la respuesta de los ratones PH es significativamente mayor que la correspondiente a ratones HT a pesar de presentar ambos el mismo grado de policitemia.

3) La respuesta a EPO exógena (relación dosis-respuesta) es similar en ambos modelos de ratones policitémicos.

4) La concentración de EPO en plasma de ratones PH expuestos a hipobaria durante 24 h es superior a 200 mU/ml, siendo no detectable por bioensayo en ratones HT tratados en forma similar;

5) el estado hipersecretorio de EPO en el ratón PH determina que la secreción de EPO en respuesta a la administración de testosterona (2.5 mg), dexametasona (500 μg). DL-isoproterenol (50 mg/kg) y cloruro de cobalto (4 y 8 μmoles) sea significativamente superior en éste que en el HT;

6) un estado hemolítico compensado crónico inducido por administración de fenilhidrazina, o hiperactividad eritropoyética inducida por administración crónica de rHu-EPO, seguidos por transfusión de eritrocitos previa a la estimulación hipobárica, determina en los ratones tratados comportamientos similares al modelo PH y no al HT.

7) el comportamiento hipersecretorio del ratón PH ocurre de manera similar en animales en los que la inducción de policitemia fue realizada mediante exposición a hipobaria contínua o discontínua;

8) el comportamiento hipersecretorio no se manifiesta durante el período de exposición crónica a hipobaria (contínua o discontínua) sino que aparece durante el período post-hipóxico.

No se ha hallado una explicación satisfactoria para este fenómeno. La disminución de la eritropoyesis que ocurre durante el período post-hipóxico, debido a la policitemia innecesaria a nivel del mar, sugeriría la existencia de algún mecanismo modulador de la secreción de EPO originado en la actividad medular. Sin embargo, el fenómeno descrito permanece como otro enigma.

Enigma 4. Hipersecreción de eritropoyetina durante quimioterapia

Como ha sido ya señalado, se acepta que el nivel de EPO circulante es controlado por la pO_2 tisular. Niveles elevados de la hormona se encuentran en humanos o animales de experimentación con hipoxia anémica o hipóxica y, circunstancialmente, en pacientes con secreción inapropiada de EPO por tumores o quistes. Sin embargo, los niveles circulantes de EPO pueden también encontrarse excesivamente elevados en pacientes con anemia aplástica y reducidos en pacientes con hiperplasia medular. Aunque estos cambios no son uniformes, han llevado a la propuesta de que cantidades apreciables de EPO son consumidas por células progenitoras o precursoras y que la disminución de ese consumo es responsable de los altos niveles de EPO en plasma en la anemia aplástica y en otras condiciones de falla medular.

Esta hipótesis puede ser discutida a la luz de los siguientes datos experimentales y clínicos:

1) Fried *et al.* (13) observaron que los niveles plasmáticos de EPO en ratones WWv (genéticamente anémicos) son significativamente superiores a ratones no-mutantes (++) con anemia inducida de la misma magnitud. Tal diferencia desaparece 7 días después de transplantar a los ratones WWv con 2 millones de células medulares obtenidas de ratones ++. En este momento, la respuesta a EPO exógena de ratones Wwv es comparable a la de ratones WWv y ++ no es debida a modificaciones de la p50 ni a aumento del clearance de EPO, por lo que se sugiere que en los ratones WWv la producción de EPO para cada nivel de anemia es modificada por la capacidad del tejido hemotopoyético de responder a la hormona.

2) Barceló & Bozzini (4) determinaron los niveles de EPO en plasma durante exposición contínua de ratones a hipobaria (456 HPA). Se observa que ratones con aplasia medular inducida por irradiación X total o administración de 5-fluorouracilo muestran niveles de EPO significativamente mayores que ratones normales expuestos en forma similar. Al no existir modificaciones del *clearance* de EPO, niveles de EPO superiores en plasma son considerados como índices superiores de producción. Estos resultados también sugieren que la producción de EPO está relacionada con la capacidad de respuesta medular a la misma.

3) Birgegard *et al.* (5) determinaron la concentración de EPO en suero de 23 pacientes antes, durante y duespués de tratamiento citostático intenso para leucemia aguda. Se observa un marcado incremento de los niveles de EPO

en plasma a partir del 1er, 2do día del tratamiento, alcanzándose el pico al 7mo día. No se observó en los pacientes durante ese lapso disminución de la concentración de hemoglobina que pueda explicar el incremento de la EPO circulante.

4) Piroso et al. (20) realizan estudios similares en 6 pacientes con leucemia aguda tratados con quimioterapia intensa. En todos los casos observan incremento de la concentración sérica de EPO a pesar de que la concentración de hemoglobina permanece estable. Los mismos autores estudian en ratas el clearance de EPO en condiciones de supresión medular por ciclofosfamida o hipertransfusión o en condiciones de estimulación medular por fenilhidrazina o hemorragia (21). El t 1/2 de EPO en plasma es similar en todos los grupos, indicando que la actividad eritroide de la médula no determina el clearance hormonal. Estos hallazgos confirman los efectuados por Bozzini (6) en perros con médula hipo, normo o hiperplástica.

Los resultados presentados sugieren una relación entre la actividad eritropoyética y la capacidad secretora de EPO, cuya interpretación exacta arrojaría nuevos conocimientos sobre la biogénesis de EPO y su regulación. Por el momento, el mecanismo de estos hallazgos permanece como otro enigma.

REFERENCIAS CITADAS

1. ABBRECHT, P.H. & LITTELL, J.K. 1972. Plasma erythropoietin in man and mice during acclimatization to different altitudes. *J. Appl. Physiol* 32: 54-58.

2. ALIPPI, R.M., BARCELÓ, A. C. & BOZZINI, C.E. 1983. Erythropoietic response to hypoxia in mice with polycythemia induced by hypoxia or transfusion. *Exp. Hematol.* 11: 122-128.

3. ALIPPI, R.M., BARCELÓ, A.C., RIO, M.E. & BOZZINI, C.E. 1983. Growth retardation in the early developing rat exposed to continous hypobaric hypoxia. *Acta Physiol. Latinoam.* 33: 1-5.

4. BARCELÓ, A.C. & BOZZINI, C.E. 1982. Erythropoietin formation during hypoxia in mice with impaired responsiveness to erythropoietin formation induced by irradiation or 5-fluorouracil injection. *Experientia* 38: 504-505.

5. BIRGERARD, G., WIDE, L. & SIMONSSON, B. 1989. Marked erythropoietin increase before fall in Hb after treatment with cytostatic drugs suggests mechanism other than anaemia for stimulation. *Brit J. Haemato.* 72: 462-466.

6. BOZZINI, C.E. 1966. Effect of the erythroid activity of the bone marrow on the plasma disappearance óf injected erythropoietin in dogs. *Nature* (Lond) 209: 1140.

7. BOZZINI, C.E., ALLIPI, R.M. & BARCELÓ, A.C. 1989. Enhanced erythropoietic response to hypobaria in hypertransfused, post-hypoxic, post-anemic or testosterone-treated polycythemic rodents. *In: Molecular biology of erythropoiesis.* Plenum Press: 23-28.

8. BOZZINI, C.E., ALIPPI, R.M. & MARTINEZ, M.A. 1971. The inhibitory effect of relative polycythemia on erythropoietin production in response to hypoxic hypoxia. *Acta Physiol. Latinoam.* 21: 293-296.

9. BOZZINI, C.E., ALVAREZ, C.A., MARTINEZ, M.A., SORIANO, G.E., ALIPPI, R.M. & GIGLIO, M. J. 1976. Production of and response to erythropoietin in the splenectomized mouse. *Exp. Hematol.* 4: 114-120.

10. DE KLERK, G., ROSENGARTEN, P.C.J. , VET, R.J. & GOUDSMIT, R. 1981. Serum erythropoietin (ESF) titers in anemia. *Blood* 58: 1164-1170.

11. ECKARDT, K. DITTMER, J., NEUMANN, R., BAUER, C. & KURTZ, A. 1990. Decline of erythropoietin formation at continuous hypoxia is nkot due to feedback inhibition. *Am. J. Physiol.* 258: F 1432-1437.

12. FRIED, W. & BARONE-VARELAS, J. 1984. Regulation of plasma erythropoietin level in hypoxic rats. *Exp. Hematol.* 12: 706-711.

13. FRIED, W., GREGORY, A., KNOSPE, H. & TROBAUGH, F.E. 1971. Regulation of plasma erythropoietin levels in mice with impaired responsiveness to erythropoietin. *J. Lab. Clin. Med.* 78: 449-456.

14. FRIED, W., PLZAK, L.F., JACOBSON, L.O. & GOLDWASSER, E. 1957. Studies on erythropoiesis III. Factors controlling erythropoietin production. *Proc. Soc. Exp. Biol. Med.* 94: 237-241.

15. KILBRIDGE, T.M., FRIED, W. & HELLER, P. 1969. The mecanism by which plethora suppresses erythropoiesis. *Blood* 33: 104-113.

16. MILLER, M.E. & HOWARD, D. 1979. Modulation of erythropoietin concentrations by manipulation of hypercarbia. *Blood Cells* 5: 389-403.

17. MIRAND, E.A., GORDON, A.S., ZANJANI, E.D., BENNET, T.E. & MURPHY, T.G.P. 1971. Disappearance of exogenous erythropoietin (ESF) from the blood of germ free mice. *Proc. Soc. Exp. Biol. Med.* 139: 161-164.

18. NAETS, J.P. & WITTEK, M. 1969. Erythropoietic activity of marrow and disappearance rate of erythropoietin in the rat. *Am. J. Physiol.* 217: 297-301.

19. NECAS, E., ZIVNY, J. & NEUWIRT, J. 1972. Oxygen tension and erythropoietin production in normal and polycythemic rats exposed to low PO_2 atmosphere. *Physiol. bohemoslov* 21: 423.

20. PIROSO, E., ERSLEV, A.J. & CARO, J. Inappropiate increase in erythropoietin titers during chemotherapy. *Am. J. Hematol.* 32: 248-254.

21. PIROSO, E., ERSLEV, A.J., FLAHARTY, K.K. & CARO, J. 1991. Erythropoietin life span in rats with hypoplastic and hyperplastic bone marrows. *Am. J. Hematol.* 36: 105-110.

22. REYNAFARJE, C., RAMOS, J., FAURA, J. & VILLAVICENCIO, D. 1964. Humoral control of erythropoietic activity in man during and after altitude exposure. *Proc. Soc. Exp. Biol. Med.* 116: 649-658.

23. RUSSELL, E.S. & KEIGHLEY, G. 1972. The relation between erythropoiesis and plasma erythropoietin levels in normal and genetically anaemic mice during prolonged hypoxia or after whole-body irradiation. *Br. J. Haemat* 22: 437-452.

24. SCHUSTER, S.J., WILSON, J.H., ERSLEV, A.J. & CARO, J. 1987. Physiologic regulation and tissue localization of renal erythropoietin messenger RNA. *Blood* 70: 316-318.

25. SHERWOOD, J.B., GOLDWASSER, E., CHILCOTE, R., CARMICHAEL, L.D. & NAGEL, R.L. 1986. Sickle cell anemia patients have low erythropoietin levels for their degree of anemia. *Blood* 67: 46-49.

26. STOHLMAN, F. & BRECHER, G. 1959. Humoral regulation of erythropoiesis V. Relationship of plasma erythropoietin level to bone marrow activity. *Proc. Soc. Exp. Biol. Med.* 100: 40-43.

III.

METABOLISMO, EJERCICIO Y ACLIMATACIÓN AGUDA A LA ALTURA

ANAEROBIC METABOLISM AT ALTITUDE: RECENT DEVELOPMENTS

Paolo Cerretelli, Bruno Grassi, Bengt Kayser

Abstract

Some aspects of anaerobic (alactic and lactic) energy metabolism at altitude are reviewed. As far as anaerobic alactic metabolism is concerned, experimental evidence indicates that neither acute nor chronic (up to 3-5 weeks) exposure to hypoxia significantly reduces maximal anaerobic alactic power. The observed reductions of the latter after longer exposures at very high altitudes seem attributable to a concomitant reduction of muscle mass. As far as anaerobic lactic metabolism is concerned, the factors possibly responsible for the well known reduction of maximal lactic acid accumulation in blood after exhaustive exercise ([La$_b$]p) in subjects acclimatized to altitude are reviewed. Such factors are: a) physical training; b) changes of lactate removal and uptake by muscle or other organs; c) enzyme activity changes along the glycolytic pathway; d) substrate availability; e) hormones (in particular cathecholamines); f) reduction of tissue buffer capacity; g) "central fatigue"; h) "tighter coupling" between ATP demand and supply and "metabolic organization" toward preferential utilization of aerobic mechanisms. It is concluded that, independent of the exact mechanisms, which are still matter for investigation, a reduction of lactate accumulation in blood and tissues at altitude may prevent changes of pH harmful for the functioning of the cell. In view of some recent developments, however, likely mechanisms implicated in the regulation of anaerobic glycolysis at altitude appear to be the modulation of the activity of glycogen phosphorylase "a" by catecholamines, and/or a central inhibition of the maximal activation of the exercising muscle mass.

Key words: Hypoxia, anaerobic metabolism, exercise, lactic acid, muscle metabolism, tissue buffer capacity, glicolisis.

Resumen

Se revisan algunos aspectos en relación al metabolismo energético (no-láctico y láctico) anaerobio en la altura. En cuanto a la capacidad máxima para el metabolismo anaerobio no-láctico la evidencia experimental indica que ni la exposición aguda a la altura ni la crónica (hasta 3-5 semanas) lo reducen significativamente. Las reducciones observadas después de exposiciones prolongadas a grandes alturas pueden atribuirse a una reducción concomitante de la masa muscular. Se revisan, en relación al metabolismo anaerobio láctico, los factores posiblemente responsables de la conocida reducción de la acumulación máxima de lactato en la sangre luego de ejercicio exhaustivo ([La$_b$]p) en sujetos aclimatados a la altura. Estos factores son: a) entrenamiento físico; b) cambios en la concentración de lactato, eliminación y acumulación por los músculos u otros órganos; c) cambios en las actividades enzimáticas a lo largo de la vía glicolítica; d) disponibilidad de sustrato; e) hormonas (en particular, las catecolaminas); f) reducción de la capacidad amortiguadora de los tejidos; g) "fatiga central"; h) buen acoplamiento entre la oferta y demanda de ATP y "organización metabólica" hacia la utilización preferencial de mecanismos aerobios. Se concluye que, independientemente de los mecanismos exactos, los cuales son todavía materia de investigación, una reducción de la acumulación del lactato en sangre y tejidos en la altura prevendría los cambios de pH perjudiciales para el buen funcionamiento celular. Sin embargo, y a la luz de algunos trabajos recientes, sería probable que los mecanismos implicados en la regulación de la glicólisis anaerobia en la altura estuvieran modulados por la actividad de la glucógeno fosforilasa "a", por catecolaminas, y/o por una inhibición central de la máxima activación de la masa muscular en ejercicio.

Palabras claves: Hipoxia, metabolismo anaerobio, ejercicio, acido láctico, metabolismo muscular, capacidad amortiguadora tisular, glicólisis.

Résumé

Ce travail passe en revue quelques aspects du métabolisme énergétique (alactique et lactique) anaérobie d'altitude. En ce qui concerne la capacité maximum pour le métabolisme alactique, l'évidence expérimentale indique que ni l'exposition aiguë à l'altitude, ni la chronique (jusqu'à 3-5 semaines) peuvent la réduire de façon significative. Les réductions observées après des expositions à hautes altitudes peuvent être attribuées à une réduction concomitante de la masse musculaire. On passe en revue, par rapport au métabolisme anaérobie lactique, les facteurs qui sont certainement responsables de la fameuse réduction de l'accumulation maximum de lactate dans la sang après un exercice épuisant ($[La_b]p$) chez des sujets acclimatés à l'altitude. Ces facteurs sont : a) entraînement physique ; b) changements dans la concentration de lactate, élimination et accumulation par les muscles ou d'autres organes; c) changements dans les activités enzymatiques tout au long de la voie glycolitique ; d) disponibilité de substrat ; e) hormones (en particulier, les cathécolamines ; f) reduction du pouvoir tampon des tissus; g) "fatigue centrale" ; h) couplage adéquat entre l'offre et la demande d'ATP et "organisation métabolique pour une utilisation préférentielle des mécanismes aérobies". On en conclue que, indépendamment des mécanismes exacts, qui font encore l'objet de recherches, une réduction de l'accumulation du lactate dans le sang et les tissus en altitude, préviendrait les changements de pH nuisibles au bon fonctionnement cellulaire. Cependant, et à la lumière de quelques travaux récents, il semblerait que les mécanismes impliqués dans la régulation de la glycolyse anaérobie en altitude soient modulés par l'activité de la glycogène phosphorilase "a", par les cathécolamines , et/ou par une inhibition centrale de l'activation maximum de la masse musculaire en exercice.

Mots clés : Hypoxie, métabolisme anaérobie, exercice, acide lactique, métabolisme musculaire, pouvoir tampon tissulaire, glycolyse .

The energy sources for ATP resynthesis in anaerobic conditions comprise essentially phosphocreatine (PCr) breakdown and anaerobic glycolysis with lactate (La) formation. The extent to which hypoxic conditions affect muscle anaerobic metabolism will be briefly reviewed in the following paragraphs.

THE ALACTIC MECHANISM

Many types of exercise are characterized by a baseline of moderate activity interrupted by sudden bursts of strenuous efforts. In these conditions, the muscle energy requirement may increase by several hundred-fold in a few tenths of a second (13). This remarkable feat can be achieved on the basis of PCr breakdown (alactic mechanism), the only process which can keep in pace with ATP utilization.

The energy yield of the alactic mechanism in humans can be studied essentially by means of two sets of methods, referred to as "average" and "instantaneous". In the "average" methods, the subject's mechanical power output ($\bar{w}_{av}$) is determined during exercises of extremely high intensity and of very short duration (<7 s) (33; 25). In the "instantaneous" methods, the "peak" ($\hat{w}$) or the "mean" maximal power output ($\bar{w}$) are determined during the pushing phase of a standard maximal jump off both feet on a force platform (11). Alternate methods have also been developed, that allow the assessment of instantaneous power during standing high jumps from the "time of flight", which is determined by means of electronic timing devices (5). The major difference between the "average" and "instantaneous" methods is that the former provide the maximal power output over several "one-leg" muscle contractions, whereas the "instantaneous" methods yield the maximal power during a single "two-legs" contraction. The latter power values are indeed 2 to 4 times higher than the former.

Only few investigations have been devoted to the study of the effects of hypoxia on maximum alactic power. di Prampero et al. (14) studied the effects of acute and chronic hypoxia on the $\bar{w}_{av}$ that can be sustained during short (<10 s) all-out efforts on the bicycle ergometer. In a study carried out on the members of the 1981 Swiss Lhotse Shar expedition, Cerretelli & di Prampero (9) assessed the effects of high-altitude acclimatization on $\hat{w}$. The results of these studies are summarized in the Table 1. It appears that: 1) acute hypoxia (12 and 14.5% O_2 in N_2) has no detectable effects on $\bar{w}_{av}$; 2) chronic hypoxia (3 weeks at altitudes of 4540 to 5200 m) does not affect either $\bar{w}_{av}$ or $\hat{w}$; 3) chronic hypoxia exceeding 5 weeks reduces significantly $\hat{w}$.

A study conducted on 6 members of the 1986 Swiss Mt. Everest expedition by Ferretti et al. (16) indicates that $\hat{w}$, upon return after a 8-10 weeks sojourn at altitudes exceeding 5000 m was slightly but significantly reduced. However, because of the concomitant decrease of the cross sectional area of the extensor muscles of the thigh, w expressed per unit cross sectional area of the muscle was unchanged, which allows to conclude that the observed decrease in power depends only on a net loss of muscle mass. Indeed, recent preliminary results obtained at the Ev-K2-CNR Pyramid Laboratory (5050 m, situated near Lobuche, Khumbu, Nepal) indicate that, in the absence of a significant reduction of body weight and muscle mass, the maximal vertical jumping height is not influenced by a 5 weeks sojourn at altitude (36). These results, coupled with the normal nerve conduction and nerve-muscle

Table 1 - Upper panel: "Average" maximal alactic power (wav) measured during a <10s effort on a cycloergometer at sea level, in acute hypoxia (breathing 14.5% and 12.1% O_2 hypoxic mixtures), and in chronic hypoxia (3 weeks at 4540 m) (14). Lower Panel: "Peak " power (w) (mean of first 5 jumps in a row) before departure, after 3 and 5 weeks at 5200 m, and after return from the expedition (9).

Altitude (m)	sea level	sea level	sea level	4.540
FIO_2	1	0.145	0.121	0.540
Exposure	acute	acute	acute	3 weeks
$\overline{w}_{av}$ ($W \cdot kg^{-1}$) $\pm SD$	11.1 ± 1.2	11.3 ± 1.0	11.2 ± 1.0	11.0 ± 0.9
n	24	24	24	24

Altitude (m)	400	5200	5200	400
FIO_2	0.209	0.209	0.209	0.209
Exposure	before	3 weeks	5 weeks	after
$\hat{w}$ ($W \cdot kg^{-1}$)	21.0 ± 1.9	20.8 ± 3.9	16.0 ± 1.8	17.4 ± 1.5
n	15	25	15	20

transmission seem to indicate that the neuro-muscular and muscular functions are preserved at altitude, and that the muscle retains its capability of sustaining short explosive efforts (27)

From the above reported results it can be concluded that neither acute nor chronic (up to 3-5 weeks) exposure to hypoxia has any effects on the maximal rate of ~P hydrolysis in muscle, at least up to an altitude of 5200 m. This finding is compatible with the data of Knuttgen & Saltin (31), who have shown that ATP and PCr concentrations are not affected by acute hypoxia, at least up to a simulated altitude of 4000 m. Raynaud & Durand (37) have shown that the O_2 debt paid within the first minute of recovery after 3 weeks at 3800 m is essentially the same as at sea level. Since this part of the debt can be taken mainly as representative of ~P resynthesis after exercise, also these data suggest that hypoxia has no major effects on this aspect of muscle metabolism. For altitudes above 5200 m and for prolonged exposures to hypoxia, however, $\hat{w}$ may undergo a substantial drop, probably as a consequence of muscle mass reduction and/or deterioration (22).

Maximal anaerobic power can also be determined by a force-velocity test and by a 30-s Wingate test (1). Whereas the first of the above measurements has the same physiological significance as the "average" methods described above for the determination of $\overline{w}_{av}$, the 30-s Wingate test is a measurement of the average power developed by the subject during a period in which not only ~P splitting but also oxidations and anaerobic glycolysis contribute a sizeable amount of energy. Bedu *et al.* (2) in a group of Bolivian, 3700 m altitude natives (7-15 yr), found that the performance of the force-velocity test was not different from that of an age matched sea-level control group, whereas that of the Wingate test was about 15 % lower. The latter is presumably a consequence of the changes in aerobic lactic metabolism occurring at high altitude (see the following paragraph).

THE LACTIC MECHANISM

Blood Lactate concentration $[La_b]$ at a given absolute work load is higher in acute hypoxia than in normoxia (24). With acclimatization to high altitude, however, $[La_b]$ values at a given work load return to values similar to those observed at sea level (15). The latter observation was also confirmed by preliminary results recently obtained by Grassi *et al.* (in preparation) at the Ev-K2-CNR Pyramid Laboratory. With regard to the maximal $[La_b]$ observed in the recovery after an exhausting exercise (peak $[La_b]$, or $[La_b]p$), this is not significantly reduced during acute hypoxia (10), whereas it decreases considerably in chronic hypoxia. Such decrease is progressive with increasing altitude, as can be seen from Fig. 1, in which the results obtained by different

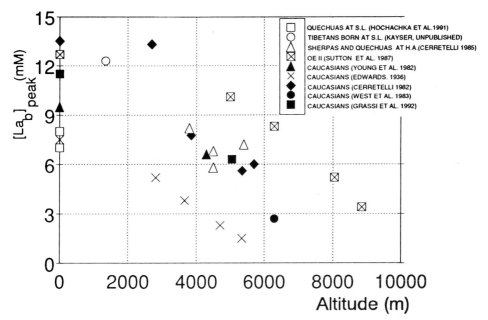

Figure 1 - Peak $[La_b]$ following exhaustive exercise in lowlanders chronically exposed to high altitude (×5; ◆10; ▲ 44; ●43; ■17), in lowlanders chronically exposed to hypoxia in a decompression chamber (⊠41), in high altitude natives examined at high altitude (△ 10) and at sea level (□21), in Tibetan born, living and examined in Kathmandu (1300 m asl) (○ Kayser *et al.*, unpublished).

authors on subjects exposed chronically to high altitude (10; 44; 43; 17) or to hypoxia in a decompression chamber (Operation Everest II; 41) are summarized. It is interesting to observe that [Lab]p values obtained in the chamber are slightly higher than those obtained on the mountains. No clear-cut explanation can be offered for such finding. Also shown on the same graph are the data obtained at altitude by Cerretelli et al. (10) on Sherpa and American Indians high altitude natives, and by Kayser et al. (personal observation) on Nepali and Tibetan natives living in Kathmandu (1300 m asl).

In the course of various expeditions to the Khumbu Valley of Nepal and to the Andes, a sizeable number (n = 41) of acclimatized and unacclimatized natives (Sherpas and Peruvian Indians) and Caucasian lowlanders were investigated at sea level, at altitude and in a hypobaric chamber by one of the authors of the present chapter (see 10) in order to assess, besides La_bp, one or more of the following variables :

a) *Resting [La$_b$].* Resting [La$_b$] is not affected by chronic hypoxia. In both Caucasians and highlanders [La$_b$] is around 1 mM, as previously shown by Edwards (15);

b) *[La$_b$]p following continuous or intermittent supramaximal work loads until exhaustion while breathing air or pure O$_2$ at ambient pressure.* As appears from Fig. 1, [La$_b$]p at an altitude of about 5350 m is reduced to about half the average sea level control value. This reduction is essentially not affected by the exercise protocol (continuous or intermittent) and/or by O$_2$ administration. The latter observation had already been made by Edwards (15) on one subject. Sherpas (n=3) exercising supramaximally after 1-year stay at sea level were able to reach [La$_b$]p up to at least 11 mM, close to the value of Caucasians breathing air at sea level (~14 mM) or in a hypobaric chamber at a simulated altitude of 3800 m (~13 mM).

c) *The relationship between blood [H$^+$] and [La$_b$] after supramaximal exercises of varying durations.* Cerretelli et al. (10) associated the decrease of the maximal lactacid capacity at high altitude to the reduction of plasma [HCO3-] consequential to the drop of Pa_{CO2}, and it was speculated that "should Pa_{CO2} at the summit of Mt Everest drop to 10 Torr, the size of the maximal lactacid O$_2$ debt would be practically nil".

The relationships between increase in venous blood [H+] and the corresponding rise in [La$_b$], determined at sea level on Caucasians and at 5350 m on acclimatized lowlanders and Sherpas appear to be linear. The buffer value for the whole body, calculated as the slope of the above lines, appears to be reduced to about half at altitude. The highest venous [H$^+$] at exhaustion is approximately the same for the two conditions, independent of [La$_b$]p (10) (Fig. 2).

d) *The kinetics of [Lab] washout during recovery following supramaximal loads while breathing air or pure O$_2$.* [La$_b$] washout kinetics in the recovery following maximal or supramaximal exercises, after an initial time lag which may be somewhat different in the two conditions, can be described both at

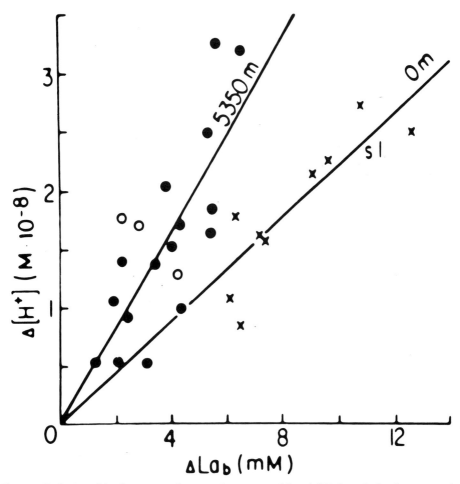

Fig. 2 - Relationship between changes in venous blood [H+] and the increases in [La$_b$], in altitude natives (○), in lowlanders acclimatized to 5350 m (●), and in sea level residents (✕). The drawn lines, forced to pass through the origin, indicate the buffer value for the whole body (10).

altitude (10; 29) and at sea level (13) by a monoexponential function, with a half-time of about 15-20 min. This seems to indicate that the La release kinetics from the exercising muscles and/or the rates of glucose resynthesis or La oxidation are not greatly influenced by altitude. In chronic hypoxia, however, the delay observed before [La$_b$] starts dropping during recovery, following a [La$_b$]p of about 6-8 mM is variable. Such delay, which occurs even at sea level for [La$_b$]p > 10 mM, is influenced by the duration of the preceding exercise, presumably by the length of altitude exposure, and by circulatory factors (*e.g.* peripheral vasoconstriction) as shown by the consequences of O$_2$ administration at altitude, which probably results from a change of the La washout kinetics from the muscles into blood (10).

Grassi *et al.* (17) have recently studied the time course of $[La_b]p$ decrease during a 5 week sojourn at 5050 m (Ev-K2-CNR Pyramid Laboratory), as well as that of the $[La_b]p$ increase upon return to sea level. The preliminary results show that: a) $[La_b]p$ kept decreasing during the first 2-3 weeks of acclimatization, reaching values 45% lower than those observed pre-expedition; b) after return to sea level, it took 4-5 weeks for $[La_b]p$ to reach pre-expedition levels; c) $[La_b]p$ during acclimatization and deacclimatization was only partially related to the acid-base status of the subjects, evaluated by arterial pH and Pa_{CO2}.

It has been recently proposed that the found reduced lactic capacity at altitude, also known as "lactate paradox" (19), may have become in altitude natives a developmental or genetic adaptation ("perpetual lactate paradox"; 21; 34). In chronically hypoxic lowlanders, on the other hand, such phenomenon is a consequence of acclimatization, since it is reversible, its expression varying with time with a halftime of about 5-10 days both for the on- and for the off-phase (acclimatization and deacclimatization, respectively), as shown by Grassi *et al.* (17). According to Hochachka's hypothesis the lactate paradox may be the consequence of a "metabolic organization" toward a preferential utilization of aerobic metabolism compared to anaerobic, and of a tighter coupling between ATP demand and supply during exercise, with the result of a lower cost of muscle work. Such hypothesis is based on observations made on a group of 6 Quechua Indian natives examined both at altitude (La Raya, 4200 m) and at sea level (21), and requires confirmation by more extensive studies on other altitude populations. Moreover, the following facts appear to be particularly relevant and must be taken into account before Hochachka's hypothesis may be accepted :

a) The Sherpas of Nepal, a much more established and genetically identified high altitude population than the Quechua Indians, undergo the same adaptive metabolic changes in chronic hypoxia as acclimatized lowlanders. In fact, they do not seem to display the so-called "perpetual lactate paradox" (10).

b) Sherpas have the same working efficiency for aerobic work as sea level residents and acclimatized lowlanders (32; 8).

c) The muscle mitochondrial volume density of Sherpas is extremely low ($3.5\% \pm 0.38$), even less than that of sedentary sea level dwellers (~4-4.5%) (30). This finding, if confirmed for the Quechuas, would be against the possibility of a metabolic organization of skeletal muscle "toward the cardiac end of the spectrum" that would be coherent with Hochachka's theory (21; 34).

d) According to Hochachka & Matheson (20), a more tight coupling in ATP demand-ATP supply is at the heart of the "perpetual lactate paradox" found in his Andean subjects. However, a tighter ATP demand-ATP supply coupling would bring about a reduction down to almost zero of the PCr hydrolysis observed in the muscle at the onset of constant-load exercises. This is the case for myocardium (26) but not for the calf muscles of Quechua

Indians (see *e.g.* Fig. 9B of the paper by Matheson *et al.*, 34). The latter appear in fact to behave, with regard to the kinetics of PCr breakdown and resynthesis, as sedentary subjects at sea level.

Apart from the possibility that the lactate paradox may perpetuate itself as a genetic feature of high altitude natives, no clear-cut explanation has been offered for this adaptational change. West (42) and Sutton & Heigenhauser (40) have indicated the following possible determinants :

a) *Physical training.* Training at altitude might hypothetically result in a progressively greater recruitment of slow twitch fibers whence the lower $[La_b]p$ levels. To the authors' knowledge this possibility is not supported by experimental evidence.

b) *A change of the rate of La removal and uptake from or by muscle or other organs.* Bender *et al.* (3) observed a decrease in the net La release from the exercising legs after 18 days acclimatization to altitude. According to these authors, such decrease could be due to a reduced production or to an increased removal of La by the muscle itself. The latter could represent a "training-like" increase in muscle La consumption during acclimatization. Young *et al.* (45), however, did not observe any "training-like" adaptations in muscle glycolytic and oxidative enzymes during altitude acclimatization. Moreover, Green *et al.* (18) have shown that in chronic hypoxia (Operation Everest II) La accumulation after exercise is drastically reduced both in blood and in muscle.

c) *Enzyme activity changes along the glycolytic pathway.* Howald *et al.* (23) have shown that the activity of hexokinase, phosphofructokinase, lactate dehydrogenase and glyceraldehyde phosphate dehydrogenase in the vastus lateralis of acclimatized mountaineers 10-12 days after return from a 6-8 weeks high altitude exposure (>5000 m) are essentially unchanged in respect to pre-expedition control values. Similar results, including data on total glycogen phosporylase, were obtained after a 15 day exposure to 4300 m by Young *et al.* (45), and by Green *et al.* (18) in the course of Operation Everest II. Thus, it would appear that the main regulatory enzymes of the glycolytic pathway are not affected by chronic hypoxia and cannot be at the basis of the "lactate paradox".

d) *Substrate availability.* High altitude acclimatization seems to have a sparing effect on muscle glycogen utilization (44; 18). By contrast, an increased dependence on blood glucose has been shown, both at rest and at exercise, possibly as a consequence of enhanced hepatic gluconeogenesis, by Brooks *et al.* (6). The muscle resting glycogen level was found to be substantially unaffected by chronic hypoxia in the course of Operation Everest II (18). The muscle glycogen sparing effect during altitude acclimatization has been attributed, among others, to a lesser beta-adrenergic stimulation of glycogenolysis (7).

e) *Hormones.* Epinephrine is known to activate phosphorylase "a" leading to enhanced muscle glycogen breakdown. During altitude acclimatization plasma epinephrine response to exercise, after a transient increase (4 hours of exposure to 4300 m) resumes sea-level control values, as shown by measurements carried out after 21 days. Plasma norepinephrine is slightly enhanced compared to control levels both in acute and chronic hypoxia (35). Thus a reduced activation of phosphorylase "a" could only occur via a down-regulation of the beta-adrenergic receptors. Richalet *et al.* (38; 39) have shown, in fact, a hypoxia-induced reduction of the beta-receptors activity of both lymphocytes and the myocardium, which could restrict the maximum rate of glycolysis and therefore maximal lactic capacity in chronic hypoxia. Experiments recently carried out with beta-blockers (46) indicate that the increased [La$_b$] at a given absolute work load seem to be mediated by catecholamines, but not the following [La$_b$] decrease during acclimatization.

f) *Reduction of the tissue buffer capacity*. The "lactate paradox" has been also associated with a reduced blood and tissue buffer capacity. This hypothesis was recently tested in humans by Kayser *et al.* (28) by sodium bicarbonate (NaHCO$_3$) (0.3 g/kg of body weight) loading before and at the end of a 35 day sojourn at 5050 m (Ev-K2-CNR Pyramid Laboratory). Net (recovery minus resting) [La$_b$]p accumulation increased significantly in 6 subjects from 12.9 to 16.6 mM at sea level but only slightly from 6.85 to 7.95 mM (NS) at high altitude (Fig. 3). The results indicate that a normalization of bicarbonate stores at high altitude, bringing the subject back to the normal "buffer line" in a situation of acute respiratory alkalosis, does not allow to resume sea level peak lactic capacity.

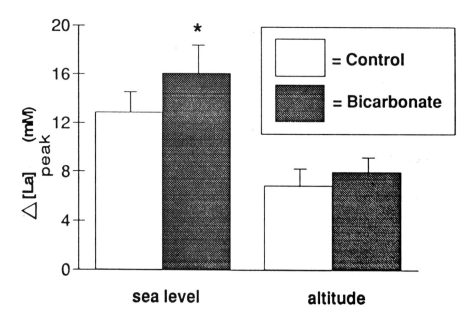

Fig. 3 - Net (peak during recovery minus resting) [La$_b$] accumulation during exhaustive exercise (Δ[La$_b$]p) at sea level and after 5 weeks at an altitude of 5050 m, in control conditions (C) and after bicarbonate ingestion (B) (28).

g) *"Central fatigue" hypothesis*. According to Bigland-Ritchie & Vollestad (4), complete neuromuscular activation may not be achieved in chronic hypobaric hypoxia. Under these conditions, inhibitory reflexes, generated from limb or respiratory muscles, would act centrally limiting maximal motor drive in relation to their O_2 availability. Such hypothesis, substantially agreed upon also by Green *et al.* (18), was put forward by Dill *et al.* (12), who stated that "It is as though the body, realizing the delicacy of the situation with regard to O_2 supply, sets up an automatic control over work which renders impossible the severe acid-base disturbances which can be voluntarily induced at sea level".

Independent of its mechanisms, which are still matter for investigation, a reduction of La accumulation in blood and in the tissues, particularly the muscles, may prevent changes of pH that could be harmful for the functioning of the cell. The blockade of anaerobic glycolysis, however, does not seem to occur through a negative feed-back via a H+-mediated inactivation of a key enzyme. The modulation of the activity of glycogen phosphorylase "a" by catecholamines appears to be the most probable mechanism responsible for the lactate paradox, even though a more complex interaction of some of the factors listed above cannot be ruled out.

REFERENCES

1. BAR-OR, O. 1987. The Wingate anaerobic test: an update on methodology, reliability and validity. *Sports Medicine* 4: 381-394.

2. BEDU, M., FELLMANN, N., SPIELVOGEL, H., FALGAIRETTE, G., VAN PRAAGH, E. & COUDERT, J. 1991. Force-velocity and 30-s Wingate tests in boys at high and low altitudes. *J. Appl. Physiol.* 70: 1031-1037.

3. BENDER, P.R., GROVES, B.M., MCCULLOUGH, R.E, MCCULLOUGH, R.G., TRAD, L., YOUNG, A.J., CYMERMAN, A. & REEVES, J.T. 1989. Decreased exercise muscle lactate release after high altitude acclimatization. *Journal of Applied Physiology* 67: 1456-1462.

4. BIGLAND-RITCHIE, B. & VOLLESTAD, N.K. 1988. Hypoxia and fatigue: how are they related? *In*: J.R. Sutton, C.S. Houston & G. Coates (eds.). *Hypoxia. The Tolerable Limits*. Indianapolis: Benchmark Press: 315-326.

5. BOSCO, C., LUTHANEN, P. & KOMI, P.V. 1983. A simple method of measurement of mechanical power in jumping. *Eur. J. Appl. Physiol.* 50: 273-282.

6. BROOKS, G.A., BUTTERFIELD, G.E., WOLFE, R.R., GROVES, B.M., MAZZEO, R.S., SUTTON, J.R., WOLFEL, E.E. & REEVES, J.T. 1991a. Incresed dependence on blood glucose after acclimatization to 4,300 m. *J. Appl. Physiol.* 70: 919-927.

7. BROOKS, G.A., BUTTERFIELD, G.E., WOLFE, R.R., GROVES, B.M., MAZZEO, R.S., SUTTON, J.R., WOLFEL, E.E. & REEVES, J.T. 1991b. Decreased reliance on lactate during exercise after acclimatization to 4,300 m. *J. Appl. Physiol.* 71: 333-341.

8. CERRETELLI, P. 1976. Limiting factors to oxygen transport on Mount Everest. *J. Appl. Physiol.* 40: 658-667.

9. CERRETELLI, P. & DI PRAMPERO, P.E. 1985. Aerobic and anaerobic metabolism during exercise at altitude. *Medicine Sport Science* 19: 1-19.

10. CERRETELLI, P., VEICSTEINAS, A. & MARCONI, C. 1982. Anaerobic metabolism at high altitude: the lactacid mechanism. *In*: W. Brendel and R.A. Zink (eds.). *High Altitude Physiology and Medicine*. Springer-Verlag: 94-102.

11. DAVIES, C.T.M. & RENNIE, R. 1968. Human power output. *Nature* 217: 770-771.

12. DILL, D.B., TALBOT, J.H. & CONSOLAZIO, W.V. 1937. Blood as a physiochemical system. XII. Man at high altitudes. *J. Biol. Chem.* 118: 649-666.

13. DI PRAMPERO, P.E. 1981. Energetics of muscular exercise. *Rev. Physiol. Biochem. Pharmacol.* 89: 143-222.

14. DI PRAMPERO, P.E., MOGNONI, P. & VEICSTEINAS, A. 1982. The effects of hypoxia on maximal anaerobic alactic power in man. *In*: W. Brendel and R.A. Zink (eds.). *High Altitude Medicine and Physiology*. Springer-Verlag: 88-93.

15. EDWARDS, H.T. 1936. Lactic acid in rest and work at high altitude. *Am. J. Physiol.* 116: 367-375.

16. FERRETTI, G., HAUSER, H. & DI PRAMPERO, P.E. 1990. Maximal muscular power before and after exposure to chronic hypoxia. *International Journal of Sports Medicine* 11 (Suppl. 1): S31-S34.

17. GRASSI, B., KAYSER, B., BINZONI, T., MARZORATI, M., BORDINI, M., MARCONI, C. & CERRETELLI, P. 1992. Peak blood lactate concentration during altitude acclimatization and deacclimatization in humans. *Pflügers Archiv* 420: R165.

18. GREEN, H.J., SUTTON, J., YOUNG, P., CYMERMAN, A. & HOUSTON, C.S. 1989. Operation Everest II: muscle energetics during maximal exhaustive exercise. *J. Appl. Physiol.* 66: 142-150.

19. HOCHACHKA, P.W. 1988. The lactate paradox: analysis of underlying mechanisms. *Ann. Sports Med.* 4: 184-188.

20. HOCHACHKA, P.W. & MATHESON, G.O. 1992. ATP ases and energy metabolism as proactive and reactive components on control of ATP turnover rates. *In*: J.R. Sutton, G. Coates & C.S. Houston (eds.). *Hypoxia and Mountain Medicine*. Burlington: Queen City Printers Inc.: 171-185.

21. HOCHACHKA, P.W., STANLEY, C., MATHESON, G.O., MCKENZIE, D.C., ALLEN, P.S & PARKHOUSE, W.S. 1991. Metabolic and work efficiencies during exercise in Andean natives. *J. Appl. Physiol.* 70: 1720-1730.

22. HOPPELER, H., KLEINERT, E., SCHLEGEL, C., CLAASSEN, H., HOWALD, H., KAYAR, S.R. & CERRETELLI, P. 1990. Morphological adaptations of human skeletal muscle to chronic hypoxia. *Int. J. Sports Med.* 11 (Suppl. 1): S3-S9.

23. HOWALD, H., PETTE, D., SIMONEAU, J.-A., UBER, A., HOPPELER, H. & CERRETELLI, P. 1990. Effects of chronic hypoxia on muscle enzyme activities. *Int. J. Sports Med.* 11 (Suppl. 1): S10-S14.

24. HUGHES, R.C., CLODE, M., EDWARDS, R.H.T., GOODWIN, T.J. & JONES, N.L. 1968. Effect of inspired O_2 on cardiopulmonary and metabolic responses to exercise in man. *J. Appl. Physiol.* 24: 336-347.

25. IKUTA, K. & IKAI, M. 1972. Study on the development of maximun anaerobic power in man with bicycle ergometer. *Res. J. Phys. Educat.* (Japan) 17: 151-157.

26. KATZ, L.A., SWAIN, J.A., PORTMAN, M.A. & BALABAN, R.S. 1989. Relation between phosphate metabolites and oxygen consumption of heart in vivo. *A. J. Physiol.* 256: H265-H274.

27. KAYSER, B., BOKENKAMP, R. & BINZONI, T. (in press). Alfa-motoneuron excitability at high altitude. *Eur. J. Appl. Physiol.*

28. KAYSER, B., FERRETTI, G., GRASSI, B., BINZONI, T. & CERRETELLI, P. 1992a. Blood lactate after exhaustive exercise at high altitude in humans: influence of bicarbonate loading. *Int. J. Sports Med.* 13: 88.

29. KAYSER, B., GRASSI, B., FERRETTI, G., COLOMBINI, A., MARCONI, C. & CERRETELLI, P. 1992b. Maximal rate of blood lactate accumulation during high altitude exposure in humans. 1992 A.P.S. Conference: Integrative Biology of Exercise; Colorado Springs (USA): Sept. 23-26.

30. KAYSER, B., HOPPELER, H., CLAASSEN, H. & CERRETELLI, P. 1991. Muscle structure and performance capacity of Himalayan Sherpas. *J. Appl. Physiol.* 70: 1938-1942.

31. KNUTTGEN, H.G. & SALTIN, B. 1973. Oxygen uptake, muscle high energy phosphates and lactate in exercise under acute hypoxic conditions in man. *Acta Physiol. Scand.* 87: 368-376.

32. LAHIRI, S., MILLEDGE, S., CHATTOPADHYAY, H.P., BHATTACHARYYA, A.K. & SINHA, A.K. 1967. Respiration and heart rate of Sherpa highlanders during exercise. *J. Appl. Physiol.* 23: 545-554.

33. MARGARIA, R., AGHEMO, P. & ROVELLI, E. 1966. Measurement of muscular power (anaerobic) in man. *J. Appl. Physiol.* 21: 1662-1664.

34. MATHESON, G.O., ALLEN, P.S., ELLINGER, D.C., HANSTOCK, C.C., GHEORGHIU, D., MCKENZIE, D.C., STANLEY, C., PARKHOUSE, W.S. & HOCHACHKA, P.W. 1991. Skeletal muscle metabolism and work capacity: a 31P-NMR study of Andean natives and lowlanders. *J. Appl. Physiol.* 70: 1963-1976.

35. MAZZEO, R.S., BENDER, P.R., BROOKS, G.A., BUTTERFIELD, G.I., GROVES, B.M., SUTTON, J.R., WOLFEL, E.E. & REEVES, J.T. 1991. Arterial chathecholamine response during exercise during acute and chronic high altitude exposure. *Am. J. Physiol.* 261: E419-E424.

36. NARICI, M., KAYSER, B., CIBELLA, F., GRASSI, B. & CERRETELLI, P. 1992. No changes in body composition and maximum alactic anaerobic performance during a 4-week sojourn at altitude. *Int. J. Sports Med.* 13: 87.

37. RAYNAUD, J. & DURAND, J. 1982. Oxygen deficit and debt in submaximal exercise at sea level and high altitude. *In*: W. Brendel and R.A. Zink (eds.). *High Altitude Physiology and Medicine*. Springer-Verlag: 103-106.

38. RICHALET, J.-P., DELAVIER, C., LE TRONG, J.-L., DUBRAY, C. & KEROMES, A., 1988a. Désensibilisation des béta récepteurs lymphocytaires humains en hypoxie d'altitude (4350 m). *Arch. Internat. Physiol. Biochim.* 96: A468.

39. RICHALET, J.-P., LARMIGNAT, P., RATHAT, C., KEROMES, A., BAUD, P. & LHOSTE, F. 1988b. Decreased human cardiac response to isoproterenol infusion in acute and chronic hypoxia. *J. Appl. Physiol.* 65: 1957-1961.

40. SUTTON, J.R. & HEIGENHAUSER, G.J.F. 1990. Lactate at altitude. *In*: J.R. Sutton, G. Coates & J.E. Remmers (eds). *Hypoxia: The Adaptations*. Toronto-Philadelphia: B.C. Decker Inc.: 94-97.

41. SUTTON, J.R., REEVES, J.T., WAGNER, P.D., GROVES, B.M., CYMERMAN, A., MALCONIAN, M.K., ROCK, P.B., YOUNG, P.M., WALTER, S.D. & HOUSTON, C.S. 1988. Operation Everest II: oxygen transport during exercise at extreme altitude. *J. Appl. Physiol.* 64: 1309-1321.

42. WEST, J.B. 1986. Lactate during exercise at extreme altitude. *Fed. Proc.* 45: 2953-2957.

43. WEST, J.B., BOYER, S.J., GRABER, D.J., HACKETT, P.H., MARET, K.H., MILLEDGE, J.S., PETERS, R.M. Jr., PIZZO, C.J., SAMAJA, M., SARNQUIST, F.H., SCHOENE, R.B. & WINSLOW, R.M. 1983. Maximal exercise at extreme altitudes on Mount Everest. *J. Appl. Physiol.* 55: 688-698.

44. YOUNG, A.J., EVANS, W.J., CYMERMAN, A., PANDOLF, K.B., KNAPIK, J.J. & MAHER, J.T. 1982. Sparing effect of chronic high-altitude exposure on muscle glycogen utilization. *J. Appl. Physiol.* 52: 857-862.

45. YOUNG, A.J., EVANS, W.J., FISHER, E.C., SHARP, R.L., COSTILL, D.L. & MAHER, J.T. 1984. Skeletal muscle metabolism of sea-level natives following short-term high-altitude residence. *Eur. J. Appl. Physiol.* 52: 463-466.

46. YOUNG, A.J., YOUNG, P.M., MCCULLOUGH, R.E., MOORE, L.G., CYMERMAN, A. & REEVES, J.T. 1991. Effect of beta-adrenergic blockade on plasma lactate concentration during exercise at high altitude. *Eur. J. Appl. Physiol.* 63: 315-322.

DÉVELOPPEMENT DES VOIES MÉTABOLIQUES AÉROBIE ET ANAÉROBIE CHEZ L'ENFANT BOLIVIEN : INTERACTIONS ENTRE L'ALTITUDE ET L'ÉTAT NUTRITIONNEL

Jean Coudert

Résumé

Le but de ce travail a été double :

(1) étudier le développement des aptitudes aérobie et anaérobie sur cycloergomètre, à Haute-Altitude (HA) (LA PAZ, 3700 m) chez des garçons âgés de 7 à 15 ans, ayant le même niveau socio-économique et le même niveau d'entraînement que le groupe contrôle de Basse Altitude (BA) (Clermont-Ferrand, 330 m).

(2) analyser l'impact des facteurs nutritionnels sur ce développement en étudiant 4 groupes d'enfants prépubères, âgés de 10 à 11 ans : 2 groupes à HA de niveau socio-économique élevé (HA1) et bas (HA2) et 2 groupes à BA (Santa Cruz de la Sierra, 420 m) de niveau socio-économique élevé (BA1) et bas (BA2).

Sur le groupe de garçons âgés de 7 à 15 ans, les faits suivants ont été observés : à HA, par rapport au groupe contrôle, le développement staturo-pondéral est identique ; la consommation maximale d'oxygène (VO_2max) est abaissée de 24,2 % en valeur absolue et de 18,1 % en valeur relative ; la fréquence cardiaque maximale (Fcmax) est plus basse de 11 b.min-1.

Les aptitudes anaérobie (dette maximale en oxygène, concentration maximale des lactates sanguins, puissance maximale anaérobie (Pmax) au cours du test Force-vitesse sont identiques et suivent le même développement qu'à BA.

Sur les groupes de niveaux socio-économiques différents, les enfants présentant un état clinique et biologique de "malnutrition marginale" ont un retard staturo-pondéral de 2 ans environ aussi bien à HA qu'à BA, par rapport aux enfants bien nourris. VO_2max est abaissée à HA dans les mêmes proportions que les bien nourris avec les mêmes réponses hématologiques (polyglobulie physiologique) et pulmonaires (augmentation du volume résiduel). Pmax mesurée au cours des tests Force-vitesse et de Wingate E de 30s (en Watt.kg-1 de poids corporel) sont significativement diminuées aussi bien à HA qu'à BA par rapport aux groupes de niveaux socio-économiques élevés.

Ces données doivent inciter à tenir compte de l'état nutritionnel, avant d'attribuer à l'altitude, ce qui revient en fait aux seuls facteurs nutritonnels.

Mots-clés : Hypoxie chronique, malnutrition marginale, consommation maximale d'oxygène, test Force-vitesse, Test de WINGATE.

Resumen

Los objetivos del estudio fueron dos:

(1) Estudiar el desarrollo de vías aerobias y anaerobias en una bicicleta ergométrica en la altura (La Paz, 3,700 m.) entre niños de 7-17 años que tuvieran el mismo estado socioeconómico y educacional que el grupo control de alturas bajas (Clermont-Ferrand, 330 m.).

(2) Analizar el efecto del estado nutricional en el desarrollo de 4 grupos de niños prepuberales de 10-11 años: 2 grupos de altura, uno de nivel socioeconómico alto (HA1) y otro de nivel socioeconómico bajo (HA2), y 2 grupos de altura baja (Santa Cruz de la Sierra, 420 m.), uno de nivel socioeconómico alto (LA1) y otro de nivel socioeconómico bajo (LA2).

Se realizaron las siguientes observaciones en el grupo de niños de 7-15 años:

- en la altura, el desarrollo biométrico (peso y talla) es igual al del grupo de control; la incorporación máxima de oxígeno (VO_2 max) cae 24.2% cuando se expresa en términos absolutos y 18.1% cuando se hace en términos relativos; el latido cardíaco máximo era menor en 11 latidos por minuto. La capacidad anaeróbica (deuda máxima de oxígeno, concentración máxima de lactato, poder anaeróbico máximo -Pmax- medido durante una prueba de velocidad forzada) fue idéntica y siguió el mismo desarrollo que a nivel del mar.

Notamos que el desarrollo biométrico (peso y talla) de niños con estados clínicos y biológicos de malnutrición marginal estaban atrasados en 2 años, tanto en la altura como a nivel del mar, cuando se les comparaba con controles de buena nutrición.

El VO_2 max se reduce en la altura en la misma magnitud, tanto en los niños con malnutrición marginal, como en los bien nutridos. Estos grupos tenían las mismas respuestas hematológicas (policitemia) y pulmonares (incremento del volumen residual). El poder anaeróbico medido durante una prueba de velocidad forzada y la prueba de 30s de Wingate (W.kg-1 de peso corporal) estaba significativamente reducido en niños con malnutrición marginal.

Los datos deberían hacernos estudiar el estado nutricional antes de atribuir a la altura lo que debe ser atribuido a factores nutricionales.

Palabras claves: Hipoxia crónica, malnutrición marginal, consumo máximo de oxígeno, prueba de velocidad forzada, prueba de WINGATE.

Abstract

The aims of this study were two:

(1) to study the development of aerobic and anaerobic pathways on a bicycle ergometer at high altitude (HA) (La Paz 3,700 m) among 7-17 year old boys, having the same socio-economic status and training levels as the control group at low altitude (LA) (Clermont-Ferrand 330m).

(2) to analyse the effect of nutritional status on the development of 4 groups of prepubertal boys of 10-11 years of age: 2 groups at HA, one of high socio-economic status (HA1) and one of low socio-economic status (HA2), and 2 groups at LA (Santa Cruz de la Sierra 420 m) one of high socio-economic status (LA1) and one of low socio-economic status (LA2).

The following observations were made regarding the group of 7-15 year old boys:

- at HA, the biometric development (height and weight) was the same as that of the control group ; the maximal oxygen uptake (VO_2max) dropped by 24.2 % when expressed in absolute terms, and by 18.1 % when expressed in relative terms ;

the maximal heart rate was lower by 11 b.min-1. The anaerobic capacity (maximal oxygen debt, maximal blood lactate concentration, maximal anaerobic power (Pmax) measured during a force velocity test) was identical and followed the same development as at LA.

We noticed that the biometric development (height and weight) of children showing a clinical and biological state of marginal malnutrition was delayed by approximately 2 years, at HA as well as LA, when compared to that of well nourished children.

VO_2max decreased at HA by the same amount in marginally undernourished and well nourished boys. These group had the same haematological (polycythemia) and pulmonary (increase in residual volume) responses. Anaerobic power measured during a force velocity test and a 30s Wingate test (W.kg-1 of body weight) was significantly lower in marginally undernourisehd boys than in well nourished boys.

The above data should encourage us to study nutritional status before attributing to altitude what shoud be attributed to nutritional factors.

Key words: Chronic hypoxia, marginal malnutrition, maximal oxygen consumption, force-velocity test, WINGATE-test.

À basse altitude (BA) il est admis que le garçon pré-pubère a un profil bioénergétique particulier : son métabolisme aérobie est relativement très développé par rapport à celui de l'adulte et subit peu de modifications durant la période de croissance, lorsqu'on l'exprime par unité de masse corporelle. Il n'en va pas de même pour le métabolisme anaérobie qui se développe particulièrement au cours de la puberté : c'est durant cette période que s'observe l'élévation des valeurs maximales des concentrations des lactates sanguins, des activités enzymatiques glycolytiques, du déficit et de la dette maximale en oxygène, ainsi que les valeurs maximales des puissances mécaniques externes développées au cours d'exercices courts et intenses (4).

Chez l'adulte, il est bien établi qu'à haute-altitude (HA) pour des altitudes supérieures ou égales à 3000 m, les possibilités maximales aérobie diminuent. Les informations concernant l'enfant sont actuellement peu nombreuses dans le domaine aérobie (7) et inexistantes dans le domaine des voies métaboliques anaérobie. C'est pourquoi nous avons entamé, dès 1984, une étude destinée à évaluer le retentissement de l'altitude sur le développement des aptitudes physiques, en particulier anaérobie du jeune garçon né et vivant en BOLIVIE. Afin d'analyser l'impact de facteurs nutritionnels, l'étude s'est déroulée en deux étapes :

1ère étape : étude d'enfants de niveaux socio-économiques élevés (SE+)

2ème étape : étude d'enfants de niveaux socio-économiques bas (SE-)

ÉTUDE D'ENFANTS DE NIVEAUX SOCIO-ÉCONOMIQUES ÉLEVÉS : (SE+)*

I.1 - Les sujets étudiés :

Il s'agissait de garçons pour la plupart nés et vivant à LA PAZ (3700 m, pression barométrique moyenne (PB) de 490 mmHg), âgés de 7 à 15 ans. Afin de permettre une comparaison avec des garçons nés et vivant à Basse-Altitude (CLERMONT-FERRAND, 330 m, PB = 730 mmHg), nous avions choisi des enfants ayant les mêmes niveaux socio-économiques et le même nombre d'heures d'activité physique hebdomadaire (5 heures par semaine, en moyenne). Les enfants de LA PAZ étaient des élèves du Lycée franco-bolivien, issus en général de familles aisées, pouvant payer les droits d'inscription relativement élevés pour le pays ; ils étaient pour la plupart métissés (métissage entre groupes d'origine AYMARA et descendants d'espagnols). Les enfants de basse altitude étaient des élèves d'écoles et lycées de la ville de CLERMONT-FERRAND.

La méthodologie employée :

L'étude a été réalisée avec le consentement des parents ; chez tous les enfants, les mesures suivantes ont été faites : poids, taille, examen clinique complet et détermination du développement pubertaire à partir des stades de TANNER, des mesures orchidométriques et du dosage de la testostérone salivaire ([Ts]) : ce dosage a été réalisé par méthode radio-immunologique sur des prélèvements de salive effectués au repos, à la même heure (3 heures après le lever, en général). Cette mesure nous a paru particulièrement intéressante, chez l'enfant : de réalisation facile, non agressive, elle fournit une information directe sur les concentrations de l'hormone biologiquement active puisqu'elle reflète le niveau de testostérone plasmatique libre.

Les données bioénergétiques ont été obtenues en utilisant un cycloergomètre adapté à l'enfant : cycloergomètre de BRUE, dont la hauteur de la selle et du guidon et la longueur du pédalier (13 cm, au lieu de 17 cm) sont ajustées à la taille de l'enfant (Ergomeca, Sorem, Toulon, France). L'ergomètre avait été préalablement étalonné, en utilisant une méthode originale (17).

Au laboratoire, les mesures bioénergétiques suivantes ont été réalisées : détermination directe de la consommation maximale d'oxygène (VO_2max), pour évaluer les aptitudes aérobie, mesure des dettes maximales en O_2 (DO_2max), détermination des seuils anaérobie ventilatoire et lactique, de la cinétique de récupération et des concentrations maximales des lactates sanguins ([L]max), et calcul des puissances maximales anaérobie (test force vitesse et test de WINGATE de 30 secondes) pour l'évaluation des aptitudes anaérobie.

---

* Travail réalisé en collaboration avec N. Fellmann, M. Bedu, H. Spielvogel, G. Falgairette et E. Van Praagh.

- VO_2max directe

La méthode utilisée a été celle des paliers ou méthode triangulaire.

Après un échauffement de 4 à 5 minutes avec une puissance d'exercice correspondant à 50 % de la puissance maximale aérobie (P.M.A.) amenant la fréquence cardiaque (Fc) à 140-150 c.min-1, l'intensité de l'exercice est augmentée par paliers de 2 minutes jusqu'à épuisement. En moyenne, 4 paliers ont été réalisés pour obtenir les valeurs maximales de VO_2. La fréquence de pédalage, imposée par un métronome et un signal lumineux, était de 70 tours par minute. Fc était enregistrée durant toute l'épreuve. Les gaz expirés étaient recueillis, durant les 30 dernières secondes pour chaque palier, dans un sac de DOUGLAS ; les volumes expirés étaient mesurés avec un spiromètre de TISSOT et les fractions expirées de O_2 et CO_2 étaient déterminées avec des analyseurs type BECKMAN OM11 et LB2. Les critères exigés pour que fussent retenues les épreuves étaient les suivants : épuisement du sujet, quotient respiratoire supérieur ou égal à 1,1, Fc voisine des valeurs maximales théoriques.

- Dette maximale en O_2

Après un repos de 10 à 20 minutes, en position allongée et en position assise sur la bicyclette, VO_2 repos a été mesurée. Ensuite, un échauffement de 4 minutes a été réalisé avec une puissance correspondant à 50 % de PMA. Après l'échauffement, la puissance est brusquement augmentée à une valeur correspondant à 115 % de PMA, calculée les jours précédents. L'enfant devait maintenir l'exercice supramaximal jusqu'à l'épuisement qui survenait en moyenne au bout de 1,5 minutes. Les gaz expirés étaient recueillis durant les 30 dernières secondes précédant l'arrêt de l'exercice, et durant les 30 minutes qui suivaient la récupération : le calcul de la dette était fait en retranchant VO_2 repos à VO_2 total mesuré durant la récupération. En moyenne, VO_2 revenait aux valeurs de repos à la 20ème minute de récupération.

- Seuils anaérobie lactiques et ventilatoires et cinétique des lactates durant la récupération : l'exercice imposé était d'intensité progressivement croissante (paliers de 17,5 W de 1,30 minutes) jusqu'à l'épuisement.

Les gaz expirés étaient recueillis durant les 30 dernières secondes et un échantillon de sang était prélevé à la fin de chaque palier et durant les 15 minutes suivant la récupération, grâce à la mise en place d'un fin cathéter veineux : le sang était immédiatement déprotéinisé et analysé par méthode enzymatique pour le dosage des lactates sanguins) (Electrode à lactate, ANALOX GM7).

Les seuils ventilatoires étaient déterminés à partir de l'accroissement non linéaire du débit ventilatoire (VE), et de l'équivalent respiratoire en O_2 (VE/VO_2) sans élévation simultanée de l'équivalent respiratoire en CO_2 (VE/VCO_2).

Les seuils lactiques correspondaient également à la zone d'accroissement non linéaire des concentrations sanguines en lactate ([L]).

La détermination des seuils a été réalisée séparément pour chaque sujet, par deux expérimentateurs.

- Test Force-vitesse :

Il consiste à faire sur le cycloergomètre une série de sprints brefs (de 5 à 8 secondes) contre une force de valeur croissante (augmentation de 0,5 kg par sprint). Après un échauffement de 3 minutes, l'enfant doit réaliser le sprint en restant assis, sur la selle. La valeur de la vitesse maximale atteinte est détectée par un tachymètre digital. Entre chaque sprint, une récupération de 3 minutes, en position allongée, est imposée à l'enfant. L'épreuve est terminée lorsqu'on atteint les valeurs maximales de puissance mécanique externe (produit vitesse par force). En moyenne, les tests ont été réalisés avec 5 à 6 sprints. Les vitesses et forces correspondant à la puissance maximale anaérobie (PMAn) sont dénommées vitesses optimales (vopt) et forces optimales (Fopt).

- Test de WINGATE de 30 secondes :

Proposé en 1970 par le "WINGATE INSTITUTE", il permettrait d'évaluer une puissance moyenne anaérobie (PAn) ou une "capacité anaérobie" (1). Pour réaliser ce test, nous avons choisi d'imposer la force optimale (Fopt) obtenue au cours du test Force-vitesse ; l'enfant doit pédaler à vitesse maximale, tout en restant assis sur la selle, contre cette force, pend·nt 30 secondes. Le travail mécanique total externe (Wt en KJ) ou la puissance mécanique moyenne (P en watts) est calculé à partir de Fopt et du nombre total de révolutions pendant 30 s. Afin de tenter d'évaluer la participation aérobie, les gaz expirés étaient recueillis durant le test pour mesurer VO_2.

L'analyse statistique des données a été, en général, réalisée pour comparer les groupes HA et BA, à l'aide de tests de t de STUDENT, non appariés.

C'est avec cet "arsenal" d'épreuves de laboratoire que nous avons tenté d'évaluer les aptitudes physiques aérobie et anaérobie du jeune résidant bolivien, vivant à LA PAZ (3 700 m) tout en le comparant au jeune européen vivant à CLERMONT-FERRAND (330 m).

Les résultats :
- L'aptitude aérobie à haute altitude :

Évaluée à partir de VO_2max, elle a toujours été inférieure à celle de basse-altitude (Tableau 1, Fig. 1).

En moyenne, VO_2max diminue à HA de 24,2 % en valeur absolue et de 18,1 % en valeur relative. Cette diminution va de pair avec un abaissement de Fcmax (11 b.min-1 en moins).

À LA PAZ, Greksa *et al.* (7) avaient trouvé chez de jeunes nageurs des valeurs de VO_2max inférieures de 10 à 20 % à celles du niveau de la mer. Nous avons observé le phénomène inverse chez des adultes résidant à LA PAZ, transplantés à Basse-altitude : après 18 jours d'acclimatement à BA, VO_2max augmentait de 15 % et Fcmax passait de 185 à 197 b.min-1 (14). Il faut insister sur le fait que la diminution des aptitudes aérobie s'observe même chez des sujets, considérés comme parfaitement adaptés aux conditions de vie en hypoxie chronique d'altitude, tels que les enfants nés et vivant à HA.

Tableau 1 : Données bioénergétiques maximales (m ± SD) à haute altitude (HA : 3700 m) et basse altitude (BA : 330 m)
VO_2max : consommation maximale d'oxygène
Fcmax : fréquence cardiaque maximale
**, p < 0,005, ***, p < 0,001

		11 ans	12 ans	14 ans
- VO_2max (I STPD.min^{-1})	HA	1,56±0,27 ***	1,59±0,29 ***	2,01±0,27 ***
	BA	2,05±0,32	1,95±0,31	2,72±0,39
- VO_2max (ml STPD.min^{-1}.kg-1	HA	43,0±0,67 ***	41,1±4,9 ***	40,5±3,8 ***
	BA	54,2±7,0	46,5±6,4	51,9±6,6
Fc max (b.min^{-1})	HA	193±6 ***	188±8 ***	188±8 ***
	BA	203±7	202±8	196±6

- Les aptitudes anaérobie à haute altitude (2, 5, 6) :

- Les dettes maximales en O_2 (DO_2 max)

Les résultats obtenus chez des enfants prépubères âgés de 11 ans à H.A. (11 garçons) étaient identiques à ceux de B.A., recueillis chez 13 garçons du même âge, aussi bien en valeur absolue (en l STPD) qu'en valeur relative (en ml STPD.kg-1 de poids corporel) (Fig. 2).

Si on admet que DO_2max est un reflet valable des aptitudes anaérobie maximales, elles seraient donc identiques chez le garçon prépubère à HA et à BA.

- Seuils anaérobie ventilatoires (VT) et lactiques (LT) :

Calculés chez des garçons âgés de 12 ans (21 sujets à HA, et 16 à BA), ils sont identiques dans les deux groupes, lorsqu'ils sont exprimés en pourcentage de VO_2max (Tableau 2).

La valeur des concentrations des lactates au seuil sont de 2,7 ± 0,5 mmol.l^{-1} à HA et de 1,8 ± 0,5 mmol.l^{-1} à BA (p < 0,001). Chez l'enfant, nous sommes donc loin des valeurs décrites chez l'adulte (seuil de 4 mmol.l^{-1}).

En outre, l'hypoxie chronique d'altitude chez l'enfant normal ne modifie pas la valeur des seuils anaérobie, contrairement à l'hypoxie chronique pathologique qui s'accompagne le plus souvent d'une diminution de leurs valeurs exprimées en % de VO_2max.

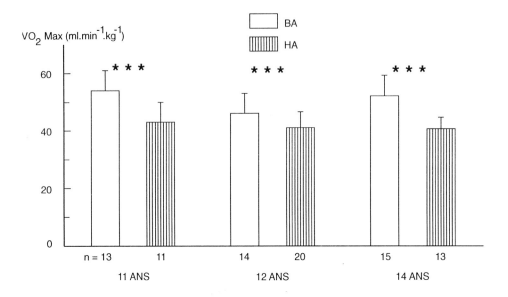

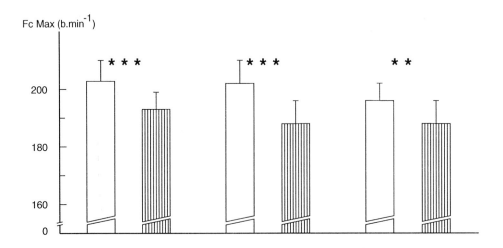

Fig. 1 - Consommation d'oxygène (VO$_2$ max) et fréquence cardiaque maximales (Fc max) mesurées à haute altitude (HA : 3700 m) et basse-altitude (BA : 330 m) m ± DS, n : nombre de garçons étudiés
***, p < 0,001 **, p < 0,005

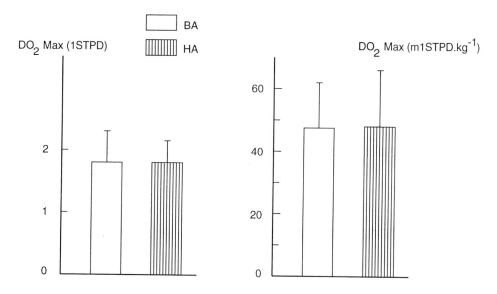

Fig. 2 - Dettes maximales en oxygène (DO$_2$ max) mesurées chez 11 garçons à haute altitude (HA, 3700 m) et 13 garçons à basse altitude (BA, 330 m) m ± DS

	n	VT %VO$_2$max	LT %VO$_2$max
HA	21	63,6 ± 7,2	67,8 ± 9,7
BA	16	64,6 ± 10,7	64,5 ± 7,4

Tableau 2 - Seuils anaérobie ventilatoires (VT) et lactiques (LT) à haute (HA) et basse altitude (BA) chez des garçons âgés de 12 ans m ± SD ; n = nombre de sujets.

- Concentrations maximales des lactates sanguins ([L]max) :

La cinétique des lactates étudiée durant les 15 premières minutes de récupération, suivant un exercice juxta maximal met en évidence que les valeurs les plus élevées sont observées autour de la 2ème minute de récupération, aussi bien à HA qu'à BA ; ce fait explique que pour détecter les pics des lactates sanguins après épreuves maximales (VO$_2$max), les prélèvements ont été faits autour de la 2ème minute de récupération. La vitesse de disparition est plus rapide à HA (t 1/2 = 8,8 ± 2,8 min) qu'à BA (t 1/2 = 14,4 ± 5,5 min).

Les valeurs de [L]max observées entre 11 et 14 ans et confrontées aux critères de maturation gonadique (stades de TANNER et [T]s) font apparaître les faits suivants (Tableau 3) :

1 - à l'âge de 11 ans : les enfants sont au stade I et [L]max sont faibles (6,0 ± 0,3 mmol.l-1 à HA et 6,7 ± 0,5 à BA) et identiques dans les 2 groupes.

Tableau 3 - Concentrations maximales des lactates sanguins ([L]max) et maturation gonadique en fonction de l'âge, à haute (HA) et basse altitudes (BA)
[T]s : concentration de la testostérone salivaire
n : nombre de sujets
**, p < 0,005, ***, p < 0,001
valeurs moyennes ± DS

	11 ans		12 ans		14 ans	
	HA	BA	HA	p	BA	BA
n	9	12	20		13	12
[L]max mmol.l-1	6,0 ±0,3	6,7 ±0,5	9,2 ±0,5	**	6,8 ±0,5	8,7 ±0,8
Stade de TANNER	I	I	III		II	III
[T]s pmol.l-1			233 ± 66	***	132 ± 30	244 ± 117

2 - à l'âge de 12 ans : des différences significatives apparaissent entre les 2 groupes : à HA, les garçons ont atteint le stade III de TANNER, avec des [T]s de 233 ± 66 pmol.l^{-1} de salive, et [L]max ont des valeurs comparables à celles qui sont décrites chez l'adulte (9,2 ± 0,5 mmol.l^{-1}) ; à BA, les sujets sont au stade II avec [T]s de 132 ± 30 pml.l^{-1} et [L]max de 6,8 ± 0,5 mmol.l^{-1} ; à l'âge de 14 ans, ils ont atteint les mêmes valeurs que le groupe HA de 12 ans (stade III, [T]s = 244 ± 117 pmol.l^{-1}, [L]max = 8,7 ± 0,8 mmol.l^{-1}).

Si on considère que les valeurs des [L]max après exercices maximaux constituent un reflet indirect mais valable de l'activité de la voie métabolique anaérobie lactique au niveau musculaire, on peut conclure, à partir de ces résultats que les garçons étudiés à LA PAZ ne présentent pas, par rapport à ceux de BA, une dépression de cette voie métabolique. Au contraire, une maturation plus précoce de cette aptitude anaérobie se manifeste à HA ; ce développement va de pair avec celui de la maturation gonadique ; nous trouvons une relation significative entre [T]s et [L]max sur l'ensemble des données (r = 0,39, p < 0,05).

Les effets directs de la testostérone sur le métabolisme du muscle ont déjà été démontrés expérimentalement chez l'animal. Par exemple, la castration du rat mâle induit une réduction des fibres musculaires et des activités enzymatiques de type anaérobie et l'injection de testostérone rétablit l'activité glycolytique (3). La régulation des gênes codant pour la synthèse des enzymes glycolytiques pourrait être sous la dépendance de la testostérone comme cela a été démontré pour la stimulation de la synthèse de la bêta-glucuronidase dans les cellules de rein de souris.

Des études complémentaires seront nécessaires pour savoir si ce phénomène est lié à l'hypoxie d'altitude ou à des facteurs ambiantaux (ensoleillement) ou autres facteurs (différences ethniques).

Les différences observées ne peuvent pas être dues aux conditions expérimentales : le matériel utilisé, les protocoles et les expérimentateurs ont toujours été les mêmes. Une différence de cinétique de disparition des lactates sanguins ne peut pas être à l'origine des plus fortes valeurs de [L]max observées à HA à l'âge de 12 ans : en effet, la cinétique plus rapide à HA tendrait plutôt à minimiser les différences.

- Test Force-vitesse (Figure 3)

Les puissances maximales anaérobie (PMan) exprimées en valeur relative (W.kg-1) augmentent significativement et de la même façon (accroissement exponentiel identique dans les 2 groupes) en fonction de l'âge aussi bien à HA qu'à BA : elles doublent pratiquement entre 7-8 ans et 14-15 ans.

Pour les mêmes groupes d'âge, on n'observe pas de différence significative entre HA et BA : l'altitude ne perturbe pas le développement des puissances anaérobie évaluées au cours de cette épreuve. Classiquement,

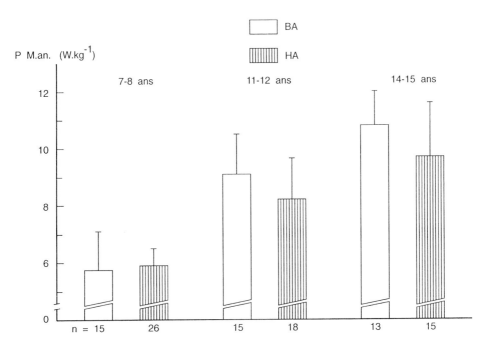

Figure 3 - Test force-vitesse
Évolution des puissances maximales anaérobie (PMan) exprimées en watt par kilo de masse corporelle, en fonction de l'âge à haute (HA) et basse altitude (BA).
n : nombre de sujets

il est admis que ce type de test, de durée brève (sprint inférieur à 10 s) sollicite essentiellement le métabolisme anaérobie alactique, qui repose sur les stocks musculaires en ATP et en phospho-créatine. Mais, plus récemment, il a été démontré que les exercices supramaximaux de durée inférieure à 10 s s'accompagnent d'une accumulation d'acide lactique, ce qui suggère également une participation vraisemblable de la glycolyse au cours du test force-vitesse (11).

   - Test de WINGATE de 30 s (Fig. 4)

   Comme pour le test force-vitesse, les valeurs des puissances mécaniques moyennes (P) obtenues au cours de ce test (exprimées en $W.kg^{-1}$) augmentent significativement en fonction de l'âge, aussi bien à HA qu'à BA. Comme pour PMan, l'accroissement est de type exponentiel, sans différence significative entre les 2 groupes.

   Mais, contrairement au test Force-vitesse, les valeurs obtenues pour un même groupe d'âge, sont significativement plus faibles à HA par rapport à celles de BA : ceci est vrai, en tous cas, pour les groupes de 11-12 ans et de 14-15 ans (Fig. 4, partie A). Pourquoi une telle différence entre 2 tests qui sont censés explorer les mêmes voies métaboliques ?

   Les résultats obtenus dans le cadre de l'étude de la participation aérobie au cours de ce test pourraient fournir en partie ou en totalité la réponse à cette question : il est clair que, pour les groupes d'âge de 11-12 ans et 14-15 ans, cette participation, évaluée à partir de l'oxygène consommé durant l'épreuve, est très significativement plus élevée à BA qu'à HA (Fig. 4, partie B). À HA, la diminution est de 20 % pour les enfants de 11-12 ans et de 17,4 % pour le groupe de 14-15 ans. Cette diminution est à rapprocher de la chute de VO_2max déjà observée dans les différents groupes à HA (diminution, en moyenne, de 18,1 % de VO_2max exprimée en ml.min-1.kg-1). Déjà, des auteurs, tels que Macek *et al.* (12) avaient insisté sur la forte participation aérobie au cours des tests de 30 s chez le jeune enfant (56,4 % VO_2max atteints au bout de 30 s après une épreuve maximale chez l'enfant, alors qu'on a seulement 35,5 % VO_2max chez l'adulte). Une diminution de VO_2max ne peut donc que réduire, en particulier chez l'enfant, le travail mécanique externe développé au cours du test de WINGATE de 30 s.

   En conclusion, chez le jeune résident bolivien vivant à 3700 m par rapport au jeune européen vivant à basse altitude (330 m),

   - L'aptitude aérobie est nettement diminuée (abaissée en moyenne de 24,2 % en valeur absolue et de 18,1 % en valeur relative). Cette diminution s'associe toujours à une baisse de la fréquence cardiaque maximale (11 b.min-1 en moins)

   - Les aptitudes anaérobie, évaluées à partir des dettes maximales en O_2, des valeurs maximales des lactates sanguins, et des puissances maximales anaérobie, recueillies au cours des tests force-vitesse, sont identiques, et se développent de la même façon, en fonction de l'âge.

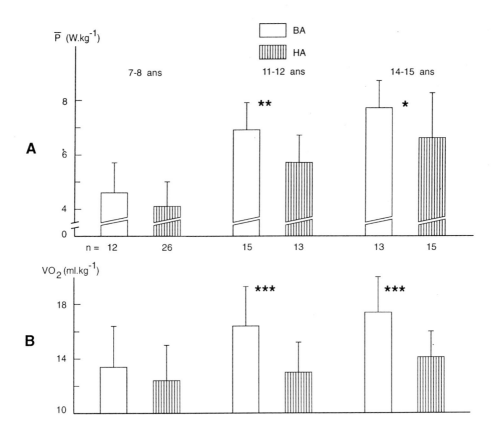

Fig. 4 - Test de wingate de 30 s.
Évolution des puissances moyennes mécaniques externes (P) exprimées en watt par kg de masse corporelle et de la participation aérobie, exprimée sous forme de volume d'oxygène consommé par kg de masse corporelle (VO_2 ml.kg^{-1}) au cours du WINGATE, en fonction de l'âge à haute (HA) et basse altitude (BA).
n : nombre de sujets, *, $p < 0,05$, **, $p < 0,01$, ***, $p < 0,001$

Les puissances mécaniques moyennes calculées au cours du test de WINGATE de 30 s sont par contre plus faibles pour un groupe d'âge donné : ce fait est vraisemblablement à relier à la diminution de la participation aérobie, au cours de ce test, elle-même conséquence de la chute de VO_2max à HA.

- Les seuils anaérobie ventilatoires et lactiques ne sont pas modifiés par l'altitude.

Toutes ces données concernent bien entendu un groupe de garçons privilégiés, bien nourris et au niveau socio-économique élevé. Il s'agit malheureusement d'une exception dans ce pays en voie de développement. Qu'en est-il chez l'enfant, tout venant, soumis à la fois aux contraintes bio-climatiques (altitude, froid) et socio-économiques (malnutrition, en particulier) ? C'est cet aspect que nous allons essayer d'aborder maintenant.

ÉTUDE D'ENFANTS DE NIVEAUX SOCIO-ÉCONOMIQUES BAS [**]

- Les sujets étudiés

Pour pouvoir aborder les interactions éventuelles entre l'altitude et l'état nutritionnel, 4 groupes de garçons prépubères, âgés de 10 à 11 ans, ont fait l'objet de l'étude : 2 groupes d'enfants ont été étudiés à LA PAZ (3700 m) : 23 provenaient du lycée franco-bolivien (groupe HA1 : niveau socio-économique élevé de Haute Altitude), 44 étaient issus d'un quartier pauvre de LA PAZ (goupe HA2 : de niveau socio-économique bas) ; les 2 groupes de Basse Altitude (BA) ont été étudiés à SANTA-CRUZ DE LA SIERRA (420 m, PB = 725 mmHg) : 48 étaient inscrits dans un collège privé, recrutant des enfants de haut niveau socio-économique (BA1), 35 étaient issus d'un *barrio* pauvre de la ville (BA2). Au total 150 enfants ont fait partie de l'étude, pour la plupart il s'agissait de métis d'espagnols et d'aymaras.

- La méthodologie employée

À côté du poids (P) et de la taille (T), les données biométriques ont été complétées par la circonférence de la partie supérieure des muscles du bras (méthode de JELLIFFE, 1966) ; la mesure des plis cutanés bicipitaux, tricipitaux, sous-scapulaires et sus-iliaques (HARPENDEN Skinfold Caliper) a permis d'estimer le pourcentage de masse grasse corporelle, en utilisant l'équation de DURNIN & RAHAMAN (2).

La masse maigre du corps a été déterminée à partir du poids du corps et de la masse grasse. Un index de masse corporelle (P/T2) a été calculé pour chaque garçon.

Une analyse d'un échantillon de sang (5 ml) prélevé au niveau d'une veine du pli du coude, entre 9h et 12h du matin a permis de mesurer les paramètres suivants : l'hématocrite (microhématocrite), l'hémoglobine (méthode de DRABKIN), le fer sérique (par spectrophotométrie), la ferritine sérique (méthode ELISA), la saturation en transferrine et la protoporphyrine du globule rouge (par hématofluorométrie). Ont été également dosées les protéines sériques totales (méthode colorimétrique), l'albumine (méthode par immunodiffusion radiale) et la préalbumine (par turbidimétrie).

Les données bioénergétiques (VO_2 max, puissance maximale anaérobie avec test Force-vitesse, et puissance maximale moyenne avec test de WINGATE de 30 s) ont été recueillies de la même façon qu'au cours de la première étape de l'étude.

[**] Travail réalisé en collaboration, dans le cadre du Contrat Européen (CI 1*/0507, avec :

1 - N. Fellmann, M. Bedu, Ph. Obert, G. Falgairette et E. Van Praagh du Laboratoire de Physiologie, Faculté de Médecine, Université d'Auvergne, Clermont-Ferrand, France.

2 - H. Spielvogel, E. Vargas, M. Villena, A. Quintela, V. Tellez, G. Parent de l'Institut Bolivien de Biologie d'Altitude (IBBA), LA PAZ, BOLIVIE et de l'ORSTOM-Nutrition (I.B.B.A.)

3 H. Kemper et B. Post, Département des Sciences de la Santé, Faculté des Sciences de la Motricité Humaine, Université d'AMSTERDAM (VRYE UNIVERSITEIT), PAYS-BAS.

Afin d'étudier l'influence du niveau socio-économique (S.E.) d'une part et de l'altitude (A) d'autre part, le test ANOVA d'analyse des variances à deux facteurs a été utilisé.

Les résultats

Données biométriques : (Tableau 4)

Les garçons de niveaux socio-économiques bas (HA2 et BA2) sont, pour un âge chronologique identique, plus petits (9 cm en moins) et plus maigres (5 à 7 kg de moins, et 3 à 4 % de masse grasse en moins).

Le périmètre supérieur des muscles du bras, considéré comme un bon critère nutritionnel est significativement plus faible. Ces différences sont uniquement liées aux niveaux socio-économiques et non à l'altitude.

Tableau 4 : Données biométriques des garçons étudiés (HA1, HA2, BA1 et BA2). Les valeurs données correspondent à la moyenne ± DS. n = nombre de sujets, HA = haute altitude, BA = basse altitude, SE+ = niveau socio-économique élevé, SE- = niveau socio-économique bas, CMSB = circonférence de la partie musculaire supérieure du bras, IMC = index de masse corporelle, ANOVA = analyse de variance, A = altitude, SE = niveau socio-économique, NS = non significatif.

	HA		BA		Probabilité du test ANOVA à 2 facteurs
	SE+	SE-	SE+	SE-	
	HA1 n=23	HA2 n=44	BA1 n=48	BA2 n=30	
Taille (cm)	140 ± 7	131 ± 5	141 ± 5	132 ± 6	A : NS,SE : < 0.001 AxSE : NS
Poids (kg)	37 ± 9	30 ± 4	36 ± 5	31 ± 4	A : NS,SE : < 0.001 AxSE : NS
Masse grasse (%)	21,3 ± 5,8	16,5 ± 3,3	21,3 ± 4,5	17,8 ± 3,6	A : NS,SE : < 0.001 AxSE : NS
Masse maigre (kg)	29 ± 5	25 ± 2	28 ± 3	25 ± 3	A : NS,SE : < 0.001 AxSE : NS
CMSB (cm)	19,5 ± 2,2	17,4 ± 1,2	18,7 ± 1,3	17,8 ± 1,3	A : NS,SE : < 0.001 AxSE : < 0,05
IMC (kg/cm²)	18,6 ± 2,9	17,2 ± 1,7	17,9 ± 1,8	17,6 ± 2,2	A : NS, SE : < 0,05 AxSE : NS

Les garçons de hauts niveaux socio-économiques (HA1 et BA1) ont un poids et une taille qui se situent dans les normes du *National Center for Health Statistics percentiles* (8).

Les données hématologiques et biochimiques : (Tableau 5)

L'hématocrite et la concentration sanguine en hémoglobine (Hb) sont significativement plus élevés à haute altitude aussi bien chez HA2 que chez HA1 : cette élévation est le reflet de la réponse induite par l'hypoxie chronique d'altitude.

Tableau 5 - Données hématologiques et biochimiques.
Les valeurs données correspondent à la moyenne ± SD, n = nombre de sujets, HA = haute altitude, BA = basse altitude, SE+ = niveau socio-économique élevé, SE- = niveau socio-économique bas, PGR = protoporphyrine du globule rouge, ANOVA = analyse de variance, A = altitude, SE = niveau socio-économique, NS = non significatif.

	HA		BA		Probabilité du test ANOVA à 2 facteurs
	SE+	SE-	SE+	SE-	
	HA1 n=23	HA2 n=44	BA1 n=48	BA2 n=30	
Hématocrite (%)	45,9 ± 2,8	45,7 ± 2,1	42,4 ± 2,3	39,9 ± 2,2	A : <0,001, SE : <0,05 AxSE : NS
Hémoglobine (g/l)	150 ± 9	153 ± 8	135 ± 9	128 ± 12	A : <0,001 SE : <0,05 AxSE : NS
Fer sérique (µg/dl)	166 ± 70	134 ± 32	154 ± 52	106 ± 33	A : <0,05 SE : <0,001 AxSE : NS
Ferritine (ng/ml)	77 ± 49	52 ± 30	58 ± 41	33 ± 18	A : <0,05 SE : <0,001 AxSE : NS
Saturation en transferrine (%)	39 ± 14	29 ± 6	30 ± 9	25 ± 7	A : <0,001 SE : <0,001 AxSE : NS
PGR (µg/dl)	27,1 ± 5,2	28,7 ± 8,0	31,9 ± 7,2	32,6 ± 8,2	A : <0,05 SE : NS AxSE : NS
Protéine totale (g/dl)	7,6 ± 0,6	7,5 ± 0,7	7,5 ± 0,4	7,9 ± 0,4	A : NS SE : NS AxSE : NS
Albumine (g/dl)	4,8 ± 0,3	4,8 ± 0,4	4,6 ± 0,4	4,5 ± 0,4	A <0,05 SE : NS AxSE : NS
Préalbumine (g/dl)	23,8 ± 5,0	19,5 ± 6,3	23,5 ± 3,7	20,1 ± 3,5	A : NS SE <0,001 AxSE : NS

Il faut noter que le bilan sanguin du métabolisme du fer ainsi que la concentration globulaire de la protoporphyrine se situent dans les limites de la normale pour l'ensemble des quatre groupes : dans la sélection des sujets, les enfants présentant une anémie, soit parasitaire, soit d'autre origine, avaient été éliminés de l'étude.

L'étude des protéines, albumine et préalbumine sanguines, utilisées également comme indicateurs de malnutrition protidique, met en évidence uniquement une chute significative de la préalbumine chez les enfants de niveaux socio-économiques bas (HA2 et LA2). Ces derniers répondent aux critères classiques de "malnutrition marginale" comme l'a confirmé l'enquête nutritionnelle réalisée parallèlement par Post *et al.* (15).

Les données bioénergétiques

- Aptitude aérobie : (Tableau 6)

Les valeurs de VO_2 max sont plus basses à HA chez les enfants aussi bien du groupe HA2 que HA1, en particulier lorsqu'elles sont exprimées par unité de masse corporelle ou par unité de masse maigre. Mais pour une même altitude, il n'y a pas de différence entre les niveaux socio-économiques.

Tableau 6 : **Données bioénergétiques aérobie obtenues après un exercice maximal pour les différents groupes (HA1, HA2, BA1 et BA2).**
Les valeurs données correspondent à la moyenne ± DS, n = nombre de sujets, PC = poids corporel, MM = masse maigre, VO_2max = consommation maximale d'oxygène, Fc max = fréquence cardiaque maximale, NS = non significatif, *p < 0,05, **p < 0,01.

	HA1 n = 23	HA2 n = 44	BA1 n = 25	BA2 n = 40	Analyse statistique
VO_2max (ml.min^{-1}.kg^{-1} pc)	37,2 ± 5,6	38,9 ± 6,4	42,5 ± 5,8	42,5 ± 5,3	HA1-HA2 : NS BA1-BA2 : NS HA1-BA1 : * HA2-BA2 : NS
VO_2max (ml.min^{-1}.kg^{-1} MM)	47,4 ± 6,3	46,7 ± 7,5	53,7 ± 6,1	51,6 ± 5,9	HA1-HA2 : NS BA1-BA2 : NS HA1-BA1 : ** HA2-BA2 : *
Fcmx (b.min^{-1})	190 ± 5	184 ± 12	197 ± 7	190 ± 10	HA1-HA2 : NS BA1-BA2 : * HA1-BA1 : * HA2-BA2 : *

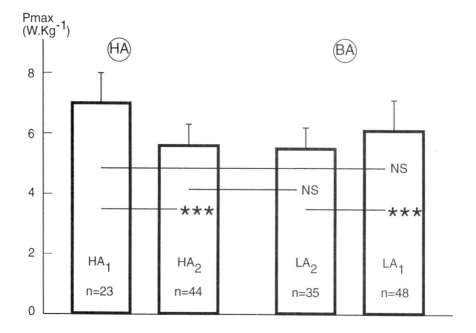

Fig. 5 - **Puissance mécanique maximale anaérobie (Pmax) obtenue au cours du test Force-vitesse chez 150 garçons prépubères âgés de 10-11 ans, à haute altitude (HA) et à basse altitude (BA) de niveaux socio-économiques élevés (HA1 et BA1) et bas (HA2 et BA2).**
n = **nombre de sujets étudiés dans chaque groupe**
NS = **non significatif - ***, p < 0,001**

Aptitudes anaérobie

Test Force-vitesse : (Figure 5)

Pour les mêmes niveaux socio-économiques, les puissances maximales anérobie (PMax) sont identiques quelque soit l'altitude. Par contre, pour une altitude donnée, PMax est significativement plus faible chez les enfants SE- (HA1 = $6,8 \pm 1,0$, HA2 = $5,5 \pm 0,8$, BA1 = $7,1 \pm 1,0$ et BA2 = $5,3 \pm 0,8$ W.kg-1 Pc).

Test de WINGATE (30 s) : (Figure 6)

Comme pour le test précédent, les valeurs des puissances maximales moyennes (P30 s) sont abaissées chez les SE-, alors qu'il n'existe pas de différence entre HA et BA, pour les niveaux SE identiques (HA1 = $5,2 \pm 0,8$, HA2 = $4,5 \pm 0,9$, BA1 = $5,2 \pm 0,7$ et BA2 = $4,0 \pm 0,6$ W.kg-1 Pc).

En définitive, les enfants prépubères présentant une malnutrition marginale se caractérisent par une altération profonde de leurs aptitudes à réaliser des exercices brefs et intenses (aptitudes anaérobie), alors que leurs possibilités aérobie sont comparables à une altitude donnée à celles des enfants "bien nourris".

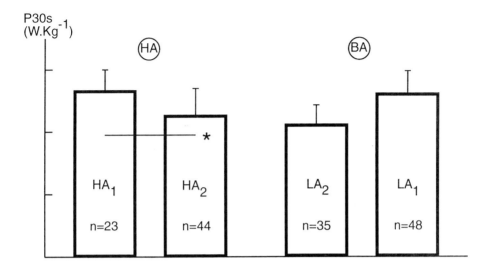

Fig. 6 - **Puissance mécanique maximale moyenne (P 30s) obtenue au cours du test de WINGATE de 30 s chez 150 garçons prépubères, âgés de 10-11 ans, à haute altitude (HA) et à basse altitude (BA), de niveaux socio-économiques élevés (HA1 et BA1) et bas (HA2 et BA2).**

Ce fait va de pair avec des observations histologiques faites à BA mettant en évidence, dans les situations de malnutrition, une réduction du diamètre des fibres musculaires du groupe II, sans modifications des fibres I (9).

CONCLUSIONS GÉNERALÉS

L'état nutritionnel constitue un des facteurs capitaux à prendre en compte pour interpréter les effets biologiques de l'altitude chez l'enfant.

Contrairement à ce qui a pu être publié (6, 5, 13 et 16) le retard staturo-pondéral observé en milieu andin est essentiellement lié au facteur nutritionnel et non au facteur altitude ; la malnutrition marginale, le plus souvent observée chez les enfants d'âge prépubertaire, nés et vivant en altitude, s'accompagne d'un effondrement de leurs aptitudes anaérobie, alors que leur aptitude aérobie est comparable à celles des enfants "bien nourris". Les réponses hématologiques induites par l'altitude ne sont pas perturbées par cet état de malnutrition ; il faut noter enfin que les modifications des volumes pulmonaires déjà décrites chez l'adulte à haute altitude (augmentation de la capacité pulmonaire totale, liée à l'accroissement du volume résiduel) (10) s'observe chez ces enfants en état de malnutrition marginale aussi bien que chez les enfants bien nourris (Fig. 7).

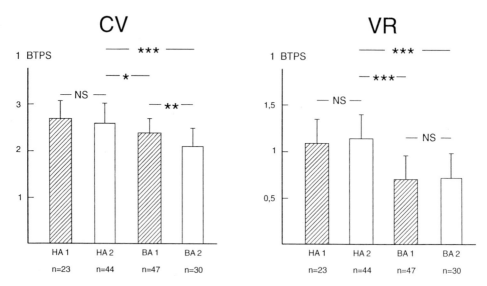

Fig. 7 - Données spirométriques recueillies chez 150 garçons prépubères, âgés de 10-11 ans, à haute altitude (HA) et à basse altitude (BA), de niveaux socio-économiques élevés (HA1 et BA1) et bas (HA2 et BA2).

CV = capacité vitale, VR = volume résiduel (méthode à l'hélium)

NS = non significatif, *p < 0,05, **p < 0,01, ***p < 0,001

REMERCIEMENTS

L'ensemble de ces travaux n'a pu être réalisé que grâce à la collaboration de nombreuses personnes que nous tenons à remercier en particulier : Alarcón de Quiroga, A.M., Arce, R.H., Cáceres, E., Gonzáles Dávila, C., Luján, C., Rodrígues, A. et Sandy, I. pour leur aide technique ; les Docteurs Ribera B. (Directeur du Centre National des Maladies Tropicales -CENETROP- de SANTA CRUZ DE LA SIERRA), Urgel, R., Romero Dávalos, A., et A.Centurion ; les Directeurs des Collèges Franco-Bolivien et Hernando Siles de LA PAZ, LA SALLE et AMBORO de SANTA CRUZ, ainsi que les Directeurs de l'IBBA (Drs E. Vargas, J.P. Dedet et M. Hontebeyrie).

REFERENCES

1. BAR-OR, O., DOTAN, R. & INBAR, O. 1977. A 30-second all-out ergometric test ; its reliability and validity for anaerobic capacity. *Israel J. Med. Sciences* 13 : 326.

2. DURNIN, J.V.G.A. & RAHAMAN, M.M. 1983 The assessment of the amount of fat in the human body from measurement of skinfold thickness. *Br. J. Nutr.* 21 : 681-689.

3. DUX, L., DUX, E., & GUBA, F. 1982. Further data on the androgenic dependency of the skeletal musculature : the effect of prepubertal castration on the structural development on the skeletal muscles. *Horm. Metab. Res.* 14 : 191-194.

4. ERIKSSON, B.O. 1980. Muscle metabolism in children. *Acta Paediatr. Scand. [Suppl]* 283 : 20-27.

5. FRISANCHO, A.R. 1978. Human growth and development among high-altitude populations. *In* : P.T. Baker, Eds, International Biological Programme 14, *The biology of high altitudes peoples.* Cambridge University Press.

6. FRISANCHO, A.R. & BAKER, P.T. 1970. Altitude and growth : a study of the patterns of physical growth of a high-altitude Peruvian Quechua population. *Am. J. Phys. Anthrop.* 32 : 279-292.

7. GRESKA, L.P., HAAS, J.D., LEATHERMAN, T.L., SPIELVOGEL, H., PAZ ZAMORA, M., PAREDES FERNÁNDEZ, L. & MORENO-BLACK, G. 1982. Maximal aerobic power in trained youths at high altitude. *Ann. Hum. Biol.* 9 : 201-209.

8. HAMILL, P.V.V., DRIZD, T.H., JOHNSON, C.L., REED, R.B., ROCHE, A.F. & MOORE, W.M. 1979. Physical growth : National Center for Health Statistics percentiles. *Am. J. Clin. Nutr.* 32 : 607-629.

9. HENRIKSSON, J. 1990. The possible role of skeletal muscle in the adaptation to periods of energy deficiency. *Eur. J. Clin. Nutr.* 44(S1) : 55-64.

10. HURTADO, A. 1964. Animals in high altitudes ; Residents man. *In* : *Handbook of Physiology*, Section 4, Adaptation to environment; Washington: American Physiological Society : 843-860.

11. JACOBS, I., TESCH, P., BAR-OR, O., KARLSON, J. & DOTAN, E. 1983. Lactate in human skeletal muscle after 10 and 30s of supramaximal exercise. *J. Appl. Physiol.* 55 : 365-367.

12. MACEK, M. & VAVRA, J. 1980. The adjustement of oxygen uptake at the onset of exercise : a comparison between prepubertal boys and young adults. *Int. J. Sports Med.* 1 : 70-72.

13. MUELLER, W.H., SCHULL, V.N., SCHULL, W.J., SOTO, P. & ROTHHAMMER, F. 1978. A multinational Andean genetic and health program : growth and development in an hypoxic environment. *Ann. Hum. Biol.* 5 : 329-352.

14. PAZ-ZAMORA, M., COUDERT, J., ERGUETTA COLLAO, J., VARGAS, E. & GUTTIEREZ, N. 1982. Respiratory and cardiocirculatory responses of acclimatization of high altitude natives (La Paz, 3,500 m) to tropical lowland (Santa-Cruz, 420 m). *In* : *High Altitude Physiology and Medicine I*, edited by W. Brendel & R. Zink. New-York : Springer-Verlag : 21-27.

15. POST, G.B., KEMPER, H.C.G., LUJAN, C., PARENT, G. & COUDERT, J. 1992. Comparison of 10-12 years old schoolboys living at high (3,700 m) and at low (420 m) altitude in Bolivia. *Int. J. Sports Med.* 13 : 88.

16. STINSON, S. 1980. The physical growth of high altitude Bolivian Aymara Children. *Am. J. Phys. Anthropol.* 52 : 377-385.

17. VAN PRAAGH, E., BEDU, M., RODDIER, P. & COUDERT, J. 1992. A simple calibration method for mechanically braked cycle ergometers. *Int. J. Sports Med.* 13 : 27-30.

FACTEURS PHYSIOLOGIQUES DE LA SURVIE EN TRÈS HAUTE ALTITUDE

Jean-Paul Richalet

Résumé

Une expédition scientifique sur le Mont Sajama (Bolivie), a permis de recueillir des données inédites sur un groupe de 10 sujets (4 femmes et 6 hommes) qui ont séjourné pendant 3 semaines à 6542 m d'altitude. Aucun accident médical grave n'est survenu au cours de l'expédition, traduisant les possibilités d'acclimatation à ce stimulus hypoxique sévère (saturation artérielle moyenne en O_2 au repos de l'ordre de 70%). La performance aérobie a diminué de 44% en hypoxie, sans modification au cours du séjour. La performance anaérobie, évaluée par le test de Wingate, n'a diminué que de 11%. La perte de poids corporel a été de 9% en moyenne, essentiellement aux dépens de la masse grasse et de la masse maigre des membres inférieurs. Cette perte de poids est essentiellement liée à une diminution des apports caloriques (-46%) pendant la première phase d'acclimatation. Une diminution du débit plasmatique rénal, du débit de filtration glomérulaire et de la réabsorption tubulaire proximale a été mise en évidence chez la plupart des sujets. Après une augmentation initiale importante de l'érythropoïèse, liée à une libération massive d'érythropoïétine, on constate chez certains sujets une stagnation voire une diminution de la concentration d'hémoglobine, vraisemblablement liée en partie à une limitation des réserves martiales. Le rôle du tubule proximal dans la libération de l'érythropoïétine a également été souligné. L'activation intense du système adrénergique en hypoxie a été retrouvée, sans être majorée par rapport à des données recueillies à des altitudes inférieures. Le phénomène de désensibilisation des ß-récepteurs en hypoxie, mis en évidence par une baisse de la réponse cardiaque à l'isoprénaline ou de la densité des ß-récepteurs lymphocytaires, présente également la même amplitude qu'à 4350 ou 4800 m. L'hypoxémie induite par l'exposition à l'altitude semble majorée par les phénomènes de ventilation périodique nocturne observés, à des degrés variables, chez tous les sujets. Au total, l'exposition à l'altitude de 6542 m entraîne une limitation importante de l'autonomie physiologique d'un individu, cette limitation persiste sans s'aggraver au cours d'un séjour de 3 semaines à la même altitude. La fonction rénale est importante à prendre en compte par son rôle modulateur dans la sécrétion d'érythropoïétine. Une alimentation correcte limite le déficit calorique principal responsable de la fonte musculaire induite par l'hypoxie. Le système adrénergique jouerait un rôle régulateur essentiel dans la plupart de ces processus, mais possèderait ses propres mécanismes limitants. La variabilité de la tolérance individuelle au stress hypoxique est un élément fondamental à considérer.

Mots clés : Andes, altitude, hypoxie, système adrénergique, fonction rénale, érythropoïétine, masse musculaire, isoprénaline, ß-récepteurs.

Resumen

Una expedición científica al Monte Sajama (Bolivia) ha permitido recoger datos inéditos sobre un grupo de 10 sujetos (4 mujeres y 6 hombres) que permanecieron 3 semanas a 6542 m de altura. Ningún accidente médico sobrevino en el curso de la expedición, indicando las posibilidades de aclimatación al estímulo de una hipoxia severa (saturación arterial media de oxígeno en reposo en el orden del 70%). El rendimiento aerobio disminuyó en un 44% en hipoxia, sin modificaciones durante toda la estadía. El rendimiento anaerobio, evaluado mediante el test de Wingate, sólo disminuyó un 11%. La media de pérdida de peso corporal fue de 9%, esencialmente a expensas de la pérdida de masa grasa y de masa magra de los miembros inferiores. Esta pérdida de peso está esencialmente ligada a una disminución de los aportes calóricos (-46%) durante la primera fase de la aclimatación. En la mayoría de los sujetos se observó una disminución del flujo plasmático renal, de la filtración glomerular y de la reabsorcíon tubular proximal. Luego de un incremento inicial importante de la eritropoiesis, ligado a una liberación masiva de eritropoyetina, se constató en algunos sujetos un estancamiento, o aún una disminución de la concentración de hemoglobina, probablemente ligada en parte a una limitación de las reservas de hierro. Se señala asimismo, el rol del túbulo proximal en la liberación de la eritropoyetina. Se comprueba la activación intensa del sistema adrenérgico en hipoxia, sin embargo, esta activación no es mayor que la descrita en estudios realizados a altitudes inferiores. El fenómeno de desensibilización de los ß-receptores en hipoxia, se demuestra por la disminución de la respuesta cardíaca al isoprenaline o por la densidad de los ß-receptores linfocíticos, con igual amplitud a 4350 que a 4800 m. La hipoxemia, producto de la exposición a la altura aumenta, en grado variable en todos los sujetos, debido a la ventilación periódica nocturna. En resumen, la exposición a la altura de 6542 m produce una limitación importante de la autonomía fisiológica de un individuo. Esta limitación persiste sin agravarse en el curso de una estadía de 3 semanas a la misma altitud. Es importante tomar en cuenta la función renal, por su rol modulador en la secreción de la eritropoyetina. Una alimentación correcta limita el déficit calórico principal, responsable del moldeo muscular inducido por la hipoxia. El sistema adrenérgico jugaría un papel regulador esencial en la mayoría de estos procesos, mas poseería sus propios mecanismos limitantes. La variabilidad de la tolerancia individual al «stress» hipóxico es un elemento fundamental a tomar en cuenta.

Palabras claves: Andes, altura, hipoxia, sistema adrenérgico, función renal, eritropoyetina, masa muscular, isoprenalina, ß-receptores linfocíticos.

Abstract

A scientific expedition to Mount Sajama (Bolivia) allowed the collection of data from 10 subjects (4 women and 6 men) who stayed 3 weeks at an altitude of 6542 m. No accidents happened during the course of the expedition, indicating the acclimatization possibilities to severe hypoxic stimulus (resting arterial oxygen saturation at rest in the order of 70%). Aerobic capacity decreased 44% in hypoxia, without modifications during the whole stage. The anaerobic capacity, measured with the Wingate test, only diminished 11%. The mean body weight loss was of 9%, essentially due to loss of fat and `mass maigre` from the lower extremities. This weight loss is esentially due to a decrease in the caloric supply (-46%) during the first stage of acclimatization. In the majority of subjects there was a reduction in the plasmatic renal flow, the glomerular filtration and the proximal tubular reabsortion. After an initial increment of erythropoiesis, associated to a massive release of erythopoietin, some subjects had a stagnation, and even a decrease of hemoglobin concentration, most likely due to a limitation of the iron reserves. The role of the proximal tubule in the release of erythropoietin is mentioned. The activation of the adrenergic system in hypoxia is observed, though this activation is not greater than that observed in studies at lower altitudes. A desensibilization of the beta-receptor is seen in hypoxia as measured by the reduction of the cardiac response to isoprenaline or of the density of lymphocytic beta-rceptors, which are the same at 4350 and at 4800 m. The hypoxemia, due to high altitude, increases in all subjects because of nocturnal periodic breathing. In summary, exposure to an altitude of 6542 m produces an important limitation of the indivudual's physiologic autonomy. This limitation persists without worsening during the three weeks of exposure. It is important to consider the renal function because of its role in the secretion of erythropoietin. A good meal limits the caloric deficit which is the main responsible of the loss of muscular mass induced by hypoxia. The adrenergic system could play an important regulatory role in the majority of these processes, though with limitations. The variability of the individual tolerance to the hypoxic `stress`should be taken into account.

Key words: Andes, altitude, hypoxia, adrenergic system, renal function, erythropoietin, muscular mass, isoprenaline, beta-receptors.

INTRODUCTION

Existe-t-il une dégradation physiologique en haute altitude? À partir de quelle limite ? Cette dégradation est-elle réversible ?

Le développement de l'alpinisme et de la randonnée en haute altitude depuis une vingtaine d'années amène un nombre croissant de personnes dans un environnement qui induit des modifications physiologiques et parfois pathologiques mal connues (29).

On distingue généralement deux zones d'altitude. De 0 à environ 5500 m, l'acclimatation semble possible. Au-delà de 5500 m, une acclimatation à long terme semble difficile : les sujets voient se dégrader leur condition physique et mentale, leur poids corporel diminue progressivement, aucune récupération n'est possible après un exercice épuisant. Il est ainsi courant de situer aux alentours de 5000-5500 mètres la limite de l'altitude «physiologique». Au-delà, le principe de la dégradation de l'organisme semble avoir été largement accepté par le milieu des alpinistes et des chercheurs intéressés par le sujet. Quels sont les données disponibles pour valider cette assertion ? Deux types d'observations peuvent être relevées. D'une part, peu de personnes vivent en permanence au-delà de 4500 m. L'habitat permanent le plus haut se situe dans les Andes et dans l'Himalaya et ne dépasse pas 5000 m, exceptés pour quelques pâturages, mais qui restent temporaires. Il est vrai que si personne ne s'installe à ces hautes altitudes, c'est peut-être parce qu'il n'y a rien à y faire où parce que l'environnement ne permet pas une activité humaine prolongée : absence d'agriculture ou d'industrie. Il y a des exceptions puisqu'au nord du Chili, des gardiens de mine à ciel ouvert vivent à 5950 m, certains depuis plusieurs années (31). D'autre part, en ce qui concerne les natifs du niveau de la mer, quelques expériences isolées ont conduit des sujets à séjourner pendant plusieurs semaines en très haute altitude. Chez les alpinistes, les expériences de survie en haute altitude sont extrêmement rares, d'autant plus que la tendance actuelle des expéditions est de rester le moins longtemps possible dans des camps situés au-delà de 6000 m.

L'expérience anglo-américaine de la «Silver Hut», en 1960-61, reste historique. Au cours de cette expédition scientifique, un groupe d'hommes a vécu pendant 100 jours à 5800 m, mais de façon intermittente (20). En 1979, Nicolas Jaeger, un médecin français, restait pendant 2 mois sous le sommet du Huascarán, à 6700 m d'altitude, sans que ses fonctions vitales ne semblent touchées (12). Depuis lors, quelques exploits isolés ont été réalisés, mais sans que des observations physiologiques ou médicales aient été rapportées.

L'objectif général de notre expédition scientifique sur le Mont Sajama (6542 m) en Bolivie était de rapporter des observations sur le comportement physiologique et psychologique au cours d'un séjour de 3 semaines à 6542 m. De nombreuses fonctions ont été explorées (cœur, rein, muscle, nutrition, sommeil, etc...), en précisant leurs modifications lors de l'arrivée à 6542 m et au cours du séjour prolongé à cette altitude.

Deux objectifs spécifiques étaient poursuivis : d'une part, la dégradation en très haute altitude est-elle réelle, et comment peut-on l'objectiver ; d'autre part, quels sont les facteurs éventuellement responsables de cette dégradation ?

EXPÉRIMENTATION

Population étudiée

Dix sujets ont participé à l'étude, 6 hommes et 4 femmes. Neuf sujets étaient natifs du niveau de la mer, une femme était native de haute altitude (La Paz, Bolivie, 3600 m) mais résidente en France depuis 5 ans. Il s'agissait de sujets moyennement entraînés, pratiquant l'alpinisme, avec une expérience variable de la haute altitude. Neuf étaient médecins, l'un était ingénieur biomédical, tous membres de l'Association pour la Recherche en Physiologie de l'Environnement. Les sujets ont donné leur consentement éclairé aux expérimentations réalisées au cours de l'expédition.

Les caractéristiques générales du groupe sont présentées dans le tableau 1.

Déroulement de l'expédition

Les sujets arrivèrent en avion à La Paz (3600 m - 4000 m), où ils séjournèrent pendant 5 jours. Puis, ils gagnèrent l'altitude de 4200 m en 3 jours en voiture. De là, ils marchèrent et escaladèrent le Mont Sajama en 10 jours, pour atteindre le sommet à 6542 m. Le laboratoire fut installé au sommet et l'ensemble des sujets y séjourna pendant trois semaines, sans activité physique intense. Les conditions atmosphériques furent défavorables pendant le début du séjour (vent violent, température extérieure sous abri moyenne de -13°C), et s'améliorèrent dans la deuxième partie (Fig. 1). Cependant, les expérimentations se sont toujours déroulées sous une tente laboratoire avec une température ambiante de +15 à +19 °C. Au terme du séjour, les sujets sont descendus à pied et ont rejoint La Paz en 3 jours et Paris en 7 jours.

Tableau 1 - Caractéristiques générales des membres de l'expédition. Altitude max : altitude maximale atteinte avant l'expédition. Moyenne ± écart-type (minimum - maximum).

Âge	34 ± 6,4	Ans	(27-44)
Poids	65,7 ± 9,6	Kg	(49-80)
Taille	172,5 ± 9,4	Cm	(159-183)
VO$_2$Max	43,5 ± 6,6	Ml/Min/Kg	(33,1 - 53,3)
Altitude Max	5875 ± 1449	M	(4350 - 8760)

Acclimatation

L'efficacité de l'acclimatation fut évaluée par un score clinique journalier de Mal aigu des montagnes (MAM) (10). Le score est calculé avec la somme de scores établis de 0 à 4 pour chaque classe de symptômes : céphalées, signes digestifs, fatigue, insomnies. Le score moyen et le profil de dénivelé sont indiqués sur la figure 2. La saturation artérielle (SaO$_2$) a été évaluée par oxymétrie transcutanée (502 Pulse oximeter, Critical Systems Inc.).

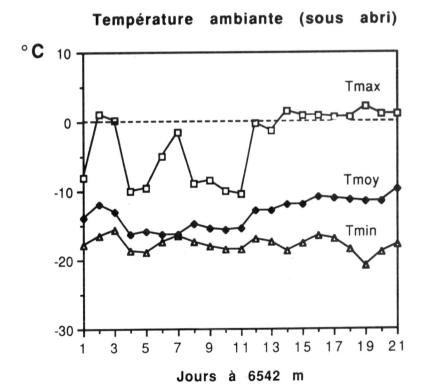

Fig. 1 - Variations des températures maximales, minimales et moyennes sous abri au cours du séjour à 6542 m.

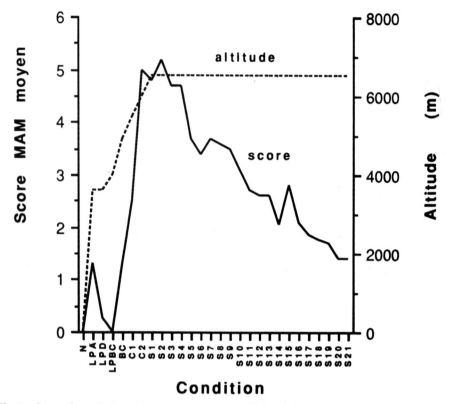

Fig. 2 - Score de mal aigu des montagnes et profil de dénivelé au cours de l'expédition.
N : normoxie, LPA : arrivée à La Paz, LPD : départ de La Paz, LPBC : trajet en
camion de La Paz au Mont Sajama, BC : camp de base (4900 m), C1 : camp 1
(5500 m), C2 : camp 2 (6000 m), S1 à S21 1 : jour 1 à 21 au sommet.

Métabolisme énergétique à l'exercice

Les deux voies métaboliques principales utilisées à l'exercice ont été
explorées : métabolisme aérobie, évalué par la mesure de la puissance maximale
obtenue au cours d'un exercice progressif par paliers ($P_{ae}max$), métabolisme
anaérobie, évalué par la mesure de la puissance maximale instantanée ($P_{an}max$)
et moyenne ($P_{an}moy$) au cours de l'épreuve de Wingate d'une durée de
30 s. Ces mesures ont été réalisées en normoxie (N), après une semaine (H1)
et trois semaines (H3) à 6542 m (28).

Fonction rénale

La fonction rénale a été explorée à l'aide de la mesure des clairances
de l'acide para-amino-hippurique (Cl_{PAH}), de l'inuline (Cl_{In}) et du lithium
(Cl_{Li}). Le débit plasmatique rénal est évalué par Cl_{PAH}, le débit de filtration
glomérulaire est évalué par Cl_{In} et le débit de réabsorption tubulaire proximal
par la différence (Cl_{In} - Cl_{Li}) (17). Ces mesures ont été réalisées en normoxie

et au cours de la deuxième semaine à 6542 m (H2). Du sang veineux a été prélevé au repos et à deux niveaux d'exercice correspondant à 40 et à 75% de P_{ae}max. Sur ces prélèvements, ont été dosées certaines hormones intervenant dans la régulation des volumes sanguins : en particulier l'activité rénine plasmatique et l'aldostérone plasmatique. Ces mesures hormonales ont été réalisées dans les conditions N, H1 et H3. (26)

Erythropoïèse

Hématocrite (Ht), concentration en hémoglobine (Hb) et en érythropoïétine sérique immunoréactive (EPO) ont été mesurés respectivement par microcentrifugation (AMES Microspin), microphotométrie (AMES M1000) et méthode radioimmunologique (^{125}I-EPO COATRIA, BioMérieux, Lyon, France), dans quatre conditions : N, H1, H2 et H3 (30).

Nutrition

Le poids corporel a été mesuré à l'aide d'un pèse-personne dans les conditions N, H2 et H3 et de nouveau en normoxie dix jours après avoir quitté le sommet. La masse grasse a été évaluée par deux méthodes différentes. Avant et après l'expédition, la masse grasse et la masse maigre ont été évaluées par double pesée dans l'air et dans l'eau, avec correction pour le volume d'air contenu dans les poumons et les voies digestives. Le pourcentage de masse grasse a également été évalué au cours de l'expédition par la méthode des plis cutanés sur 10 zones de mesure, à l'aide d'une pince à pression constante de Holtain dans les conditions N, H1, H2 et H3 (6). Le volume des membres a été évalué par des mesures sériées des diamètres du membre supérieur et du membre inférieur du même côté. Sept points de mesure, répartis sur chaque membre, ont été utilisés. À partir des diamètres et des hauteurs relevées, le volume de chaque membre est calculé en considérant chaque segment de membre comme un tronc de cône (16). La prise alimentaire et de boissons a été notée sur des carnets personnels à 4 reprises, sur des périodes de trois jours consécutifs : normoxie, pendant la phase d'ascension (HA), et au cours de la première (H1) et la troisième (H3) semaine. La composition des aliments, le calcul des calories et des différents constituants de l'alimentation a été réalisé en utilisant un logiciel de calcul nutritionnel «CE.RE.AL.», établi à partir de plusieurs tables de composition alimentaire (19 ; 21).

Système adrénergique

Le niveau d'activation du système adrénergique a été évalué par la mesure des concentrations plasmatiques de catécholamines (noradrénaline, adrénaline, dopamine) au repos et à deux niveaux d'exercice. La réponse chronotrope à la stimulation adrénergique a été évaluée par la relation fréquence cardiaque/dose d'isoprénaline lors d'une épreuve de perfusion à dose progressive d'isoprénaline (1 ; 27). La densité des récepteurs adrénergiques sur les lymphocytes circulants a été mesurée à l'aide d'un ligand spécifique (23) en normoxie et à H3.

Apnées du sommeil

Le sommeil a été exploré par un enregistrement polygraphique nocturne en normoxie et en début de séjour à 6542 m. Un dispositif Medilog 9000 a été utilisé pour enregistrer 4 voies d'électroencéphalogramme, 1 voie électrooculogramme, 1 voie électrocardiogramme + électromyogramme et deux voies pour les mouvements respiratoires, thoraciques et abdominaux. SaO_2 était mesurée en continu par la méthode décrite plus haut (18).

RÉSULTATS

Acclimatation (Fig. 2)

Le score moyen de MAM augmente transitoirement lors de l'arrivée à La Paz puis réaugmente lors de l' ascension du Mont Sajama. Les scores les plus élevés ont été observés lors de l'ascension au-dessus de 6000 m et pendant les 4 premiers jours à 6542 m. Les scores diminuent ensuite progressivement sans néanmoins atteindre zéro, sauf pour deux sujets en fin de séjour. Deux sujets ont présenté en début de séjour des signes de gravité (désorientation, somnolence pour l'un, dyspnée de repos sévère pour l'autre) ayant nécessité une recompression d'une durée d'une heure dans un sac de recompression portable (11). Au total, sur un plan clinique, l'ensemble des sujets se sentaient mieux en fin qu'en début de séjour, sauf pour deux sujets dont l'un qui a présenté des signes respiratoires importants pendant l'ensemble du séjour.

Exercice musculaire

La saturation artérielle en O_2 (SaO_2) atteint des valeurs très basses en début de séjour, puis augmente légèrement, du fait de l'acclimatation au cours du séjour, aussi bien au repos qu'à l'exercice maximal (Fig. 3). La puissance maximale aérobie a diminué de 44% en altitude, sans modification au cours du séjour (Fig. 4). La fréquence cardiaque maximale diminue de 16% puis 18% en altitude (Fig. 4). Au retour en normoxie, puissance maximale aérobie et fréquence cardiaque maximale n'ont pas encore totalement retrouvé leurs valeurs de base. Au cours de l'épreuve de Wingate, la puissance pic au cours de l'épreuve (témoin de la puissance anaérobie alactique) n'a pas diminué de façon significative, alors que la puissance moyenne (témoin de la puissance anaérobie lactique) a diminué de 11 % en altitude (Fig. 5).

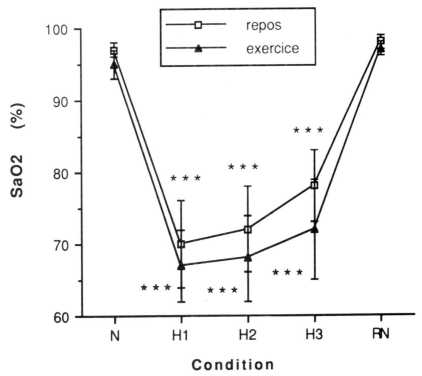

Fig. 3 - Variations de la saturation artérielle en O_2 (SaO_2) au repos et à l'exercice maximal, au cours du séjour à 6542 m. N: normoxie, H1, H2, H3 : 1ère, 2ème, 3ème semaine à 6542 m, RN: 10 jours après la redescente du sommet. Statistique: hypoxie *vs* normoxie: * : $p<0,05$, ** : $p<0,01$, *** : $p<0,001$; valeurs présentées : moyenne ± écart-type.

Fonction rénale

Les paramètres de la fonction rénale sont présentés dans le tableau 2. On note une baisse de 34% du débit plasmatique rénal (DPR), une baisse non significative du débit de filtration glomérulaire (DFG), avec une augmentation de 22% de la fraction de filtration (=DFG/DPR*100). Le débit de réabsorption tubulaire proximal (APR) a diminué de 14 %. Il faut noter que l'un des sujets a un comportement particulier sur le plan rénal, puisqu'il augmente nettement sa filtration glomérulaire en hypoxie, contrairement à l'ensemble du groupe. Le bilan hormonal met en évidence une diminution très nette de l'activité rénine et de la concentration d'aldostérone plasmatique en altitude, aussi bien au repos qu'à l'exercice (Fig. 6 et 7).

Érythropoïèse

Après une augmentation initiale importante, EPO a diminué chez la plupart des sujets entre H1 et H2, puis est resté stable, en moyenne entre H2 et H3 (Fig. 8). Cependant, il existe une grande variabilité individuelle dans

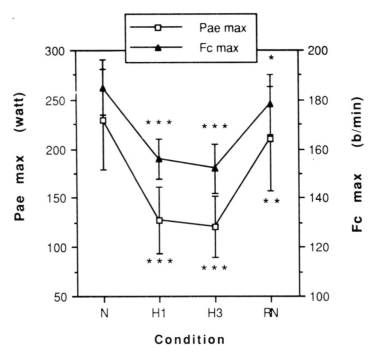

Fig. 4 - Variations de la puissance maximale aérobie (Pae max) et de la fréquence cardiaque maximale (Fc max) au cours du séjour à 6542 m. Conditions et statistiques : voir légende figure 3.

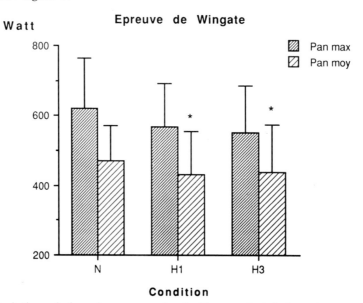

Fig. 5 - Variations de la puissance maximale (Pan max) et de la puissance moyenne (Pan moy) au cours de l'épreuve de Wingate. Conditions et statistiques : voir légende figure 3.

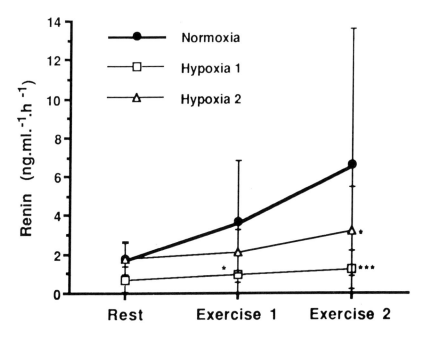

Fig. 6 - Variations de l'activité rénine plasmatique, au repos et à deux puissances d'exercice (Exercice 1 : 40% Pae max ; Exercise 2 : 75% Pae max) en normoxie (Normoxia) et en hypoxie (Hypoxia 1 : 1ère semaine, Hypoxia 2 : 3ème semaine).

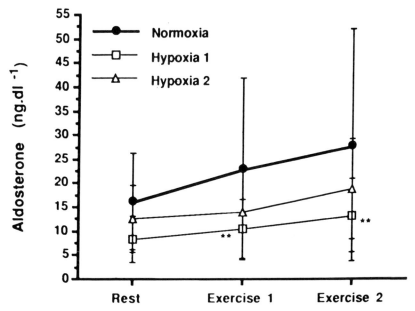

Fig. 7 - Variations de l'aldostérone plasmatique, au repos et à deux puissances d'exercice en normoxie (Normoxia) et en hypoxie (Hypoxia 1 : 1ère semaine, Hypoxia 2 : 3ème semaine).

Tableau 2 - Modifications des paramètres de la fonction rénale en haute altitude. DPR : débit plasmatique rénal; DFG : débit de filtration glomérulaire, APR : débit de réabsorption tubulaire proximale. *** : p<0,001.

	Normoxie	Hypoxie
DPR (Ml/Min)	562 ± 85	371 ± 110***
DFG (Ml/Min)	104 ± 15	87 ± 31
APR (Ml/Min)	65 ± 14	56 ± 27

la réponse de EPO au stimulus hypoxique. En particulier, des différences nettes sont apparues entre les hommes et les femmes : chez les femmes, EPO est resté élevé pendant tout le séjour en altitude. Comme on pouvait également s'y attendre, une polyglobulie s'est développée, comme en témoigne l'augmentation à H1 de Ht et de Hb (Fig. 8). Plus étonnante est la diminution observée de Ht et Hb entre H2 et H3, alors que les sujets séjournent à la même altitude.

Nutrition et composition corporelle

Le poids corporel a diminué de 9% en altitude et ne s'est pas restauré à la fin du séjour ; les sujets ont déjà récupéré en moyenne près de la moitié du poids perdu après dix jours de retour en basse altitude (Fig. 9). La masse grasse évaluée par hydrodensitométrie avant et après l'expédition n'est pas modifiée car le délai entre la redescente du sommet et la mesure au retour était trop long. Le pourcentage de masse grasse, évalué au cours du séjour, a diminué en moyenne de 26,5% (Fig. 9). Le volume des membres supérieurs a baissé en moyenne de 5%, celui des membres inférieurs de 13% (Fig. 10). La ration calorique s'est révélée très abaissée pendant la phase d'ascension, sans que l'équilibre entre les différents constituants ne soit profondément modifié (Tableau 3). Parallèlement aux apports caloriques, les apports de différents sels et oligo-éléments ont été très inférieurs à la normale pendant la phase d'ascension, en particulier l'apport en fer (-58%).

Système adrénergique

Les concentrations de noradrénaline ont augmenté en altitude, aussi bien au repos qu'à l'exercice (Fig. 11), alors que l'adrénaline n'a pas varié de façon significative (résultats non présentés). La réponse chronotrope à l'isoprénaline a diminué de 42 % à H1 puis ne s'est pas modifiée au cours du séjour en altitude (Fig. 12). La densité des ß-récepteurs adrénergiques lymphocytaires (Bmax) a diminué de 41% en altitude (Bmax N : 26,2 ± 8,0 ; H3 : 15,3 ± 9,0 fmol/mg.prot), sans modification de l'affinité des récepteurs pour un ligand spécifique.

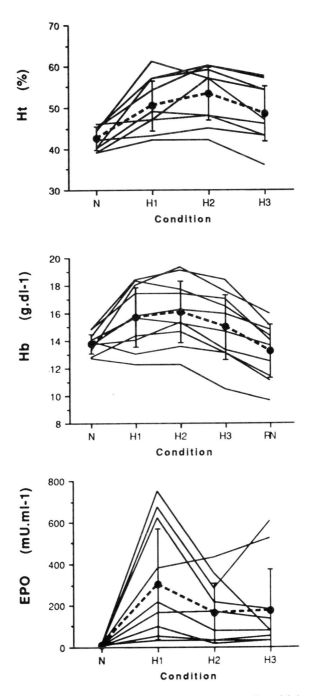

Fig. 8 - Variations de l'hématocrite (Ht) et de la concentration d'hémoglobine (Hb) et d'éryhtropoïétine (EPO), au cours du séjour à 6542 m. Conditions et statistiques : voir légende figure 3.

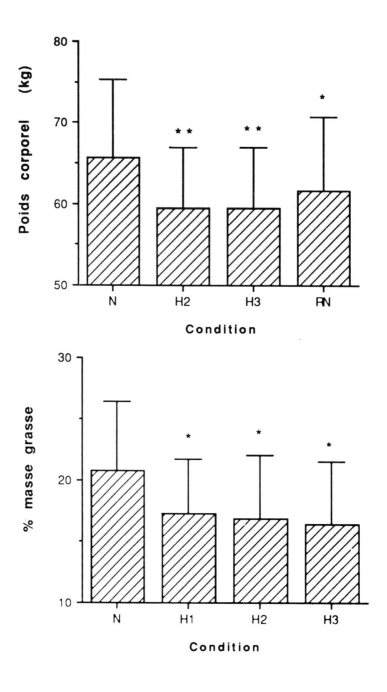

Fig. 9 - Variations du poids corporel et du pourcentage de masse grasse. Conditions et statistiques : voir légende figure 3.

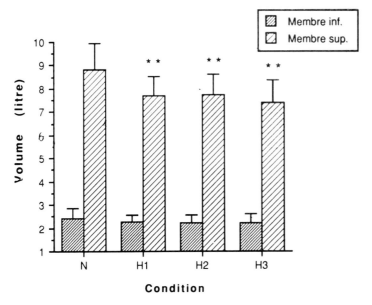

Fig. 10 - Variations du volume des membres inférieurs et supérieurs au cours du séjour en altitude. Conditions et statistiques : voir légende figure 3.

	N Normoxie	HA Ascension	H1 6542 M 1 SEM	H3 6542 M 3 SEM
Apport Énerg. (Kcal/J)	1863 ± 432	1005 ± 327***	1857 ± 729	1955 ± 839
Protides (% Kcal Tot)	16,3 ± 1,9	14,8 ± 3,1	13,3 ± 1,5***	15,0 ±2,3
Lipides (% Kcal Tot)	33,6 ± 6,6	25,2 ± 5,9*	30,6 ± 6,3	31,0 ± 6,7
Glucides (% Kcal Tot)	48,4 ± 7,2	58,5 ± 7,1*	54,7 ± 6,7*	52,6 ± 6,3
Sodium (Mg/J)	2004 ± 749	1438 ± 664	2832 ± 1061*	1726 ± 778
Potassium (Mg/J)	2669 ± 625	1357 ± 661***	2831 ±755	2631 ± 927
Calcium (Mg/J)	1149 ± 416	557 ± 202***	709 ± 264*	888 ± 267
Fer (Mg/J)	10,3 ± 1,8	4,3 ± 2,4***	12,1 ± 3,9	12,9 ± 3,9*

Tableau 3 - Ration calorique et apport en différents constituants alimentaires au cours du séjour en altitude. ***: p<0,001 ; **: p<0,01 ; *: p<0,05.

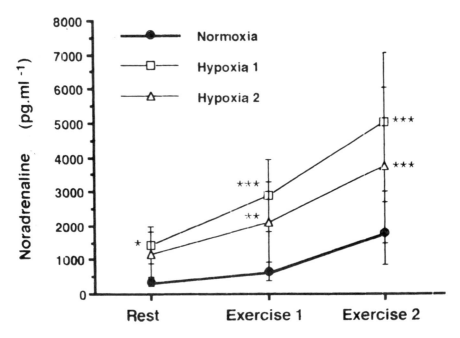

Fig. 11 - Variations de la concentration plasmatique de noradrénaline au repos et à deux niveaux d'exercice en normoxie (Normoxia) et en hypoxie (Hypoxia 1 : 1ère semaine, Hypoxia 2 : 3ème semaine).

Test à l'isoprénaline

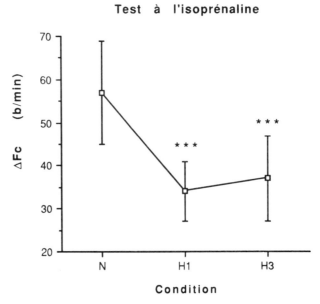

Fig. 12 - Variation de la réponse chronotrope (ΔFc) à une dose de 0,06 µg/kg/min d'isoprénaline au cours du séjour à 6542 m. Conditions et statistiques : voir légende figure 3.

Apnées du sommeil

En haute altitude, le temps total de sommeil était inchangé, le pourcentage de temps d'éveil intercurrent pendant le sommeil a nettement augmenté (Tableau 4). Le temps passé en stades 1 et 2 a augmenté, aux dépens des stades 3 et 4. Le sommeil paradoxal était inchangé. Le temps passé en respiration périodique en altitude était en moyenne de 36%, avec des variations de 1 à 80 % selon les individus. Les épisodes de respiration périodique duraient de 1 à 57 minutes et la durée de chaque apnée observée était de 7 à 20 secondes. La saturation artérielle en O_2 pendant le sommeil a atteint des valeurs très basses : 53 ± 13 %. Le temps passé par chaque sujet en respiration périodique était bien corrélé à la réponse individuelle à l'hypoxie évaluée avant le départ (Fig. 13) (25).

Tableau 4 - Caractéristiques du sommeil au cours du séjour à 6542 m. TST : temps total de sommeil, éveil : temps passé en éveil intercurrent (en % TST), SP : temps passé en sommeil paradoxal (en % TST) ''' : p<0,001 ; '' : p<0,01 ; ' : p<0,05.

	TST (MIN)	Éveil (%)	Stade 1+2 (%)	Stade 3+4 (%)	SP (%)
Normoxie	410 ± 49	6 ± 5	45 ± 12	38 ± 7	18 ± 11
Hypoxie	434 ± 109	33± 11***	64 ± 9*	18 ± 6**	18 ± 7

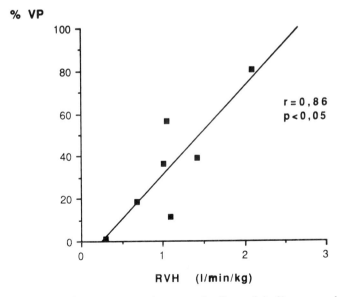

Fig. 13 - Relation entre le temps passé en respiration périodique pendant la nuit en altitude (VP, en % du temps total de sommeil) et la réponse ventilatoire à l'hypoxie (RVH) mesurée à l'exercice avant le départ.

DISCUSSION

Il est d'emblée possible de constater que l'acclimatation fût possible à cette altitude extrême. En aucun cas l'évacuation à une altitude inférieure ne s'est révélée nécessaire, même si certains l'auraient souhaité en début de séjour, lorsque les conditions atmosphériques étaient très défavorables. Les aspects psychologiques sont alors très importants à considérer mais ils ne seront pas discutés ici. Deux sujets sur dix paraissaient moins «en forme» à la fin qu'au début du séjour, mais il est difficile de mettre cela sur le compte d'une détérioration physique ou d'une baisse de la motivation. Pourtant, le stress hypoxique était sévère, comme en témoignent les valeurs de SaO_2, parfois proches de 60% en début de séjour. Cependant, SaO_2 augmente nettement au cours du séjour, ce qui témoigne d'une acclimatation ventilatoire efficace (Fig. 3).

Malgré cette acclimatation, la performance aérobie, profondément altérée en début de séjour, ne s'améliore pas significativement au cours du séjour. Ce phénomène avait déjà été relevé par d'autres auteurs, bien qu'à des altitudes inférieures (5). La baisse de 44% trouvée ici pour l'altitude de 6542 m correspond aux valeurs relevées au cours de l'expédition américaine de 1981 à l'Everest (32). Il existe une dissociation nette entre la fatigue subjective, ressentie lors d'un exercice épuisant, et la puissance effectivement atteinte au cours de l'épreuve sur bicyclette ergométrique. Ainsi, les sujets se sentent plus à l'aise en fin de séjour, alors qu'ils n'améliorent guère leurs performances. L'épreuve de Wingate, qui correspond à un exercice intense supramaximal de 30 secondes, est particulièrement pénible à réaliser en haute altitude. La récupération s'accompagne d'une dyspnée intense et d'une sensation de malaise pendant plusieurs minutes. La puissance de pointe instantanée n'est pas modifiée, mais la puissance moyenne est diminuée. Cependant, rapportée au poids corporel, cette puissance n'est pas significativement diminuée par rapport à la normoxie. Ces résultats sont les premiers obtenus à cette altitude ; ils concordent avec des données obtenues chez des enfants natifs de haute altitude à 3600 m (2) ou chez des aldultes natifs du niveau de la mer transplantés à 4350 m [observations personnelles]. La filière métabolique anaérobie alactique semble ainsi moins touchée par l'hypoxie que la filière aérobie, semblant montrer que la mobilisation de l'ATP et de la créatine phosphate musculaires n'est pas altérée par une diminution de l'apport d'O_2. Cependant, la mise en jeu au cours de l'épreuve de Wingate de processus anaérobies lactiques, voire aérobies est probable, en particulier au-delà des 10 premières secondes.

La fonction rénale a rarement été explorée en altitude. Les données présentées ici sont les premières à objectiver une vasoconstriction artériolaire rénale, s'accompagnant d'une baisse (chez 9 sujets sur 10) de la filtration glomérulaire et de la réabsorption tubulaire proximale. La diminution de la filtration glomérulaire avait déjà été pressentie à l'exercice, à 4350 m (17). Les modifications hormonales observées confirment celles déjà obtenues lors d'études contrôlées en plus basse altitude (3 ; 17) : le système rénineangiotensine-aldostérone est complètement inhibé. Jusqu'à présent, peu d'hypothèses convaincantes avaient été avancées pour expliquer ce phénomène (15). Une légère augmentation de la pression artérielle, trouvée ici (résultats non présentés), pourrait inhiber la libération de rénine, mais elle n'a pas été notée dans d'autres circonstances. L'hypokaliémie, associée à l'alcalose respiratoire de l'altitude, pourrait être responsable de la diminution de l'aldostéronémie mais ne rendrait pas compte de la baisse de la rénine. Le système adrénergique est stimulé en hypoxie, ce qui devrait favoriser la libération de rénine, à moins qu'une désensibilisation des récepteurs adrénergiques intra-rénaux, comparable à celle observée dans le coeur de rat (13) ou les lymphocytes humains (ici et réf. 23), ne survienne également en hypoxie chronique.

La polyglobulie d'altitude semble une réaction extrêmement variable d'un individu à l'autre. Divers facteurs peuvent être invoqués. La libération d'EPO par le rein dépend de l'apport d'O_2 à un capteur situé vraisemblablement à proximité du tubule proximal (7). La fonction tubulaire rénale semble donc avoir un rôle modulateur sur la libération d'EPO. Dans le présent travail, nous avons trouvé une excellente corrélation entre la concentration d'EPO à H2 et APR, principal déterminant de la consommation d'O_2 du néphron (Fig. 14). La réponse de la moelle osseuse à l'érythropoïétine dépend également de la disponibilité en substrats nécessaires à la fabrication du globule rouge. Il est vraisemblable que les réserves de fer se sont trouvées amoindries au cours de ce séjour prolongé en haute altitude, en particulier du fait de la baisse des apports alimentaires en fer pendant les 10 jours de la phase d'ascension (Tableau 3). Il est intéressant de constater que la «résistance à l'EPO», observée à partir de H2 a été particulièrement marquée chez les femmes, pour lesquelles il est bien connu que les réserves en fer sont plus limitées. Chez l'une des participantes, un véritable état anémique a été constaté au retour en normoxie (Hb = 9,5 g/dl), alors qu'aucun saignement ou syndrome inflammatoire n'était survenu pour l'expliquer.

La perte de poids lors de séjour prolongés en haute altitude est une donnée bien établie (4). Le perte observée ici (environ 9% du poids corporel de base) est relativement limitée. Il est important de relever que cette baisse est observée en début de séjour et que le poids corporel se maintient par la suite, malgré la persistance du stimulus hypoxique. La perte s'est faite aux dépens de la masse grasse, mais elle a également touché la masse maigre. Une fonte musculaire est objectivée par la diminution du volume des membres, particulièrement des membres inférieurs. La mesure de la masse grasse par la méthode des plis cutanés peut être entachée d'erreur du fait d'un oedème sous-cutané qui majorerait la valeur du pli en altitude. La perte de poids est essentiellement liée à la négativation des bilans calorique et hydrique qui survient pendant la phase d'ascension (HA). Pendant cette période, les signes de MAM (nausées) gênent la prise de nourriture. Par ailleurs, les conditions de confort sont limitées et ne favorisent pas la prise de repas. En revanche, lors du séjour au sommet, l'installation d'une cuisine confortable et l'activité

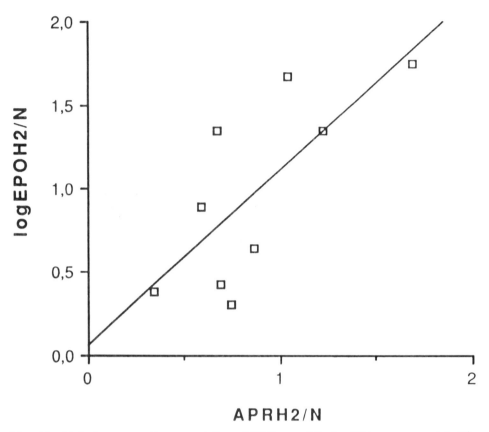

Fig. 14 - Relation entre l'augmentation d'EPO en altitude (H2 par rapport à N) et la variation du débit de réabsorption tubulaire proximal (APR à H2 par rapport à N).

culinaire à temps plein de l'une d'entre nous a permis d'offrir des conditions d'alimentation satisfaisantes et une nourriture la plus variée et la plus agréable possible, compte tenu de l'environnement particulier du camp. Ces conditions relativement confortables sont bien différentes de celles observées au cours d'expéditions sportives où les impératifs de poids de portage et de temps disponible sont tels que l'alimentation est limitée, peu variée et souvent insuffisante. Cela explique peut-être la dégradation relatée au cours d'expédition et que nous n'avons pas retrouvée ici. La carence d'apport en fer, parallèle à la carence générale d'apport nutritif, a pu jouer un rôle déterminant dans la limitation de la réponse érythropoïétique, contribuant à limiter la quantité disponible de substrat nécessaire à l'érythropoïèse (30).

Le système adrénergique est stimulé en hypoxie, comme en témoigne l'augmentation observée par tous les auteurs des concentrations de noradrénaline circulante en hypoxie aiguë et chronique (23). Il en résulte en particulier une augmentation de la fréquence cardiaque de repos. En réponse à une stimulation permanente, les ß-récepteurs cardiaques font vraisemblablement l'objet d'une désensibilisation (13 ; 23). La baisse de la réponse cardiaque à l'isoprénaline et de la densité des ß-récepteurs lymphocytaires n'avaient jusqu'à présent été observée qu'à des altitudes plus basses (4350 à 4800 m). Il semble que les baisses observées ici soient du même ordre. Les concentrations de catécholamines, au repos et à l'exercice, sont d'ailleurs équivalentes à celles obtenues à 4350 ou 4800 m (23). Il semble donc qu'un stimulus hypoxique plus sévère n'ait pas entraîné une activation adrénergique plus intense et une désensibilisation plus marquée. Ce phénomène de désensibilisation, qui protège le cœur contre une trop forte consommation d'oxygène (24), semble donc lié à l'action de l'agoniste adrénergique lui-seul et non à l'hypoxie *per se*. Il s'agirait d'une réaction homéostatique non spécifique induite par l'augmentation de l'activation adrénergique.

Le sommeil est profondément perturbé en altitude (8 ; 9). Les stades de sommeil profonds (3+4) sont altérés, au profit d'un sommeil plus léger (stades 1+2). Le phénomène de ventilation périodique est trouvé, avec une proportion variable, chez tous les sujets. La relation nette entre réponse à l'hypoxie et temps passé en ventilation périodique avait déjà été notée à des altitudes plus basses (14). Cette relation témoigne de l'importance du gain de la boucle de régulation de la ventilation en réponse au stimuli O_2 et CO_2. Ces phénomènes ventilatoires nocturnes ne semblent donc pas être péjoratifs, en termes de risque pathologique puisqu'ils surviennent plus fréquemment chez les sujets possédant une bonne réponse ventilatoire à l'hypoxie, c'est-à-dire une moins grande sensibilité au MAM. En revanche, si la saturation artérielle moyenne au cours du sommeil est plus faible chez les sujets présentant une ventilation périodique importante, le stimulus de la sécrétion d'EPO doit être plus intense chez ces sujets et pourrait induire une polyglobulie accrue, à condition qu'il n'y ait pas de résistance à l'EPO. Cependant, il a été noté, chez des natifs de haute altitude, que la saturation artérielle moyenne pouvait être conservée, malgré une ventilation périodique importante ; en effet, une hypoventilation globale moyenne peut induire une hypoxémie sévère sans qu'il y ait ventilation périodique (22). Les perturbations du sommeil, se traduisant par de très nombreux réveils nocturnes, peuvent contribuer à une dégradation progressive physique et psychologique, d'autant plus que l'on ne note aucune amélioration au cours du séjour (8).

En conclusion, il est possible, à partir de cette série exceptionnelle d'expérimentations réalisées pour la première fois en très haute altitude, de tirer les enseignements suivants : (1) : l'exposition à l'altitude de 6542 m entraîne une limitation importante de l'autonomie physiologique d'un individu, se traduisant par une baisse du poids corporel, de la masse musculaire et de la performance musculaire surtout aux dépens des processus aérobies; (2) : ces diminutions persistent sans s'aggraver au cours d'un séjour de 3 semaines à la même altitude, alors que la sensation subjective de bien-être s'améliore chez la plupart des sujets ; (3) : la fonction rénale est importante à prendre en compte, non seulement par son rôle éventuel dans la physiopathologie du MAM, mais également par son rôle modulateur dans la sécrétion d'érythropoïétine ; (4) : la nutrition constitue un élément fondamental dans le maintien de l'homéostasie, en limitant le déficit calorique principal responsable de la fonte musculaire induite par l'hypoxie ; (5) : en réponse au stress hypoxique, le système adrénergique jouerait un rôle régulateur essentiel dans la plupart de ces processus, mais il existerait des contre-mécanismes venant moduler l'action du système adrénergique, limitant ainsi les capacités d'autonomie de l'organisme mais le préservant néanmoins d'un coût énergétique élevé, dangereux dans une situation d'hypoxie sévère ; (6) : dans une situation limite pour les possibilités d'acclimatation, la variabilité de la tolérance individuelle à un tel stress hypoxique est un élément fondamental à considérer. L'écart sera faible entre une acclimatation possible et une dégradation inéluctable.

REMERCIEMENTS

Cette expédition scientifique a été possible en premier lieu du fait de ses membres, qui ont à la fois participé en tant qu'expérimentateurs et que volontaires pour l'ensemble des épreuves. Qu'ils en soient remerciés : Ana-Maria Antezana, Hélène Barthélémy, Vincent Bonaldi, Patrick Bouchet, Emmanuel Cauchy, Jean-Bernard Duchemin, Jean-Louis Le Trong, Michèle Marchal, Chantal Para et Jean-Paul Richalet.

La logistique de l'expédition a largement bénéficié de l'aide de l'Institut Bolivien de Biologie d'Altitude (IBBA) à La Paz, ainsi que du régiment Tocopilla de Curahuara de Carangas pour l'acheminement des 2 tonnes de matériel au sommet du Sajama. Nous remercions également pour leur collaboration le Département de Biologie Humaine de l'Université de Maastricht (Hollande), le Département de Physiologie de l'Université de Genève (Suisse), Le Laboratoire de Physiologie de la Faculté de Médecine de Besançon et le Laboratoire de Physiologie de la Faculté de Médecine Necker à Paris.

Enfin, cet ensemble d'expérimentations entre dans le cadre du partenariat scientifique avec les laboratoires Sandoz France et Sandoz Nutrition (Suisse), mené depuis 1983.

RÉFÉRENCES

1. ANTEZANA, A.-M., RICHALET, J.-P., KACIMI, R., BONALDI, V., DUCHEMIN, J.-B. & BOUCHET, P. 1992. Response to isoproterenol at extreme altitude (6542m, 3 weeks). *Int. J. Sports Med.* 13: 77.

2. BEDU, M., FELLMANN, N., SPIELVOGEL, H., FALGAIRETTE, G., VAN PRAAGH, E., & COUDERT, J. 1991. Force-velocity and 30-s Wingate tests in boys at high and low altitudes. *J. Appl. Physiol.* 70: 1031-1037.

3. BOUISSOU, P., RICHALET, J.-P., GALEN, F. X., LARTIGUE, M., LARMIGNAT, P., DEVAUX D. C., F. & KÉROMÈS, A. 1989. Effect of ß-adrenoceptor blockade on renin-aldosterone and a-ANF during exercise at altitude. *J. Appl. Physiol.* 67: 141-146.

4. BOYER, S. J. & BLUME, F. D. 1984. Weight loss and changes in body composition at high altitude. *J. Appl. Physiol.* 57: 1580-1585.

5. DILL, D. B. & ADAMS, W. C. 1971. Maximal oxygen uptake at sea level and at 3090 m altitude in high school champion runners. *J. Appl. Physiol.* 30: 854-859.

6. DURNIN, G. V. G. A. & WOMERLEY, G. 1974. Body fat assessed from total body density and its estimation from skinfold thickness: Measurement on 481 men and women aged from 16 to 72 years. *Br. J. Ntr.* 32: 77-97.

7. ECKARDT, K.-U., KURTZ, A. & BAUER, C. 1989. Regulation of erythropoietin production is related to proximal tubular function. *Am. J. Physiol.* 256 (*Renal Fluid Electrolyte Physiol.* 25): F942-F947.

8. GOLDENBERG, F., RICHALET, J.-P., KÉROMÈS, A., VEYRAC, P., JOUHANDIN, M. & GISQUET, A. 1988. Effects of loprazolam on high altitude insomnia and ventilation during sleep. In : *Sleep' 86.* W. P. Koella, Obal, F., Schulz, H. & Visser, P., Gustav Fischer Verlag, Stuttgart, New-York: 340-342.

9. GOLDENBERG, F., RICHALET, J.-P., ONNEN, I. & ANTEZANA, A.-M. 1992. Sleep apneas and high altitude newcomers. *Int. J. Sports Med.* 13: S34-S36.

10. HACKETT, P. 1992. The Lake Louise Consensus on the Definition and Quantification of Altitude Illness. In : *Hypoxia and Mountain Medicine.* J. R. Sutton, Coates, G. and Houston, C. S., Queen City Printers Inc., Burlington, USA: 327-330.

11. HERRY, J.-P., RICHALET, J.-P., RATHAT, C. & BENOZILLO, J.-P. 1990. Le caisson de recompression portable (CHP) dans le traitement de la pathologie de haute altitude. *Urgences* 9: 145-148.

12. JAEGER, N. 1979. *Carnets de solitude.* Denoël, Paris, pp. 236.

13. KACIMI, R., RICHALET, J.-P., CORSIN, A., ABOUSAHL, I. & CROZATIER, B. 1992. Hypoxia-induced downregulation of ß-adrenergic receptors in rat heart. *J. Appl. Physiol.* 73: 1377-1382.

14. MASUYAMA, S., KOHCHIYAMA, S., OKITA, T., KUNITOMO, F., TOJIMA, T., KIMURA, H., KURIYAMA, T. & HONDA, Y. 1987. Relationship between disordered breathing during sleep at high altitude and ventilatory chemosensitivities to hypoxia and hypercapnia. *Am. Rev. Resp. Dis.* 135: A184.

15. MILLEDGE, J. S., CATLEY, D. M., WILLIAMS, E. S., WITHEY, W. R. & MINTY, B. D. 1983. Effect of prolonged exercise at altitude on the renin-aldosterone system. *J. Appl. Physiol.* 55: 413-418.

16. NARICI, M., KAYSER, B., CIBELLA, F., GRASSI, B. & CERRETELLI, P. 1992. No change in body composition and maximum alactic anaerobic performance during a 4-week sojourn at altitude. *Int. J. Sports Med.* 13: 87.

17. OLSEN, N. V., KANSTRUP, I.-L., RICHALET, J.-P., HANSEN, J. M., P. G., & G. F. X. 1992. Effects of acute hypoxia on renal endocrine function at rest and during graded exercise in hydrated subjects. *J. Appl. Physiol.* (in press).

18. ONNEN, I., ANTEZANA, A.-M., PARA, C., HOURY, J. & RICHALET, J.-P. 1992. Periodic breathing during sleep at 6542m. *Int. J. Sports Med.* 13: 80.

19. OSTROWSKI, Z. L. 1978. *Les aliments. Table des valeurs nutritives.* J. Lanore.

20. PUGH, L. G. C. E. 1962. Physiological and medical aspects of the Himalayan Scientific and Mountaineering Expedition, 1960-1961. *Br. Med. J.* 2: 621-627.

21. RANDOIN, L. 1982. *Table de composition des aliments.* J. Lanore.

22. RAYNAUD, J. 1989. Sommeil et fonctions cardio-respiratoires chez le sujet normal et le polyglobulique en haute altitude. *Première réunion internationale Alpes Andes de physiologie et physiopathologie d'altitude*, La Paz, Bolivia.

23. RICHALET, J.-P. 1990. The heart and adrenergic system in hypoxia. *In : Hypoxia. The adaptations* . J. R. Sutton, Coates, G. and Remmers, J. E., B.C. Dekker Inc., Toronto: 231-240

24. RICHALET, J.-P. 1990. Prédiction des conditions d'oxygénation myocardique à l'exercice maximal en haute altitude. *Arch. Int. Physiol. Biochim.* 98: A226.

25. RICHALET, J.-P. 1991. Acute mountain sickness: risk factors. *In : A colour atlas of mountain medicine* . Wolfe Medical Pub., London: 54-56, 212.

26. RICHALET, J.-P., DÉCHAUX, M., BIENVENU, A., LABORDE, K., LAMBERTO, C., PARA, C., THIRIET, I., BONALDI, V. & SOUBERBIELLE, J.-C. 1992. Renal function during prolonged exposure to extreme altitude (6542m). *Int. J. Sports Med.* 13: 78-79.

27. RICHALET, J.-P., LARMIGNAT, P., RATHAT, C., KÉROMÈS, A., BAUD, P. & LHOSTE, F. 1988. Decreased human cardiac response to isoproterenol infusion in acute and chronic hypoxia. *J. Appl. Physiol.* 65: 1957-1961.

28. RICHALET, J.-P., MARCHAL, M., LAMBERTO, C., LE TRONG, J.-L., ANTEZANA, A.-M. & CAUCHY, E. 1992. Alteration of aerobic and anaerobic performance after 3 weeks at 6542 m (Mt. Sajama). *Int. J. Sports Med.* 13: 86-87.

29. RICHALET, J.-P., RATHAT, C. 1991. *Pathologie et altitude.* Masson éd., Paris: pp. 211.

30. RICHALET, J.-P., SOUBERBIEL, J.-C., ZITTOUN, J., ANTEZANA, A.-M. & CAUCHY, E. 1992. Control of erythropoiesis during prolonged exposure to extreme altitude. *Arch. Int. Physiol. Biochim.* 100: A122.

31. WEST, J. B. 1986. Highest inhabitants of the world. *Nature (Lond.)* 324: 517.

32. WEST, J. B., BOYER, S. J., GRABER, D. J., HACKETT, P. H., K. MARET, H., MILLEDGE, J. S., PETERS, R. M. J., PIZZO, C. J., SAMAJA, M., SARNQUIST, F. H., SCHOENE, R. B. & WINSLOW, R. M. 1983. Maximal exercise at extreme altitudes on Mount Everest. *J. Appl. Physiol.* 55: 678-687.

HUMAN TOLERANCE TO EXTREME ALTITUDES

John B. West

Abstract

Over the last 15 years, considerable progress has been made in understanding how human beings tolerate extreme altitudes. The highest inhabitants of the world are apparently the caretakers of the Aucanquilcha mine in north Chile, altitude 5950 m, barometric pressure 372 mmHg. Only a small proportion of the miners can live at this great altitude. The first ascent of Mt. Everest, 8848 m, without supplementary oxygen was made by Messner and Habeler in 1978. The 1981 American Research Expedition to Everest, and the low-pressure chamber simulated ascent, Operation Everest II in 1985 concentrated on the physiology of extreme altitude. Humans can only reach the highest point in the world because the barometric pressure considerably exceeds that predicted from the Standard Atmosphere. Extreme hyperventilation at these great altitudes reduces the alveolar P_{CO_2} to as low as 7-8 mmHg on the Everest summit. The alveolar P_{O_2} is about 35 but the arterial P_{O_2} is only 28-30 mmHg because of diffusion limitation of oxygen transfer across the blood-gas barrier. The very low P_{CO_2} causes marked respiratory alkalosis which accelerates loading of oxygen in the pulmonary capillary. Although ventilation is greatly increased, cardiac output in relation to work rate is the same as at sea level. However myocardial contractility is well maintained to altitudes of over 8000 m. Maximal oxygen consumption falls to just over 1 l/min on the Everest summit, and the oxygen cost of ventilation may be a limiting factor during exercise. In spite of the great reduction in aerobic capacity, and anaerobic glycolysis is also severely restricted, but the mechanism is unclear.

Key words: Highest inhabitants, barometric pressure, alveolar gas composition, blood gases, diffusion limitation, respiratory alkalosis, hyperventilation, hypoxic ventilatory response, cardiac output, myocardial contractility, maximal oxygen consumption, maximal work capacity, anaerobic glycolysis.

Resumen

En los últimos 15 años se ha progresado considerablemente en el entendimiento de cómo los seres humanos toleran las alturas extremas. Los pobladores que viven en las alturas más grandes son, aparentemente, los cuidadores de las minas de Aucanquilcha en el norte de Chile, altura: 5950 m, presión barométrica: 372 mmHg. Sólo una pequeña proporción de mineros puede vivir allí. El primer ascenso al Monte Everest, 8848 m, sin oxígeno suplementario fue realizado por Messner y Habeler en 1978. La Expedición Americana de 1981 al Everest, y el ascenso simulado en cámara de baja presión, Operación Everest II de 1985, se concentraron en la fisiología de la altura extrema. Los humanos pueden llegar al punto más alto de la tierra porque la presión barométrica excede considerablemente a lo que se ha predicho de la Atmósfera Standard. La hiperventilación extrema reduce el P_{CO_2} alveolar en la cima del Everest a 7-8 mmHg. El P_{O_2} alveolar es alrededor de 35 pero el P_{O_2} arterial es sólo 28-30 mmHg debido a la limitación de la difusión en la transferencia de oxígeno a través de la barrera sangre-gas. El P_{CO_2} tan bajo causa una marcada alcalosis respiratoria que acelera la carga de oxígeno al capilar pulmonar. Si bien la ventilación aumenta notablemente, la eficiencia cardíaca en relación a la tasa de trabajo es la misma que a nivel del mar. La contractilidad miocárdica se mantiene bien en alturas por encima de los 8000 m. El consumo máximo de oxígeno cae hasta 1 l/min en la cima del Everest, y la demanda de oxígeno de la ventilación puede ser el factor limitante durante el ejercicio. A pesar de la gran reducción de la capacidad aeróbica, hay una restricción de la glicólisis anaeróbica, pero el mecanismo es desconocido.

Palabras claves: Habitantes más altos, presión barométrica, composición del gas alveolar, limitación de difusión, alcalosis respiratoria, hiperventilación, respuesta ventilatoria a la hipoxia, contractilidad miocárdica, consumo máximo de oxígeno, capacidad máxima de trabajo, glicolisis anaeróbica.

Résumé

Au cours des 15 dernières années, on a considérablement progressé dans la compréhension de la tolérance humaine aux altitudes extrêmes. Les personnes qui vivent aux altitudes les plus élevées sont apparemment surveillants des mines de Aucanquilcha au nord du Chili, altitude : 5950 m, pression barométrique 372 mmHg. Seule, une petite quantité de mineurs peut y vivre.

La première ascension de l'Everest, 8848 m, sans oxygène supplémentaire a été réalisée par Messmer et Habeler en 1978. L'expédition américaine à l'Everest en 1981 et l'ascension simulée en chambre à basse pression, opération Everest II en 1985, se concentrèrent sur l'étude de la physiologie en altitude extrême. Les humains peuvent arriver au point le plus haut du globe parce que la pression barométrique dépasse considérablement ce que l'on a dit précédemment de l'Atmosphère Standard. L'hyperventilation extrême réduit la P_{CO_2} alvéolaire à la cime de l'Everest à 7-8 mmHg. La P_{O_2} alvéolaire est d'environ 35, mais la P_{O_2} artérielle est seulement de 28-30 mmHg, à cause de la limitation de la diffusion dans le transfert d'oxygène à travers la barrière alvéolo-capillaire. Une P_{CO_2} aussi basse provoque une alcalose respiratoire marquée qui accélère la charge d'oxygène des capillaires pulmonaires. Si la ventilation augmente effectivement de façon notable, l'efficacité cardiaque en relation au taux de travail est le même qu'au niveau de la mer. La contractilité myocardique se maintient bien au-dessus de 8000 m. La consommation maximum d'oxygène baisse jusqu'à 1l/min. à la cime de l'Everest et la demande de l'oxygène de la ventilation peut être un facteur limitant durant l'exercice. Malgré la réduction importante de la capacité aérobie, il y a une restriction de la glycolyse anaérobique, mais le mécanisme n'est pas connu.

Mots clés : Habitants les plus hauts, presssion barométrique, composition du gaz alvéclaire, limitation de diffusion, alcalose respiratoire, hyperventilation, réponse ventilatoire à l'hypoxie, contractilité myocardique, consommation maximale d'oxygène, capacité maximale de travail, glycolyse anaérobie.

INTRODUCTION

It is indeed a pleasure to contribute to this volume in honor of my friend Professor Carlos Monge-C. No doubt others in the book will summarize the enormous contributions that Professor Monge has made to our knowledge of acclimatization and adaptation to high altitudes. May I just say that, beginning with his illustrious father Professor Carlos Monge-M., the Lima school has pioneered research on permanent residents of high altitude, and thereby done a great service to Peru and to the high altitude world in general.

It was Professor Carlos Monge-C.'s father who wrote extensively of the role of «climatic aggression» in the development of Andean man (18). In his influential book *Acclimatization in the Andes* he discussed how the harshness of the high altitude climate harmed the Spanish conquerers and how the permanent residents of high altitude developed a resistance to the «climatic noxiousness». An interesting related question is: what is the highest altitude that human beings can tolerate? Of course this questions only makes sense if we are thinking of tolerance in terms of more than a few seconds. Air force pilots have been exposed to extremely low pressures for brief periods of time and have recovered. However here we ask the question in terms of tolerance to very high altitudes, first for years, and then for days, or even only hours. The first group are the highest inhabitants of the world, and the second group are the elite mountain climbers. For the second group we analyze the physiological mechanisms which allow the extraordinary tolerance to severe hypoxia.

HIGHEST INHABITANTS OF THE WORLD

In his foreword to Carlos Monge-M.'s book *Acclimatization in the Andes*, the geographer Isaiah Bowman stated that he came across the remains of a permanent habitation in Peru at an altitude of 17,400 ft. (5300 m) during a traverse across the Peruvian Cordillera in 1911 (3). Although precolumbian structures have been found near the summit of Llullaillaco (6723 m) and an Inca body was discovered at about 6300 m on Cerro del Toro, it has been argued that these were associated with mountain worship and were only briefly visited for that purpose (32). On the other hand, a three-roomed dwelling was found at an alitude of about 6600 m on Llullaillaco in 1961 suggesting that the visits may have been longer (7).

However for many years the highest inhabitants of the world were believed to be the miners of the Aucanquilcha mine camp at an altitude of 5340 m in north Chile. They were visited by the 1935 International High Altitude Expedition to Chile who reported that about 150 people lived at the mine camp which is «probably the highest permanent community in the world» (15). The expedition members reported that the sulphur mine itself was at the extreme height of «nearly 19,000 ft.» (5800 m), and that the miners went up and down to the mine on foot, the climb up taking about an hour and a half with the return about 25 minutes. Work was continuous throughout the year except for brief periods during storms.

The expedition measured the barometric pressure at the camp as 401 mmHg which fits reasonably well with the stated altitude at that latitude. They also reported that an attempt was made to put the camp closer to the mine, and that for more than 6 months, a camp was maintained at 18,500 ft

(5640 m). However the miners apparently suffered from increasing persistent headaches and sleeplessness, and preferred to climb to the mine daily rather than live at the higher altitude. On the basis of this report, the altitude of 5340 m was widely quoted as the highest at which human beings could live indefinitely, though it was recognized that only a subset of the population could tolerate this altitude. In fact most of the miners are Bolivian natives who normally reside between 2000 and 4000 m.

That there might be a small group of people living higher was suggested by an article in the July 1, 1979 «Sunday Magazine» from the newspaper El Mercurio of Santiago, Chile. The article described how the reporter, Armando Araneda, visited the mine itself which he thought was at an altitude of 6000 m, and found 6 men permanently stationed there. It was not clear why the men were there. The reporter stated that they were required to fill the buckets of the aerial tramway which transported the sulphur ore (caliche) down to the lower level. However since the miners walked up each day to do this, it was not clear why 6 men actually resided there. Conditions were said to be primitive with only a tin hut for accommodation, and three beds between 6 men. A translation of the newspaper article was sent to me by David B. Dill Jr., a mining engineer, and the son of David Bruce Dill, the eminent exercise and environmental physiologist, and a member of the 1935 expedition.

When I was invited to attend a meeting in Santiago in October 1985, I said that I would very much like to visit the mine which apparently had been ignored by physiologists for 50 years in spite of the great interest of it being the highest permanent habitation in the world. Arrangements were kindly made through the help of Dr. Raimundo Santolaya, Director of the *Centro de Investigaciones Ecobiológicas y Médicas de Altura*, de Codelco-Chile. This Institute is situated in Chuquicamata, site of one of the largest open-cut copper mines in the world. We set off very early one morning in a four-wheel drive vehicle across the Atacama desert, passing enormous salt lakes with myriads of pink flamingos. When we reached the vicinity of the mine, I learned that the old camp at an altitude of 5340 m had been abandoned, and the miners now lived at Amincha at an altitude of 4200 m. The miners were driven up to the mine each day in hugh Mack trucks.

When we reached the mine itself I was intrigued to find that 4 caretakers lived permanently at the mine (35). One man, Señor Justo Copa, had been in residence for two years (Fig. 1). His dusky appearance suggested that he had severe polycythemia, but otherwise I was not able to get any further information. Most of the caretakers lived there for shorter periods of time, and they all descended by truck by Amincha on Sundays to play football.

Although the 1935 expedition stated that the altitude of the mine was nearly 5800 m, I obtained a large scale contour map of the area (Institute of Military Geography, Santiago, 1972) which clearly showed that the altitude of the mine was 5950 m. In addition we measured the barometric pressure

Fig. 1 - Señor Justo Copa (right), one of the four caretakers of the Aucanquilcha mine (5950 m) in October 1985. Dr. Raimundo Santolaya (left) is holding a digital barometer showing a pressure of 381 mmHg. This photograph was taken a short distance below the mine. At the mine itself the pressure was 373 mmHg.

using an accurate digital barometer (Fig. 1) and obtained a figure of 373 mmHg. Dr. Robert B. Schoene who visited the mine in March 1986 measured the pressure as 371 mmHg. The pressure-altitude relationship is latitude-dependent, and the latitude of Aucanquilcha is 21° South, similar to that of Mt. Everest (28° North) where the relationship has been accurately measured (40). This confirms an altitude of approximately 5950 m.

Few physiological data are available on these men. The mine is privately owned and the management are understandably reluctant to draw a great deal of attention to this unusual working environment. Although the maximal oxygen consumption of the miners is not known, they are certainly capable of heavy work because they break up large pieces of the caliche with sledge hammers (16).

The barometric pressure of 371-373 mmHg means that the P_{CO_2} of moist inspired gas is only 68 mmHg. If their alveolar P_{O_2} and P_{CO_2} conform to the pattern previously described for acclimatized lowlanders and high altitude residents (23, 41) they would have alveolar P_{O_2} and P_{CO_2} values of approximately 42 and 22 mmHg respectively (Fig. 2). In March 1986, arterial blood samples were taken from three of the men while they were visiting Ollague (3700 m, PB 490 mmHg) and these gave a mean hematocrit of 61% which is similar

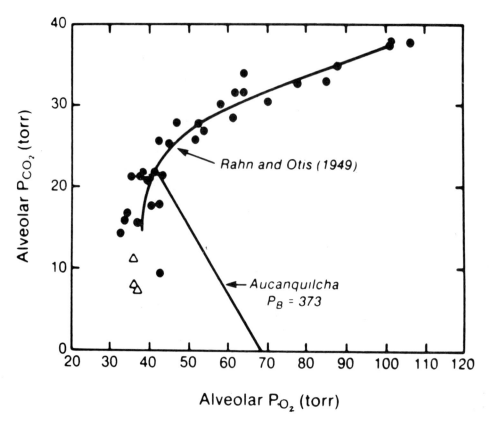

Alveolar P_O₂ (torr)

Fig. 2 - Oxygen-carbon dioxide diagram showing the alveolar gas composition of permanent residents, and lowlanders acclimatized to high altitude. Most of the data were collected by Rahn & Otis (23). The three triangles (bottom left) were obtained at extreme altitudes on Mt. Everest (41). The diagonal line shows a respiratory exchange ratio of 0.85 for a barometric pressure of 372 mmHg and predicts that the caretakers of the Aucanquilcha mine at 5950 m will have alveolar P_{O_2} and P_{CO_2} values of approximately 42 and 22 mmHg respectively (35).

to that of acclimatized lowlanders at a similar altitude. Some physiological data are available on the Aucanquilcha miners who worked in the mine but resided considerably lower in Amincha (4200 m) (26). At the mine, the mean P_{O_2}, P_{CO_2} and pH of their arterial blood were 34•5 mmHg, 27•5 mmHg and 7•40 respectively. However these people should not be confused with the caretakers who lived at the mine.

According to Ward (31) reports from Chinese sources suggest that Tibetan miners have lived and worked at altitudes approaching 6000 m in the Tangulla Range although accurate documentation of the altitudes is not available. Thus until someone comes up with additional information, the caretakers of the Aucanquilcha mine can claim the distinction of being the highest inhabitants of the world.

PHYSIOLOGY ON THE SUMMIT OF MT. EVEREST

While nearly 6000 m is apparently the highest altitude for permanent human habitation, elite climbers have ascended to the highest point on earth, the summit of Mt. Everest (8848 m). However there is considerable evidence that this is very near the limit of human tolerance to hypoxia. For example, Norton got to within 300 m of the summit in 1924 without supplementary oxygen (19) but the mountain was not climbed without oxygen until 1978. Thus the last 300 m took 54 years? Again, when the summit was eventually reached without supplementary oxygen by Messner and Habeler in 1978, they reported that the last 100 m took more than an hour to climb (17). Finally recent measurements of the maximal oxygen uptake ($\dot{V}O_{2max}$) in well acclimatized subjects with an inspired P_{O_2} of 43 mmHg (the same as on the Everest summit) show that the value is only a little over 1 l/min (40, 29) (see below). It is a remarkable coincidence that the highest point on earth is so close to the limit of human tolerance to hypoxia. One of first comprehensive analyses of the physiological problems at the summit of Mt. Everest was made in 1921 by A.M. Kellas whose contributions have been almost completely overlooked (36). His paper «A consideration of the possibility of ascending Mt. Everest» was unfortunately only published in French in a very obscure place (14). On a basis of extensive study he concluded that «Mt. Everest could be ascended by a man of excellent physical and mental constitution in first-rate training, without adventitious aids [supplementary oxygen] if the physical difficulties of the mountain are not too great». It was not until almost 60 years later that this prediction was fulfilled.

During the last 15 years, two major experiments have clarified the physiology of man at the summit of Mt. Everest. In 1981, the American Medical Research Expedition to Everest (AMREE) placed laboratories at 5400 and 6300 m, and a number of physiological measurements were made above 8000 m including the first measurements on the Everest summit itself (Fig. 3). In 1985, an Everest ascent was simulated in a low pressure chamber experiments lasting 40 days. This was Operation Everest II (OE II) with principal investigators C. S. Houston, J. R. Sutton and A. Cymerman (12). A chamber experiment has the advantage that more invasive procedures such as cardiac catheterization and muscle biopsies can be carried out. However there is evidence that the degree of acclimatization is better in a field experiment. The two types of investigation are therefore complementary. Most of what follows is based on the results of these two experiments.

First we should look briefly at the barometric pressure at extreme altitudes on Mt. Everest because there has been considerable confusion on this important topic. As long ago as 1878, Paul Bert gave a figure of 248 mmHg for the barometric pressure on the Mt. Everest summit which is essentially correct (2). Of course this was extrapolated from measurements made at much lower altitudes. Confusion arose after World War I when it became advantageous to develop a «Standard Atmosphere» with a barometric

Fig. 3 - Dr. Christopher Pizzo collecting alveolar gas samples on the summit of Mt. Everest during AMREE, October 24, 1981.

pressure-altitude relationship that could be universally used for calibrating altimeters, low-pressure chambers, and other devices. The Standard Atmosphere (13) was never intended to be used to predict the actual barometric pressure at a particular location, because it has been known from the beginning of the century that the pressure-altitude relationship is both temperature and latitude dependent. Nevertheless, when respiratory physiologists started using low-pressure chambers in World War II, they incorrectly applied the Standard Atmosphere to mountains of interest particularly Mt. Everest (11, 22). The result was that the barometric pressure for the Everest summit (8848 m) was predicted to be 236 mmHg which is far too low.

The error became apparent when expeditions to high mountains resumed after World War II. For example Pugh noted that the barometric pressures in the Himalayas considerably exceeded those predicted from the Standard Atmosphere (20). During AMREE, barometric pressures were measured on Mt. Everest at accurately known altitudes including the first measurement on the summit, and it was shown that the pressures were much higher than predicted from the Standard Atmosphere. Indeed the difference in pressure on the summit was found to be approximately 17 mmHg, or 7% of the actual pressure (42). This is sufficient to cause a large change in VO_{2max} (see below).

Meteorological data also showed that the pressure on the Everest summit varied by about 12 mmHg between mid-summer when it was highest, and mid-winter when it was lowest. This change in barometric pressure is certainly sufficient affecting the maximum work capacity. It also became clear that if Mt. Everest were located at a higher latitude, for example the latitude of Mt. McKinley (64° N) the barometric pressure would be approximately 220 mmHg, and the mountain would certainly be inaccessible without supplementary oxygen. Thus it is only the proximity of Mt. Everest to the equator and the consequent bulge of barometric pressure associated with the high temperature there, that allows human beings to reach the highest point on earth without supplementary oxygen (33).

One of the most important features of acclimatization to high altitude is an increase in alveolar ventilation, and this is critically important at extreme altitude. Figure 2 shows how the alveolar P_{O_2} and P_{CO_2} of acclimatized subjects both fall from sea level (top right) to the Everest summit (bottom left). The solid line was drawn by Rahn & Otis (23) based on data from a number of investigators at increasing altitudes. The three triangles show data obtained on AMREE including the Everest summit (bottom-most triangle). The data fit well with the extrapolation of the line.

Note that the bottom part of the line, and its extrapolation, are almost vertical indicating that above a certain altitude (about 7000 m) the alveolar P_{O_2} is essentially constant at a value of about 35 mmHg. This means that successful climbers are able to defend their alveolar P_{O_2} by the process of extreme hyperventilation. This is one of the most important features of acclimatization to extreme altitude.

Also note that the alveolar P_{CO_2} values on the summit were between 7 and 8 mmHg (41). In order to generate the enormous ventilations required for these extremely low P_{CO_2} values, the successful climber needs an adequate hypoxic ventilatory response. There is evidence that climbers who are unlucky enough to be born with a low hypoxic ventilatory response tolerate extreme altitudes poorly (27) though there are exceptions. It is interesting that the alveolar P_{CO_2} values found on OE II were not quite so low (Malconian *et al.*, personal communication) probably because the degree of acclimatization was less than in the field experiment AMREE (38). In a similar low pressure experiment, Operation Everest I, carried out by Houston and Riley in 1946, when the rate of ascent was almost the same as in OE II, Rahn & Otis (23) pointed out that there was very little acclimatization at the extreme altitudes.

Although the alveolar gas values shown in Fig. 3 are of interest, in terms of the delivery of oxygen to the peripheral tissues it is clearly desirable to know the arterial blood gases. Arterial P_{O_2}, P_{CO_2} and pH were measured during Operation Everest II at inspired P_{O_2} values of 63, 49 and 43 mmHg corresponding to altitudes on Mt. Everest of about 6450, 8100 and 8848 m respectively (29). The last altitude is the Everest summit. At each altitude, arterial blood was taken at rest, and at two or three levels of exercise, obtained by means of a bicycle ergometer.

Both the arterial P_{O2} and P_{CO2} declined with altitude, and at any given altitude, with increasing work level. The mean arterial P_{O2} on the summit was 30 mmHg at rest, and this fell to 28 mmHg during exercise levels of 60 and 120 watts. Resting arterial P_{CO2} fell from 20 at an inspired P_{O2} of 63, down to 11 on the summit. Exercise on the summit reduced the arterial P_{CO2} to 10 mmHg.

The very low P_{CO2} values on the summit resulted in a marked degree respiratory alkalosis. The highest arterial pH seen on OE II was 7.56 which was the resting value on the summit. However on AMREE where the P_{CO2} values were much lower, and base excess was measured on venous blood taken the following morning after the summit climb, calculated arterial pH exceeded 7.7 (41). The extreme respiratory alkalosis increases the oxygen infinity of hemoglobin and results in more rapid loading of oxygen in the pulmonary capillary. This is advantageous because oxygen transfer across the blood-gas barrier is diffusion-limited under these extraordinary conditions, and the advantage of the increased loading in the pulmonary capillary outweighs the disadvantage of the decreased unloading in the peripheral tissues (1). The reason for the diffusion limitation of oxygen transfer at extreme altitude is that the effective slope of the oxygen dissociation curve is very high. First, oxygen exchange is occurring on a very steep part of the curve, and second, the polycythemia increases the change in the oxygen concentration of the blood per unit change of P_{O2}.

The very low P_{CO2} values referred to above imply enormous increases in ventilation. Since the alveolar P_{CO2} at sea level is 40 mmHg, and carbon dioxide production for a given work level is independent of altitude, the data shown in Fig. 2 imply an increase in alveolar ventilation to approximately 5 times normal. We have anecdotal evidence for this from a tape recorded by Dr. Christopher Pizzo on the Everest summit. He had to pause for breath between every two or three words. It is likely that these enormous ventilations at extreme altitude incur such an oxygen cost that they limit the amount of work that a climber can carry out (33).

Although ventilation is enormously increased at extreme altitudes, it is a paradox that the other great convection system for transporting oxygen, that is the cardiac output, is not changed in acclimatized subjects at high altitudes compared with sea level. In other words the relationship between cardiac output and oxygen uptake (or power) is the same in acclimatized subjects at high altitudes as it is at sea level (21, 24). The reasons for this are obscure. It is well known that cardiac output for a given work level increases during acute hypoxia (30). Why the relationship returns to the sea level value in acclimatized subjects is unknown. It should be pointed out that because polycythemia develops during acclimatization, hemoglobin flow in relation to power is increased. However why the body does not take advantage of the possible increase in the delivery of oxygen to the peripheral tissues by raising cardiac output is a mystery.

At one time it was thought that cardiac function was extremely vulnerable to the severe hypoxia of high altitude. For example as late as 1934, Leonard Hill stated that «degeneration of the heart and other organs due to low oxygen pressure in the tissues, is a chief danger which the Everest climbers have to face» (10). However measurements made during OE II showed surprisingly that myocardial contractility was well maintained up to simulated altitudes of about 8010 m. The measurements were made by cardiac catheterization and two-dimensional echocardiography (24, 28). Indeed there was a suggestion that contractility was even better under these conditions of extreme hypoxemia when the arterial P_{O_2} was about 33 mmHg, than at sea level, when the P_{O_2} is between 90 and 100 mmHg. This is a fascinating finding indicating as it does that the normal myocardium is extremely tolerant of severe tissue hypoxia. It emphasizes the fundamental difference between hypoxemia and ischemia. Of course it should not be assumed that someone with coronary artery disease is not at increased risk at high altitudes (37), although this has actually been suggested (25).

Maximal work rate (power) and maximal oxygen consumption ($\dot{V}O_{2max}$) fall precipitously with increasing altitude at extreme heights, and as pointed out earlier, it is a remarkable coincidence that the $\dot{V}O_{2max}$ of a climber near the summit of Mt. Everest is just sufficient to allow him to reach the highest point on earth without supplementary oxygen. Figure 4 shows measurements of $\dot{V}O_{2max}$ on both AMREE and OE II down to the inspired P_{O_2} of the summit of Mt. Everest (43 mmHg). The AMREE measurements were made on extremely well-acclimatized subjects at an altitude of 6300 m with the subjects breathing air, 16 and 14% oxygen respectively (40). The last gave an inspired P_{O_2} of 43 mmHg equivalent to that on the Everest summit where the $\dot{V}O_{2max}$ was 1.07 l/min. The data from OE II were obtained after 40 days of exposure to simulated high altitude (6) and, as noted earlier, the subjects were apparently not as well acclimatized as those on AMREE. The summit measurements were made at a barometric pressure of 240 mmHg with the subjects breathing a slightly enriched oxygen mixture giving the same inspired P_{O_2} of about 43 mmHg. In spite of this difference between the two studies, the agreement on $\dot{V}O_{2max}$ is extraordinarily close. Note that the AMREE subjects had higher $\dot{V}_{O_{2max}}$ levels at sea level but nevertheless the values on the Everest summit were extremely close.

An oxygen consumption of about 1 l/min is equivalent to that produced by walking slowly on level ground. It therefore only permits a very slow climbing rate and calculations show that it fits reasonably well with the climbing rate of about 2 m/min reported by Messner and Habeler near the summit on their first ascent on Everest in 1978 (33).

It might be thought that the great reduction in aerobic capacity at extreme altitudes as illustrated in Figure 4 would be partly compensated for by a substantial increase in anaerobic glycolysis. This is well known to occur in acute hypoxia where the reduction in aerobic power evinces substantial anaerobic glycolysis (34). Surprisingly this is not the situation at extreme altitude.

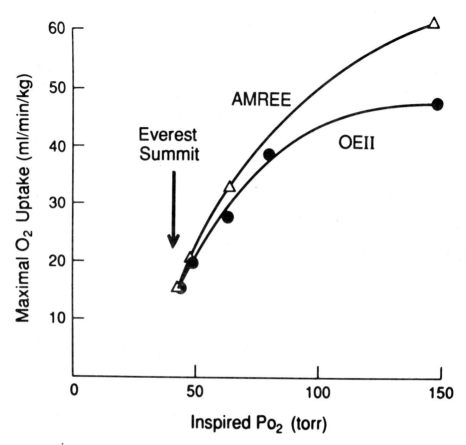

Figure 4 - VO_{2max} plotted against inspired P_{O2} as measured during the 1981 American Medical Research Expedition to Everest (AMREE) and the low pressure chamber simulated ascent, Operation Everest II (OE II). At the inspired P_{O2} corresponding to the Everest summit, VO_{2max} was about 1.07 l/min. From West (39).

Edwards (8) during the 1935 International High Altitude Expedition to Chile was the first to show that blood lactate levels are low in acclimatized subjects at high altitudes even during maximal work. He plotted blood lactate against power at various altitudes up to 5340 m and showed that when the subjects were well acclimatized, all the points fell on the same line. This means that blood lactate for a given work level was independent of tissue P_{O2}. Since maximal work capacity declines rapidly with increasingly altitude (Fig. 4) this finding also implies that maximal blood lactate falls in acclimatized subjects as altitude increases.

Cerretelli (4) has done extensive studies on this topic and a summary of his results is shown in Figure 5 together with additional data obtained at an altitude of 6300 m on AMREE (40). A provocative prediction from these data is that during maximal exercise at altitudes exceeding 7500 m there will be no increase blood lactate at all in spite of the extreme oxygen deprivation! This is indeed a paradox.

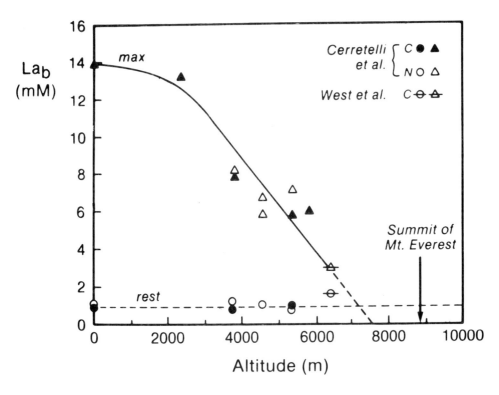

Figure 5 - Blood lactate concentration (Lab) plotted against altitude in acclimatized Caucasians (C) and high altitude natives (N). Most of the data are redrawn from Cerretelli *et al.* (5). The data for 6300 m are from West *et al.* (41). From West (34).

The reasons for the low blood lactate levels during maximal exercise in acclimatized subjects at high altitude are not fully understood. It should be pointed out that a low blood lactate per se does not necessarily mean a reduced lactate production, because the blood level depends on a balance between production and removal. However muscle biopsies of the vastus lateralis taken on OE II showed that lactate levels in the muscle were indeed reduced. For example at a barometric pressure of 282 mmHg, muscle lactate concentration (m mol/kg dry wt) was 39.2 compared to 113 at sea level after exhaustive exercise (9). The «lactate paradox» as it has been dubbed, is a topic of intense research at the present time.

REFERENCES

1. BENCOWITZ, H.Z., WAGNER, P.D. & WEST, J.B. 1982. Effect of change in P50 on exercise tolerance at high altitude: a theoretical study. *J Appl Physiol* 53: 1487-1495.

2. BERT, P. 1878. *La Pression Barométrique*. Paris, Masson: English translation by M.A. Hitchcock and F.A. Hitchcock, College Book Co., 1943.

3. BOWMAN, I. 1916. *The Andes of southern Peru, geographical reconnaissance along the seventy-third meridian*. New York: H. Holt and Company.

4. CERRETELLI, P. 1980. Gas exchange at high altitude. *In*: J.B. West (ed.), *Pulmonary Gas Exchange Vol. II*. New York: Academic Press: 97-147.

5. CERRETELLI, P. 1982. Anaerobic metabolism at high altitude: the lactacid mechanism. *In*: W. Brendel & R.A. Zink (eds.), *High Altitude Physiology and Medicine*. New York: Springer-Verlag.

6. CYMERMAN, A., REEVES, J.T., SUTTON, J.R., ROCK, P.B., GROVES, B.M., MALCONIAN, M.K., YOUNG, P.M., WAGNER, P.D. & HOUSTON, C.S. 1989. Operation Everest II: maximal oxygen uptake at extreme altitude. *J Appl Physiol* 66: 2446-2453.

7. ECHEVARRÍA, E. 1968. The South American Indian as a pioneer alpinist. *Alpine Journal* 73: 81-88.

8. EDWARDS, H.T. 1936. Lactic acid in rest and work at high altitude. *Amer J Physiol* 116: 367-375.

9. GREEN, H.J., SUTTON, J., YOUNG, P., CYMERMAN, A. & HOUSTON, C.S. 1989. Operation Everest II: muscle energetics during maximal exhaustive exercise. *J Appl Physiol* 66: 142-150.

10. HILL, L. 1934. Foreword. *In*: A. Campbell & E.P. Poulton (eds.), *Oxygen and Carbon Dioxide Theraphy*. London: Oxford University Press.

11. HOUSTON, C.S. & RILEY, R.L. 1947. Respiratory and circulatory changes during acclimatization to high altitude. *Amer J Physiol* 149: 565-588.

12. HOUSTON, C.S., SUTTON, J.R., CYMERMAN, A. & REEVES, J.T. 1987. Operation Everest II: man at extreme altitude. *J Appl Physiol* 63: 877-882.

13. INTERNATIONAL CIVIL AVIATION ORGANIZATION. 1964. *Manual of the ICAO Standard Atmosphere*. Montreal, Quebec: Int. Civil Aviation Org.

14. KELLAS, A.M. 1921. Sur les possibilités de faire l'ascension du Mont Everest. *Compt. Rendus des Séances* 1: 451-521.

15. KEYS, A. 1936. The physiology of life at high altitude: the International High Altitude Expedition to Chile 1935. *Scientific Monthly* 43: 289-312.

16. MC INTYRE, L. 1987. The High Andes. *National Geographic Magazine* 171: 422-459.

17. MESSNER, R. 1979. *Everest: Expedition to the Ultimate*. London: Kaye & Ward.

18. MONGE, C. 1948. *Acclimatization in the Andes*. Baltimore: Johns Hopkins Universtiy Press.

19. NORTON, E.F. 1925. *In*: *The Fight for Everest, 1924*. London: Arnold: 120-143.

20. PUGH, L.G.C.E. 1957. Resting ventilation and alveolar air on Mount Everest: with remarks on the relation of barometric pressure to altitude in mountains. *J Physiol (Lond)* 135: 590-610.

21. PUGH, L.G.C.E., GILL, M.B., LAHIRI, S., MILLEDGE, J.S., WARD, M.P. & WEST, J.B. 1964. Muscular exercise at great altitudes. *J Appl Physiol* 19: 431-440.

22. RAHN, H. & FENN, W.O. 1955. A Graphical Analysis of the Respiratory Gas Exchange. *American Physiological Society*.

23. RAHN, H. & OTIS, A.B. 1949. Man's respiratory response during and after acclimatization to high altitude. *Amer J Physiol* 157: 445-462.

24. REEVES, J.T., GROVES, B.M., SUTTON, J.R., WAGNER, P.D., CYMERMAN, A., MALCONIAN, M.K., ROCK, P.B., YOUNG, P.M. & HOUSTON, C.S. 1987. Operation Everest II: preservation of cardiac function at extreme altitude. *J Appl Physiol* 63: 531-539.

25. RENNIE, D. 1989. Will mountains trekkers have heart attacks? *J Amer Med Assoc* 261: 1045-1046.

26. SANTOLAYA, R.B., LAHIRI, S., ALFARO, R.T. & SCHOENE, R.B. 1989. Respiratory adaptation in the highest inhabitants and highest Sherpa mountaineers. *Respirat Physiol* 77: 253-262.

27. SCHOENE, R.B., LAHIRI, S., HACKETT, P.H., PETERS, R.M.,JR., MILLEDGE, J.S., PIZZO, C.J., SARNQUIST, F.H., BOYER, S.J., GRABER, D.J., MARET, K.H. & WEST, J.B. 1984. Relationship of hypoxic ventilatory response to exercise performance on Mount Everest. *J Appl Physiol* 56: 1478-1483.

28. SUAREZ, J., ALEXANDER, J.K. & HOUSTON, C.S. 1987. Enhanced left ventricular systolic performance at high altitude during Operation Everest II. *Amer J Cardiol* 60: 137-142.

29. SUTTON, J.R., REEVES, J.T., WAGNER, P.D., GROVES, B.M., CYMERMAN, A., MALCONIAN, M.K., ROCK, P.B., YOUNG, P.M., WALTER, S.D. & HOUSTON, C.S. 1988. Operation Everest II: oxygen transport during exercise at extreme simulated altitude. *J Appl Physiol* 64: 1309-1321.

30. VOGEL, J.A. & HARRIS, C.W. 1967. Cardiopulmonary responses of resting man during early exposure to high altitude. *J Appl Physiol* 22: 1124-1128.

31. WARD, M.P. 1986. Across Tibet. *Alpine Journal* 91: 84-89.

32. WARD, M.P., MILLEDGE, J.S. & WEST, J.B. 1989. *High Altitude Medicine and Physiology*. London: Chapman and Hall.

33. WEST, J.B. 1983. Climbing Mt. Everest without oxygen: an analysis of maximal exercise during extreme hypoxia. *Respirat Physiol* 52: 265-279.

34. WEST, J.B. 1986a. Highest inhabitants in the world. *Nature* 324: 517. 33.

35. WEST, J.B. 1986b. Lactate during exercise at extreme altitude. *Fed Proc* 45: 2953-2957.

36. WEST, J.B. 1987. Alexander M. Kellas and the physiological challenge of Mt. Everest. *J Appl Physiol* 63: 3-11.

37. WEST, J.B. 1988a. Rate of ventilatory acclimatization to extreme altitude. *Respirat Physiol* 74: 323-333.

38. WEST, J.B. 1988b. In Reply-The Safety of Trekking at High Altitude After Coronary Bypass Surgery. *J Amer Med Assoc* 260: 2218-2219.

39. WEST, J.B. 1990. Limiting factors for exercise at extreme altitude. *Clin Physiol* 10: 265-272.

40. WEST, J.B., BOYER, S.J., GRABER, D.J., HACKETT, P.H., MARET, K.H., MILLEDGE, J.S., PETERS JR., R.M., PIZZO, C.J., SAMAJA, M., SARNQUIST, F.H., SCHOENE, R.B. & WINSLOW, R.M. 1983a. Maximal exercise at extreme altitudes on Mount Everest. *J Appl Physiol* 55: 688-698.

41. WEST, J.B., HACKETT, P.H., MARET, K.H., MILLEDGE, J.S., PETERS, R.M., JR., PIZZO, C.J. & WINSLOW, R.M. 1983b. Pulmonary gas exchange on the summit of Mt. Everest. *J Appl Physiol* 55: 678-687.

42. WEST, J.B., LAHIRI, S., MARET, K.H., PETERS, R.M. & PIZZO, C.J. 1983c. Barometric pressures at extreme altitudes on Mt. Everest: Physiological significance. *J Appl Physiol* 54: 1188-1194.

IS HIGH ALTITUDE A RISK FACTOR FOR PATIENTS WITH CORONARY HEART DISEASE?

Robert F. Grover

Abstract

In healthy young men, ascent to high altitude is associated with sympathetic stimulation and an increase in circulating norepinephrine. This results in an increase in hearth rate, increase in myocardial contractility, and in some individuals an impressive rise is systemic arterial pressure, all factors know to increase myocardial oxygen demand. Initially, myocardial oxygen supply is augmented by increasing coronary blood flow. However, within a few days, a greater extraction of oxygen from the coronary arterial blood permits coronary blood flow to decrease, thereby lessening the demands on the coronary circulation. Myocardial oxygen supply is well maintained and myocardial function is preserved even when arterial PO_2 falls as low as 30 Torr.

How well do patients with coronary artery disease tolerate high altitude? Definitive studies are lacking, but limited data indicate no increase in the frequency of myocardial ischemia. Furthermore, among 150,000 persons trekking to Everest Base Camp at 17,000 feet, there were no cardiac deaths. A sojourn at high altitude has even been advocated by some for the rehabilitation of patients following recovery from a myocardial infarction or coronary bypass surgery. Hence, given a patient with stable coronary disease and a reasonably good exercise tolerance, there is no justification for advising against travel to moderate altitude.

Key words: Hypoxia adaptation, coronary disease, cardiac physiology.

Resumen

En hombres jóvenes el ascenso a la altura se asocia a estimulación simpática y a un incremento de la norepinefrina circulante. Esto resulta en un incremento de la frecuencia cardíaca, incremento de la contractilidad miocárdica y, en algunos individuos, en un impresionante aumento de la presión arterial sistémica, todos estos factores que aumentan la demanda de oxígeno miocárdico. Inicialmente el suministro de oxígeno aumenta con el incremento del flujo sanguíneo coronario. Sin embargo, al cabo de unos días la mayor extracción de oxígeno por la sangre arterial coronaria reduce el flujo coronario, decreciendo así la demanda sobre la circulación coronaria. El sumistro de oxígeno miocárdico se mantiene y se preserva la función miocárdica aún cuando el PO_2 arterial cae hasta 30 Torr.

¿Cuán bien toleran los pacientes con enfermedad coronaria la altura? Aunque no hay estudios definitivos, los poco datos disponibles indican que no hay un incremento en la frecuencia de isquemia miocárdica. Es más, no hubieron muertes por problemas cardíacos entre las 150,000 personas que realizaron caminatas al Campamento Base del Everest a 17,000 pies. Muchos han aconsejado viajes a la altura para la rehabilitación de pacientes que se recuperan de infartos al miocardio o bypass coronario. De esta manera, dado un paciente con enfermedad coronaria y razonable tolerancia al ejercicio no se justifica la prohibición de viajes a alturas moderadas.

Palabras claves: Adaptación a la hipoxia, enfermedad coronaria, fisiología cardíaca.

Each year millions of people visit the mountains of the western United States for recreation, camping, fishing, hiking, skiing, playing golf, or simply enjoying the magnificant scenery. Many of the most popular recreation areas are located at altitudes between 2500 and 3500 meters (8,000 to 11,500 feet). With modern transportation, rapid ascent to these areas is commonplace. Visitors include men, women and children of all ages, some with a variety of health problems. Among these are older men with coronary heart disease. For such men, does exposure to these moderate altitudes constitute a significant risk of a sudden cardiac event? Surprisingly, there is little definitive information to answer that question.

NORMAL CORONARY CIRCULATION

The primary function of the coronary circulation is to adjust coronary blood flow, and hence arterial oxygen supply, to meet changing oxygen demands by the myocardium. Myocardial oxygen requirements are determined by the magnitude of the pressure generated within the left ventricle during systole, the rate at which this pressure is generated, i.e. contractility, and the frequency of systole, i.e. the number of contractions per minute (heart rate). As we shall see, an increase in each of these factors occurs at high altitude.

One of the most readily observable early responses to high altitude is tachycardia (6). For example, during the first few days at 3100 m, heart rate is increased 10-20%. An exercise load generating a heart rate of 110/min at sea level will elevate heart rate to 135/min at this altitude. However, with adaptation over 1-3 weeks, this tachycardia usually diminishes. This increase in heart rate would increase myocardial oxygen requirements.

In most previous studies conducted at high altitude, only isolated measurements of blood pressure have been made, but these tend to show a modest rise (6). In 1991, the first 24 hour measurements of ambulatory blood pressure were obtained in healthy young men. Observations were made on two separate days at sea level, and at three intervals during adaptation to 4300 m (13). Although three of the five men showed only a modest rise in systolic pressure, the other two showed a rise of 20 mmHg by the second day, and this rise increased to a remarkable 50 mmHg rise by day 18. On occasion, systolic pressure approached 200 mmHg. Obviously the rise in blood pressure is variable, and from these limited data the frequency of such extreme elevations in systolic pressure in otherwise healthy young individuals is unknown. Nevertheless, any rise in systolic pressure would further increase myocardial oxygen demands.

Echocardiography has made it possible to assess myocardial contractility noninvasively. It has been employed during at least three investigations of human altitude exposure, and revealed increases in such indices of contractility as ejection fraction and velocity of wall motion (12). This, too, would augment myocardial oxygen needs.

The underlying mechanism producing the increases in heart rate, systolic blood pressure, and myocardial contractility is stimulation of the sympathetic nervous system by the stress of hypoxemia. Evidence for this is the progressive rise in plasma catecholamines and in the 24 hour excretion of norepinephrine over the first days at high altitude (6).

Meeting myocardial oxygen demands depends upon coronary arterial oxygen transport. With ascent to 3100 m altitude, the lowering of atmospheric pressure from 760 mmHg to 525 mmHg is associated with a fall in arterial oxygen tension (pO_2) from 92 mmHg to 60 mmHg at rest, with a further reduction to 55 mmHg during exercise. In older men, whose lungs provide less efficient gas exchange, even lower oxygen tensions would be expected. As a consequence, arterial oxygen saturation, normally about 97% at sea level, would be reduced at 3100 m to about 90%. If hemoglobin concentration were to remain unchanged, coronary arterial oxygen content would then be reduced by about 10%. However, within hours of arrival at high altitude, hemoconcentration begins, elevating both hematocrit and hemoglobin concentration. This is sufficient to offset the arterial desaturation and preserve arterial oxygen content at pre-ascent levels both at rest and during exercise (4). In other words, at moderate altitude, arterial desaturation per se does not compromise coronary oxygen transport.

Within the capillary bed of the myocardium, oxygen diffuses from the coronary arterial blood into the surrounding myocardial tissue. As a result, blood pO_2 falls progressively from its level in the arteries until it is in equilibrium with the pO_2 of surrounding tissue. This minimum pO_2, as reflected in the venous blood draining from the myocardium into the coronary sinus, is 18 mmHg even in the absence of exercise. In view of this low pO_2, it is generally assumed that oxygen extraction from the coronary circulation is virtually maximal at all times. This suggests that oxygen delivery to the myocardium cannot be augmented by increasing extraction, and hence can only be accomplished by increasing coronary blood flow.

If this assumption were correct, then when ascent to moderate altitude increases myocardial oxygen demands (through sympathetic stimulation), one would expect to see an increase in coronary blood flow. However, direct measurements indicate this is not the case (3). In fact, coronary blood flow is virtually the same as at sea level, both at rest and during exercise. This is made possible by a decrease in the affinity of hemoglobin for oxygen, perhaps from an increase in red cell 2,3-diphosphoglycerate (2,3 DPG) (2). Recall that the coronary circulation is apparently regulated to maintain a constant myocardial tissue pO_2 (1); hence, the coronary sinus blood pO_2 also remains constant (at 18 mmHg). When the affinity of hemoglobin decreases (P50 increases), the coronary blood oxygen saturation must then fall if an increase in pO_2 is to be avoided. Apparently this is exactly what happens. Coronary sinus blood oxygen saturation does decrease from a value of 30% at sea level down to 20% at 3100 m while pO_2 remains unchanged at 18 mmHg (3). In other words, with ascent to moderate altitude, oxygen extraction (arterio-venous difference in oxygen content) from the coronary blood increases significantly, both at rest as well as under the demands of exercise. Consequently, even though the oxygen requirements of the myocardium have been increased, these can now be met with no greater coronary blood flow than was required at sea level. In other words, ascent to moderate altitude places only minimal demands on the coronary circulation in spite of increased myocardial oxygen requirements.

CORONARY ARTERY DISEASE

Patients with documented coronary disease (CAD) have never been the subjects of a definitive study of exposure to high altitude. However, limited evidence indicates that such patients tolerate moderate altitude exposure without difficulty. Such evidence consists of surveys of populations who visit high altitude regions, pilot studies of small numbers of CAD patients taken to high altitude specifically for study, and patients with known CAD and myocardial infarction undergoing rehabilitation in centers located at high altitude in Peru.

Trekking in Nepal has become a very popular activity in recent years. Frequently, visitors fly from Kathmandu situated at 4,500 ft (1,380 m) to Lukla at 9,000 ft (2,750 m), then trek into the Khumbu region for several days, eventually reaching Mount Everest Base Camp at 17,700 ft (5,400 m). Only serious climbing expeditions proceed higher. In a recent 3 1/2 year period, nearly 150,000 persons made this trek. Considering the considerable expense of such a trek, these tend to be older individuals. No cardiac deaths were reported, and only 3 (perhaps 6) men required helicopter evacuation for known cardiac problems (11). In addition, there are anecdotal reports of men with coronary artery bypass surgery making this trek without ill effect. The authors conclude that «if altitude is an increased risk for sudden coronary events, this effect is difficult to detect.»

Skiing in the Colorado Rockies is also a very popular sport. Many of the major ski resorts are situated between 8,000 and 9,000 ft (2,400 and 2,700 m) where visitors sleep and eat. For skiing, they ascend via lifts to altitudes of 12,000 ft (3,600 m) to begin their descent. Grover and his associates (5) reasoned that such strenuous exercise in the cold and hypoxic mountain environment might prove to be particularly stressful for older men with latent CAD. To test this hypothesis, using radio-telemetry, they recorded electrocardiograms during active skiing above 10,000 ft (3,100 m) in 149 men, two thirds of whom were at least 40 years old. In this older age group, despite remarkable tachycardia, the incidence of abnormal ST segment changes was only 5.6%, no higher than has been reported in asymptomatic older men tested at sea level. In other words, the myocardial requirements for exercise at high altitude were met quite adequately, even in older men.

Two other reports deal specifically with CAD patients. In a pilot study, Okin (9) studied eleven men with documented previous myocardial infarction and/or angina during a standardized step test, first at their resident altitude of 5,200 ft (1,600 m), and again after driving into the mountains to 8,000 ft (2,400 m) and then to 10,400 ft (3,200 m). In spite of higher heart rates, no patient who had a normal Master's Test at lower altitude had a positive Master's Test at higher altitude. Likewise, no patient developed symptoms at higher altitude who did not have them at the lower altitude. Hence, ischemic changes could not be produced in these patients with know CAD despite ascent from 5,200 ft to 8,000 and 10,400 ft.

In one other study (7), a hypobaric chamber was employed to simulate ascent to high altitude. Thirty men with proven stabilized CAD performed a double Master's two-step exercise test at sea level. They then entered the decompression chamber and over 10 minutes were taken to a simulated altitude of 15,000 ft (4,500 m). After a 40 minute rest, they repeated the exercise test. None of the subjects manifested any symptoms or arrhythmias during exercise testing at sea level or in the decompression chamber. The electrocardiographic response to the Master's Test was positive in 17 of the subjects at sea level, and increased slightly to 20 at simulated altitude. The authors concluded that it is quite safe to subject persons with stabilized ischemic heart disease to exercise in an hypoxic environment.

Finally, exposure to high altitude has actually been employed to facilitate rehabilitation of patients with coronary heart disease. In Peru, Marticorena et al. (8) have been taking patients with healed myocardial infarction, some following coronary bypass surgery, to La Oroya at 3,730 meters (12,300 feet) to participate in an extended rehabilitation program. Although detailed results have not been published, the authors report that the patients have a good response to this altitude exposure with no untoward effects. This unconventional approach to treatment will be followed with great interest.

In conclusion, considering the limited available evidence, given a patient with stable CAD and a reasonably good exercise tolerance at sea level, exposure to moderate altitude does not appear to constitute an added risk factor, and there is no justification for depriving him of the pleasure of mountain travel (10).

REFERENCES

1. DUVELLEROY, M.A., MEHMEL, H. & LAVER, M.B. 1973. Hemoglobin-oxygen equilibrium and coronary blood flow: an analog model. *J Appl Physiol* 35: 480-484.

2. EATON, J.W., BREWER, G.J. & GROVER, R.F. 1969. Role of red cell 2,3-diphosphoglycerate in adaptation of man to altitude. *J Lab Clin Med 73:* 603-609.

3. GROVER, R.F., LUFSCHANOWSKI, R. & ALEXANDER, J.K. 1976. Alterations in the coronary circulation of man following ascent to 3,100 m altitude. *J Appl Physiol* 41: 832-838.

4. GROVER, R.F., REEVES, J.T., ROWELL, L.B., PIANTADOSI, C.A. & SALTZMAN, H.A. 1993. The influence of environmental factors on the cardiovascular system. *In* R.C. Schlant, C.E. Rackley, E.H. Sonnenblick & N.K. Wenger (eds.), *The Heart. Arteries and Veins.* New York: McGraw-Hill: (in press).

5. GROVER, R.F., TUCKER, C.E., McGROARTY, S.R. & TRAVIS, R.R. 1990. The coronary stress of skiing at high altitude. *Arch Int Med* 150: 1205-1208.

6. GROVER, R.F., WEIL, J.V. & REEVES, J.T. 1986. Cardiovascular adaptation to exercise at high altitude. *In* K.B. Pandolph (ed.), *Exercise and Sport Sciences Reviews, vol. 14.* New York: Macmillan: 269-302.

7. KHANNA, P.K., DHAM, S.K. & HOON, R.S. 1976. Exercise in an hypoxic environment as a screening test for ischaemic heart disease. *Aviat, Space and Environ Medi* 47: 1114-1117.

8. MARTICORENA, E.A., MARTICORENA, J.M., MARTICORENA, J.E. et al. 1984-1985. Nueva técnica en rehabilitación cardíaca y prevención primaria coronaria: utilización de las grandes alturas. *Archivos del Instituto de Biología Andina* 13: 189-206.

9. OKIN, J.T. 1970. Response of patients with coronary heart disease to exercise at varying altitudes. *Advas Cardiol* 5: 92-96.

10. RENNIE, D. 1989. Will mountain trekkers have heart attacks? *JAMA* 261: 1045-1046.

11. SHLIM, D.R. & HOUSTON, R. 1989. Helicopter rescues and deaths among trekkers in Nepal. *JAMA* 261: 1017-1019.

12. SUAREZ, J., ALEXANDER, J.K. & HOUSTON, C.S. 1987. Enhanced left ventricular performance at high altitude during Operation Everest II. *Amer J Cardiol* 60: 137-142.

13. WOLFEL, E.E., YARON, M., SELLAND, M., MAZZEO, R.S., CYMERMAN, A., GROVER, R. & REEVES, J.T. 1992. Increases in systemic arterial pressure after 3 weeks residence at 4300 m. A sympathetic effect. *Clin Res* 40: 22A.

IV.

MAL DE MONTAÑA
CRÓNICO

CHRONIC MOUNTAIN SICKNESS IN PERU, CHILE, AND NEPAL: 1978-1987

Robert M. Winslow

Abstract

Beetween 1978 and 1987, the author and Dr. Monge collaborated on studies of Chronic Mountain Sickness (CMS) in Peru, Chile, and Nepal. These culminated in the book, *Hypoxia, Polycythemia, and Chronic Mountain Sickness* (Baltimore: The John Hopkins University Press, 1987). In CMS, the final equilibrium between O_2 supply and red cell concentration is influenced by many factors, including cardiopulmonary function, ventilatory control, sleep patterns, physical conditioning, and, probably, genetics. Many of these, in turn, are also influenced by age and environment. One useful concept is the «vicious cycle hypothesis»: polycythemia, arising from a normal stimulus (hypoxia), can become self propagating if decreased blood flow resulting from increased viscosity causes further hypoxia. In the kidney, this would imply higher and higher erythropoietin production as hematocrit rises, rather than the reverse. This concept remains controversial, underscoring the need for further work both in the laboratory and in the mountains.

Key words: Chronic mountain sickness, polycythemia, erythropoietin, hypoxia, hematocrit.

Resumen

Entre los años 1978 y 1987, el autor y el Dr. Monge colaboraron en estudios sobre el Mal de Montaña Crónico (MMC) en Perú, Chile y Nepal. Estos estudios se plasmaron en el libro, *Hypoxia, Polycythemia, and Chronic Mountain Sickness* (Baltimore: The John Hopkins University Press, 1987). En el MMC el equilibrio final entre el aporte de O_2 y la concentración de glóbulos rojos está influenciado por muchos factores, incluyendo la función cardiopulmonar, el control de la ventilación, los patrones de sueño, la condición física, y, probablemente, la genética del individuo. Muchos de estos factores a su vez, están también influenciados por la edad y el ambiente. Una hipótesis conveniente es la del «ciclo vicioso»: la policitemia, producto de un estímulo natural (hipoxia), puede autopropagarse si disminuye el flujo sanguíneo como resultado de un aumento de la viscocidad, causando más hipoxia. En el riñón ésto implicaría una síntesis de eritropoyetina cada vez mayor a medida que se eleva el hematocrito y no lo contrario. Este concepto es aún controversial, y plantea la necesidad de llevar a cabo más investigación en este campo, tanto en el laboratorio como en las montañas.

Palabras claves: Mal de montaña crónico, policitemia, eritropoyetina, hipoxia, hematocrito.

Résumé

Entre 1978 et 1987, l'auteur et le Dr. Monge collaborèrent aux études sur le Mal de Montagne Chronique (MMC) au Pérou, au Chili et au Népal. Ces études débouchèrent sur le livre *Hypoxia, polycythemia, and Chronic Mountain Sickness* (Baltimore: The Johns Hopkins University press, 1987).

Dans le MMC, l'équilibre final entre l'apport de O_2 et la concentration de globules rouges est influencé par de nombreux facteurs, y compris la fonction cardiopulmonaire, le contrôle de la ventilation, les types de sommeil, la condition physique et, probablement, la génétique des individus. Beaucoup de ces facteurs, à leur tour, sont influencés par l'âge et le milieu ambiant. Une hypothèse satisfaisante est celle du "cercle vicieux" : la polycythémie, conséquence d'une stimulation naturelle (hypoxie) peut s'autopropager si le flux sanguin diminue, conséquence d'une augmentation de viscosité, provoquant plus d'hypoxie.

Dans le rein, ceci provoquerait une synthèse d'érythropoïétine chaque fois plus élevée à mesure qu'augmente l'hématocrite, et non le contraire. Ce concept est encore controversé et fait apparaître la nécessité de développer encore plus la recherche dans ce domaine, aussi bien en laboratoire qu'enaltitude.

Mots clés : Mal de Montagne Chronique, polycythémie, érythropoïétine, hypoxie, hématocrite.

INTRODUCTION

In 1987 Dr. Monge and I summarized our studies in patients with Chronic Mountain Sickness (CMS) in a book published by the Johns Hopkins University Press (17). We expressed the view that polycythemia is a normal response to hypoxia, but that this response is exaggerated in CMS patients. This view led us to question whether polycythemia is an advantageous adaptive mechanism under any circumstance.

This view was not always obvious to us. In fact, our initial studies, carried out in 1978 in Morococha, were designed simply to remeasure the blood oxygen equilibrium curve (OEC) in high altitude natives. This seemed like an appropriate starting point for a systematic study of the clinical entity, because the earlier measurements of Hurtado (1, 8) were badly out of date. The initial studies led to broader ones in Peru, Chile, and Nepal and included experimental observations with many other collaborators in the areas of pulmonary, gas exchange, exercise, and sleep physiology. Over the decade that our experiments together spanned, we came to appreciate CMS as a complex interaction of multiple normal adaptive mechanisms. That is, there may be no single etiological factor. Data collected by us and by others subsequent to publication of our book have served to consolidate and support our views. Dr. Monge and I met for the first time after a seminar he conducted at the University of Maryland in 1976. Both he and I had our roots at the Johns Hopkins University, and so Baltimore seemed an appropriate place to begin our long friendship and collaboration.

The Baltimore meeting occurred at the urging of a young Italian postdoctoral student working in my laboratory at the National Institutes of Health (NIH), Dr. Miki Samaja. Dr. Samaja and I were collaborating on studies on the precise measurement of the whole blood OEC, but he previously had been part of an Italian scientific expedition to Mt. Everest with Dr. Paulo Cerretelli, and was fascinated with high altitude physiology. At the time, I had no interest in high altitude, and my only familiarity with CMS was as a result of my clinical training in hematology.

In his seminar, Dr. Monge showed a graph of hemoglobin concentrations in high-altitude natives. The Gaussian distribution particularly impressed me. We had recently conducted studies in normal sea-level subjects which showed a similar Gaussian distribution of P50 values. The lowest P50's often were seen in patients with elevated carboxyhemoglobin or genetic abnormalities of hemoglobin structure. We discussed at length the significance of these parallel observations, and my naive idea was that perhaps those Andean natives with the highest hematocrit also had the lowest P50.

In our work at the NIH, we had developed very precise methods for the continuous recording of the OEC (25). This method was capable of distinguishing between experimental and biological variation (23), and we concluded that in normal sea-level persons, variation in the P50 value does occur which cannot be explained by the known effectors of oxygen affinity, pH, , and 2,3-DPG. Thus, it seemed possible that a negative relationship might occur between P50 and hemoglobin concentration.

In his characteristic way, Dr. Monge encouraged me to develop the idea of a link between P50 and hemoglobin concentration in high-altitude natives, even though he surely must have considered this to be very unlikely. The result was a proposal to the National Science Foundation for a small travel grant for me, a technician (Nancy Statham, now Nancy Winslow), an engineer (Carter Gibson, NIH), and a colleague (Dr. Sam Charache, Johns Hopkins University) to measure the OEC in the high altitude natives of Peru using the methods we had developed at the NIH.

MOROCOCHA 1978

In my first visit to Lima in the summer of 1978, Drs. Monge, Charache and I met with Professor Hurtado in his home. Although his age was quite advanced at that time, Dr. Hurtado was lucid, and his recollections about his life's research were most impressive. He showed us volumes of data on measurements of the OEC using the van Slyke apparatus, and was very proud to tell us that every point on the OEC required 14 corrections! I was convinced that our modern methods would provide more accurate data.

After moving our team and equipment to Morococha, we began a systematic study of arterial blood gases and blood OEC's in about 50 male native residents with a range of hematocrit (mean 61 ± 8%, s.d.). These studies disproved our initial hypothesis that a causative relationship might exist between blood P50 and hematocrit. In fact, these studies questioned the dogma, originally established by Hurtado, that an increased P50 is an adaptive mechanism (21). In essence, we found that high altitude natives have a chronic respiratory alkalosis which results in increased red cell 2,3-DPG, which raises P50 by its direct effect on hemoglobin and by lowering red cell pH, but which also decreases P50 by the alkaline Bohr effect. In other words, Hurtado's claim of increased P50 was based on correcting the data to pH 7.4 («standard» conditions), but at the *in vivo* pH, higher at altitude, the average P50 is exactly the same as at sea level. We also showed that the Bohr effect in high altitude natives was no different from that in sea level residents (22), a concept that had been based on measurements on Sherpas (14). Our conclusions were eventually accepted by our peers, but we learned that dogmatic ideas die slowly.

During the course of the Morococha work, we also studied iron metabolism, carboxyhemoglobin, and methemoglobin in all of our subjects and were not able to show any significant differences in any respect between CMS patients and «normal» volunteers. We also studied arterial (PO_2)and saturation and could not show any correlation between either and hemoglobin concentration or hematocrit.

Although Dr. Monge had extensive clinical experience in the mountains, examination of CMS patients was particularly impressive to me. They demonstrated cyanosis, clubbing, dependent edema, and impaired (in some cases severely) mental function, especially when the hematocrit was greater than 70%. These observations led us to question whether inadequate transport led to polycythemia or if polycythemia led to decompensated transport. This line of thinking was prompted, I am sure, by the studies we were conducting at the NIH in sickle cell anemia patients. There, we showed that exchange transfusion with normal red cells (no change in hematocrit) could significantly improve objective parameters of blood oxygenation and exercise tolerance (12). Thus, we decided to attempt to determine whether reduction of hematocrit in CMS cases would have objective effects on transport and exercise capacity.

The effect of the environment in Morococha could not be ignored. Dr. Monge and I visited the mines where we observed men working underground in the midst of large amounts of dust generated by the mining activities. The men had been issued face masks by the mining company, but many chose not to wear them. We were intrigued then at the question of how much chronic lung disease contributes to hypoxemia in these natives and, thus, to polycythemia.

CERRO DE PASCO 1979

After the Morococha experience we were not confident that interpreting our data with respect to the etiology of CMS was possible, and became convinced that we should find another site for working which did not suffer the same degree of air pollution. Dr. Monge suggested we conduct our next set of experiments at Cerro de Pasco, where the mining was done above ground, and subjects could be selected who never had been exposed to the same conditions as our Morococha subjects. So in 1978 we set off across Junin Province in a caravan of Brazilian Volkswagens. Cerro de Pasco, while slightly more remote, was also more civilized at the time, with better weather and better services available to us. The living facilities were also better, and Sr. Atencio and our cook, Betty, took excellent care of us.

The first Cerro expedition was intended only as a pilot study. We wished to collect the same type of blood data as we had in Morococha, but, in addition, we wanted to make some measurements of overall physical capacity, so we could judge the advantages and disadvantages of polycythemia. We selected another cohort of about 25 subjects and essentially repeated the Morococha measurements. Our budget was low and our exercise protocol was rather simple: it consisted of pedalling on a cycle ergometer in stages, 1 minute each, of increasing work until the subject stopped because of exhaustion. We took blood samples at each stage to measure gases and lactic acid, and we collected expired gas in meteorological balloons in order to measure uptake and release (24).

We considered this Cerro de Pasco expedition to be a transition year. We had 3 years of funding from the NSF, and we intended the third to be our definitive study of the relationships between blood gas transport, polycythemia, and exercise. But one of our subjects was a severely polycythemic man who required therapeutic phlebotomy. We were able to study this man at several hematocrits, and we found that not only did his exercise tolerance improve, but his arterial lactic acid concentrations were lower and increased more slowly during exercise at lower hematocrits. These findings seemed to confirm our general belief that polycythemia serves no useful purpose in high altitude natives.

1979 was also a transition year for me in other ways. My interest in high altitude physiology was deepening, and I was invited to join the 1981 American Medical Expedition to Everest (AMREE), led by Prof. John West at the University of California, San Diego. Dr. West was a scientist of substantial reputation, and the invitation was irresistible to me because of the opportunity to learn firsthand something about pulmonary and exercise physiology from experts. However, my employer, the NIH did not share my enthusiasm, and preferred me to focus my scientific interests on subjects perceived to be of more immediate practical importance. Since we were unable to resolve this difference, I elected to move instead to the Centers for Disease Control in Atlanta. This move allowed me to pursue my high altitude interests. One significant disadvantage to me, however, was that in my first year in Atlanta, Dr. Monge spent much of 1980 at the NIH campus in Bethesda as a Senior Fogarty Fellow, an appointment I had worked hard for. I had anticipated a year of close collaboration with him.

CERRO DE PASCO 1980

The 1980 Cerro de Pasco expedition was, judging from productivity, our most successful expedition. Joining us that year, in addition to Nancy Statham (Winslow) were Dr. Frank Sarnquist (Anesthesiologist from Stanford, also an AMREE member), Dr. Harvey Klein (NIH Clinical Center Blood Bank), Dr. Ed Brown (Mount Sinai Medical Center, New York), and a number of technical associates. Our instrumentation was quite sophisticated, considering the environment. We had been working on our exercise protocol and the computer hardware and software (16) to make data collection noninvasive and automatic. The participation of Drs. Sarnquist and Klein meant that we could place arterial and Swann-Ganz catheters with safety and convenience (4), and carry out sophisticated blood exchange protocols to study the effects of exercise.

Although we continued to expand our database on blood gases and hematologic measurements, our most useful observations were made with one subject. This man had a hematocrit of approximately 65% and typical symptoms of CMS. In addition, he was able to cooperate fully with our exercise protocol, and was willing to undergo a stringent program of hematocrit reduction. This case study (20) convinced all of us of the physiological futility of polycythemia as a response to high altitude. Not only did this subject's symptoms decrease as his hematocrit reduced from 65 to 42%, but his pulmonary function improved, ventilation/perfusion match was better, pulmonary artery pressures were lower, and cardiac output increased into the normal range at all exercise levels. However, we still were not much closer to understanding the etiology of CMS.

Studies on CMS were interrupted, temporarily, by my participation in AMREE. This ambitious project occupied me for most of 1981, and little was done to plan further CMS studies. However, the experience was important, because it introduced me to high altitude natives of Nepal, who never seem to develop CMS. In fact, that is not quite true; we did discover one Sherpa who had a hematocrit of 72% after returning from extreme altitude, and he had typical CMS symptoms. However, as a general rule, hematocrits in the Himalayas did not seem to be as high as in the· Andes. As I trekked in the Himalayas and talked to other scientists on the expedition, I wondered if it would ever be possible to conduct studies in Nepal, similar to those we had done in the Andes.

The years immediately following AMREE were filled with analysis of data and the many presentations that follow a successful expedition, especially one with as much visibility as AMREE. The expedition had been a success both in its science and its mountaineering, and there were many opportunities to meet with world leaders in high altitude physiology. In this period the nagging question kept returning as to the difference between natives of the Andes and Himalayas at similar altitudes, and a plan was formulated to study the two groups.

During the period after AMREE, Dr. Monge and I decided to consolidate our data from our 3 expeditions in Peru, and to formulate our ideas about CMS. To achieve that goal, we reached an agreement with the Johns Hopkins University Press to publish our book, *Hypoxia, Polycythemia, and Chronic Mountain Sickness*, and we plunged into the task of assembling the world's literature on CMS, a task that took us several years. But it also allowed us to formulate our ideas, and to plan more expeditions. A key to our subsequent studies was Dr. Duane Blume, California State University at Bakersfield. Dr. Blume had been the Logistical Leader of AMREE, and is a biologist with a long interest in high altitude physiology. Dr. Blume supplied the organization for our unfocussed ideas about a comparative Andean-Himalayan study, and, once again, we turned to the National Science Foundation for support. To our surprise, we were successful.

In general, we planned to carry out studies similar to the ones we had done earlier in Cerro de Pasco, but in matched subjects at equal altitudes in the two locations. In addition to these studies, we planned to expand in a number of areas. First, we felt that measurements of erythropoietin (EPO) should be made, to examine the possibility of altered control of erythropoiesis in the two populations. Second, we felt that we should make some measurements of sleep ventilation in light of the work that had been done in Colorado to suggest a link between the control of ventilation and CMS (9). Finally, we wanted to measure plasma volume to study the control of red cell mass independent of hemoglobin concentration because of a nonlinear relationship discovered in Quechua Indians (19). These were very ambitious goals, and we were not to be successful in all of them.

In 1985 I relocated again, this time to San Francisco, to work on a project for the U.S. Army directed at developing artificial blood. Our CMS project went forward, however, with Dr. Blume as its logistical leader. For the comparative studies, we added personnel as well. Dr. Sukhamay Lahiri, from AMREE, joined us with his assistant, Mike Cola, to study sleep patterns. Dr. Brownie Schoene, Dr. Peter Hackett, and Rick Peters, also from AMREE, joined us to help with pulmonary and exercise tests, and my long-time associate, Dr. Samaja, from Milan, helped with the blood work. Keith Chapman, an invaluable colleague from San Francisco, supplied most of the energy for organization.

Our first major obstacle came from my new association with the Army: because of the political unrest in Peru, we were not permitted by the State Department to work there, and we had to find another Andean location. Dr. Monge asked Dr. Raimundo Santolaya, of Santiago, to help, and he, together with Codelco, Chile, rescued us with a laboratory facility in Ollagüe. Actually, it was a school house, but it served us well for our studies.

OLLAGÜE, CHILE 1987

The 1987 expedition to Ollagüe was too big, and suffered because the goals of the team were not clearly set. Consequently, many of the studies were not completed or the data were not usable. However, the blood analyses were useful, and our erythropoietin measurements (actually made by Dr. Eugene Goldwasser, University of Chicago) were excellent. In any case, since we had much data on Andean residents, this was considered to be a preliminary to the Himalayan expedition, scheduled for the next year. The main lesson I learned was that expeditions should be small with well-defined goals. Our group was so unmanageable that we were almost nonfunctional on many days. Dr. Monge, however, refused to become involved in personal issues and instead turned our attention to interesting questions about the blood of viscachas, llamas, and sheep.

KHUNDE, NEPAL 1988

Dr. Monge had never visited Nepal, but of course he and I had been close through my AMREE years, so we had discussed at great length the possible differences between Sherpas and Quechua Indians. Our book was published late in 1987, and, that burden complete, we felt prepared to undertake the real comparative study in Sherpas. Although I knew Dr. Monge to be a man of considerable physical stamina, I was concerned about the rigors of trekking in Nepal. On his way to Kathmandu, he and I spent several days in San Francisco preparing and selecting personal equipment for the trip. Due to other obligations, Dr. Lahiri and I could not leave with the other expedition members, but had to join them approximately a week later.

When Dr. Lahiri and I finally joined the group at Khunde, Nepal, we found Dr. Monge in fine spirits and condition, immersed, as usual, in the day-to-day work of the laboratory which had been set up in a private home in the town. My misgivings about the effects of physical hardships in Nepal were dispelled. In contrast to the Ollagüe expedition, the Khunde work was smooth and successful. We collected blood samples from many Sherpas, and essentially repeated all the measurements we had made earlier in Morococha and Cerro de Pasco. In essence, we found these people to be leaner and without the «barrel» chest conformation usually found in the Andes (3). Their hematocrits were slightly lower, in accord with the data in Tibetans (2) and their erythropoietin concentrations were also slightly lower, implying that their level of hemoglobin is more appropriate for the degree of hypoxic exposure (18). In other words, Sherpas seem to be better acclimatized to hypoxia than do Quechua Indians living at the same altitude

We felt the degree of ventilatory «blunting» was less in the Himalayas than in the Andes, but our data were not considered to be definitive. Sleep studies carried out in children showed disturbances which were not expected, based on previous studies, but these data were quite difficult to interpret, and have not been fully published. Similarly, our exercise studies in Khunde have not been published in detail, but do not show appreciable differences between the two study populations.

After completing our studies in Nepal, we spent more time than we wanted to in Namche Bazaar. Namche is very close to Khunde, and the accommodations there are quite civilized. But our delay there was caused by the start of the Monsoon season. We had contracted with Royal Nepal Airlines to take us by helicopter from Namche back to Kathmandu, but they were unable to reach us because of low ceilings, and the alternative was to trek on foot. I knew the trek well, having made in 1981, and had no desire to retrace my earlier footsteps. The route passes through steaming tropical jungles, complete with leeches, fleas, and other vermin, and would take approximately 2 weeks at a civilized pace. Fortunately, a small window in the weather opened, and we were able to leave, only a little delayed. However, we used the idle hours in Namche to discuss the differences and similarities between the Andes and Himalayas.

In our book, Dr. Monge and I formulated the concept that CMS has many etiologies. We believe that the final equilibrium between supply and red cell concentration was influenced by many factors, including cardiopulmonary function, ventilatory control, sleep patterns, physical conditioning and, probably, genetics. Subsequent studies have generally supported our views with respect to EPO production (5, 10), pulmonary function (11, 15), and genetic, or at least anthropologic, differences in populations (7). Many of these, in turn, are also influenced by age (13) and environment.

One concept that has persisted after all the studies is the «vicious cycle hypothesis». That is, polycythemia which arises from a normal stimulus (hypoxia), can become self propagating if decreased flow resulting from increased viscosity causes further hypoxia (11). With respect to the kidney, this would imply higher and higher EPO production as hematocrit rises, rather than the reverse. This concept has been controversial (6) and work needs to be done to test the hypothesis. But perhaps the best way to test it is in the laboratory, not the mountains.

For me personally, the high-altitude expeditions have been classrooms and laboratories. Every project has provided insight into integrative physiological mechanisms. In this era of molecular biology, it seems such overall views, provided in the past by men like Bernard, Barcroft, Monge Medrano, and Hurtado, are less and less popular. I believe this is because we do not like to think of complex answers to simple questions. An enduring lesson I learned from Dr Monge is that a scientific life well lived is as an unbiased observer of biological systems over which we can have no control. We cannot make CMS a simple entity, even though we would like to. As new tools become available, however, we should return again and again to earlier unsolved mysteries, like CMS. My last direct interaction with Dr. Monge was in the fall of 1987, when I visited Lima on the occasion of the NIH centennial. I was invited to give a lecture at the Cayetano Heredia University to mark the occasion, and I had the opportunity to meet and renew friendships with many Latin American scientists interested in high-altitude problems. As usual, I found it to be extremely exciting to interact with these people, especially Dr. Monge. Unfortunately, it appears that high altitude work in Peru is now less attractive because of the civil unrest there, but my continued correspondence with Dr. Monge indicates that he still actively works in the mountains.

Perhaps the most important lesson learned from Dr. Monge is that one does what one can even under adverse conditions. My first introduction to this philosophy was in our 1978 expedition. The North American team arrived in Lima at the start of a holiday weekend, and we were unable to receive our equipment from customs. We spent several days with Dr. Monge in his home, unable to work. Faced with a large amount of idle time (this happens often in high-altitude expeditions), Dr. Monge showed us that without books, equipment, or other materials, we could entertain ourselves with intellectual activity. The many hours spent in his living room were devoted to discussions about high altitude physiology and related subjects, and were extremely important to me in formulating subsequent ideas. For all these lessons, and many more, I am forever grateful to Dr. Monge for his patient and even guiding hand.

REFERENCES

1. ASTE-SALAZAR, H. & HURTADO, A. 1944. The affinity of hemoglobin for oxygen at sea level and at high altitudes. *Am J Physiol* 142: 733-743.

2. BEALL, C.M. 1983. Reappraisal of Andean high altitude erythrocytosis from a Himalayan perspective. *Sem Resp Med* 5(2): 195-201.

3. BLUME, F.D., SANTOLAYA, R., SHERPA, M.G. & MONGE-C., C. 1988. Anthropometric and lung volume measurements in Himalayan and Andean natives. *FASEB J* 2(5): A1281.

4. BROWN, E.G., KROUSKOP, R.W., MCDONNELL, F.E., MONGE-C., C., SARNQUIST, F., WINSLOW, N.J. & WINSLOW, R.M. 1985. Simultaneous and continuous measurement of breath-by-breath oxygen uptake and arterial-venous oxygen content. *J Appl Physiol* 58(4): 1138-1139.

5. DAINIAK, N., SPIELVOGEL, H., SORBA, S. & CUDKOWICZ, L. 1989. Erythropoietin and the polycythemia of high-altitude dwellers. *Adv Exp Med Biol* 271: 17-21.

6. ERSLEV, A.J., CARO, F. & BESARAB, A. 1985. Why the kidney? *Nephron* 41: 213-16.

7. FRISANCHO, A.R. 1988. Origins of differences in hemoglobin concentration between Himalayan and Andean populations. *Resp Physiol* 72(1): 13-18.

8. HURTADO, A. & ASTE-SALAZAR, H. 1948. Arterial blood gas and acid-base balance at sea level and at high altitudes. *J Appl Physiol* 1: 304-325.

9. KRYGER, M.H. & GROVER, R.F. 1983. Chronic mountain sickness. *In*: T.L.Petty & R.M.Cherniack (eds.): *Seminars in respiratory medicine* Vol 5, Man at Altitude. New York: Thieme-Stratton: 164-68.

10. LEÓN-VELARDE, F., MONGE-C., C., VIDAL, A., CARCAGNO, M., CRISCUOLO, M. & BOZZINI, E. 1991. Serum immunoreactive erythropoietin in high altitude natives with and without excessive erythrocytosis. *Exp Hematol* 19: 257-260.

11. MANIER, G., GUENARD, H., CASTAING, Y., VARENE, N. & VARGAS, E. 1988. Pulmonary gas exchange in Andean natives with excessive polycythemia - effect of hemodilution. *J Appl Physiol* 65(5): 2107-17.

12. MILLER, D.M., WINSLOW, R.M., KLEIN, H.G., WILSON, K.C., BROWN, F.L. & STATHAM, N.J. 1980. Improved exercise performance after exchange transfusion in subjects with sickle cell anemia. *Blood* 56(6): 1127-1131.

13. MONGE, C., LEÓN-VELARDE, F. & ARREGUI, A. 1988. Increasing prevalence of excessive polycythemia with age among healthy high-altitude miners (letter). *N Engl J Med* 321(18): 1271.

14. SAMAJA, M., VEISTEINAS, A. & CERRETELLI, P. 1979. Oxygen affinity of blood in altitude Sherpas. *J Appl Physiol* 47(2): 337-41.

15. TEWARI, S.C., JAYASWAL, R., KASTHURI, A.S., NATH, C.S. & OHRI, V.C. 1991. Excessive polycythemia of high altitude. Pulmonary function studies including carbon monoxide diffusion capacity. *J Assoc Phys India* 39(6): 453-455.

16. WINSLOW, R.M. & MCKNEALLY, S.S. 1986. Analysis of breath-by-breath exercise data from field studies. *Int J Clin Monit Comput* 2: 167-180.

17. WINSLOW, R.M. & MONGE-C., C. 1987. *Hypoxia, Polycythemia, and Chronic Mountain Sickness.* Baltimore: Johns Hopkins University Press.

18. WINSLOW, R.M., CHAPMAN, K.W., GIBSON, C.C., SAMAJA, M., MONGE-C., C., GOLDWASSER, E., SHERPA, M.G. & BLUME, D. 1989. Different hematologic responses to hypoxia in Sherpas and Quechua Indians. *J Appl Physiol* 66(4): 1561-1569.

19. WINSLOW, R.M., KLEIN, H.G. & MONGE-C., C. 1985. Red cell mass and plasma volume in Andean natives with excessive polycythemia. *Archivos de Biología* 13: 85-94.

20. WINSLOW, R.M., MONGE-C., C., BROWN, E.G., KLEIN, H.G., SARNQUIST, F. & WINSLOW, N.J. 1985. The effect of hemodilution on transport in high-altitude polycythemia. *J Appl Physiol* 59(5): 1495-1502.

21. WINSLOW, R.M., MONGE-C., C., STATHAM, N.J., GIBSON, C.G., CHARACHE, S., WHITTEMBURY, J., MORAN, O. & BERGER, R.L. 1981. Variability of oxygen affinity of blood: human subjects native to high altitude. *J Appl Physiol* 51: 1411-1416.

22. WINSLOW, R.M., MONGE-C., C., WINSLOW, N.J., GIBSON, C.G. & WHITTEMBURY, J. 1985. Normal whole blood Bohr effect in Peruvian natives of high altitude. *Resp Physiol* 61(2): 197-208.

23. WINSLOW, R.M., MORRISSEY, J.M., BERGER, R.L., SMITH, P.D. & GIBSON, C.G. 1978. Variability of oxygen affinity or normal blood: an automated method of measurement. *J Appl Physiol* 45: 289-297.

24. WINSLOW, R.M., STATHAM, N., GIBSON, C.G., DIXON, E., MORAN, O. & DEBROT, J. 1979. Improved oxygen delivery after phlebotomy in polycythemic natives of high altitude. *Blood* (abstract) American Society of Hematology.

25. WINSLOW, R.M., SWENBERG, M.L., BERGER, R.L., SHRAGER, R.I., LUZZANA, M., SAMAJA, M. & ROSSI-BERNARDI, L. 1977. Oxygen equilibrium curve of normal human blood and its evaluation by Adair's equation. *J Biol Chem* 252(7): 2331-2337.

FACTORES PREDOMINANTES EN LA ETIOPATOGENIA DE LA ENFERMEDAD DE MONGE (EPA) EN LA PAZ, BOLIVIA (3.600 - 4.000 M.)

Enrique Vargas P., Mercedes Villena C.

Resumen

Se presenta una síntesis de los principales estudios de la función respiratoria en pacientes portadores de la "Enfermedad de Monge" o Eritrocitosis Patológica de Altura (EPA), entidad nosológica de carácter regional en Bolivia que, a causa de su frecuencia (5,2% en la población de La Paz) con evidente aparición en la población masculina joven, constituye un problema médico social entre la población residente de altura. El enfoque etiopatogénico caracteriza algunos de los probables mecanismos participantes a la altura de la ciudad de La Paz (3600-4000 m.), entre los que sobresalen: la hipoventilación alveolar crónica, provocada por una disminución de la sensibilidad de los quimioreceptores periféricos a la hipoxia, (respuesta ventilatoria al test de hipoxia: aumento de VE en el grupo EPA =12%, en grupo control = 46% - $FIO_2 = 8\%$). Esta depresión de la VE en vigilia es aún mayor durante las etapas de respiración periódica (RP) del sueño, que por su profundidad provocan una caída considerable de SaO_2. Otro factor constituye la disminución de la relación ventilación-perfusión (VA/Q< a 0, 1), sin un verdadero cortocircuito a nivel alvéolo-capilar, cuyo valor mejora con la hemodilución, tanto del débito cardíaco (Q de 5, 5 + 1, 2 a 6, 9 + 1, 2 l/min.) como de la ventilación (VE de 8, 5 + 1, 4 a 9, 6 + 1, 3 l/min.). Debemos mencionar igualmente un incremento en el gradiente alvéolo-arterial de oxígeno (Δ A-aO$_2$) que sumado a los otros factores mencionados dan lugar a una hipoxemia progresiva y a una moderada retención de CO_2. La resultante, una eritrocitosis y un hematocrito anormalmente elevados que producen gradualmente un efecto nocivo por alteración de la microcirculación pulmonar, conformando un círculo vicioso: la eritrocitosis ejerce una acción sobre la hipoxia· y ésta a su vez estimula y aumenta la eritrocitosis. Al final analizamos los resultados obtenidos en un ensayo terapéutico con el bismesilato de almitrina administrado a diferentes concentraciones.

Palabras claves: Altura, desadaptación, mal de montaña crónico, Eritrocitosis Patológica de Altura (EPA), zona andina boliviana, regulación ventilatoria, intercambio gaseoso, circulación pulmonar, terapéutica de la enfermedad de Monge.

Résumé

Ce travail présente une synthèse des principales études de la fonction respiratoire chez des patients porteurs de la "Maladie de Monge" ou Érythrocytose Pathologique d'Altitude (EPA), entité nosologique à caractère régional en Bolivie qui, par sa fréquence (5,2% de la population de La Paz) et par une claire apparition parmi la population masculine jeune, constitue un problème médical social chez la population résidant en altitude. L'optique etiopathogénique caractérise quelques uns des éventuels mécanismes inhérents à l'altitude de la ville de La Paz (3600-4000 m), parmi lesquels ressortent : l'hypoventilation alvéolaire chronique, provoquée par une diminution de la sensibilité deschémorécepteurs périphériques à l'hypoxie (réponse ventilatoire au test de l'hypoxie : augmentation de VE dans le groupe EPA + 12%, dans le groupe controle = 46%-FIO_2 = 8%). Cette baisse de la VE en veille est encore plus importante au cours des étapes de respiration périodique (RP) du sommeil, qui par leur intensité provoquent une chute considérable de SaO_2. La diminution de la relation ventilation/perfusion est un autre facteur (VA/Q < 0,1), sans véritable shunt au niveau alvéo-capillaire, dont la valeur s'améliore avec l'hemodilutión, aussi bien du débit cardiaque (Q de 5,5 + 1,2 a 6,9 + 1,2 l/min.) que de la ventilation (VE de 8,5 + 1,4 a 9,6 + 1,3 l/min.). Il faut également mentionner une augmentation du gradient alvéolo-artériel d'oxygène (Δ A-aO_2) qui, ajoutés aux autres facteurs mentionnés, provoquent une hypoxie progressive et une rétention de CO_2. Il en résulte une Érythrocytose et un hématocrite anormalement élevé qui entraînent graduellement un effet nocif par altération de la micro circulation pulmonaire formant un cercle vicieux : l' Érythrocytose exerce une action sur l'hypoxie et celle-ci, à son tour, stimule et augmente l'Érythrocytose. Nous analysons enfin les résultats obtenus dans un essai thérapeutique avec le bismesilate d'almitrine administré à différentes doses.

Mots clés : Désadaptation, Mal des Montagnes Chronique, Érythrocytose Pathologique d'Altitude (EPA), zone andine bolivienne, régulation ventilatoire, échanges gazeux, circulation pulmonaire, thérapeutique de la maladie de Monge.

Abstract

We present a synthesis of respiratory function studies in patients with "Monge's disease" or Pathological High Altitude Eryhtrocytosis (PHAE), a disease entity with a regional character in Bolivia that constitutes a medical and social problem among high altitude inhabitants because of its high frequency (5.2% in the population of La Paz). Among the possible pathogenic mechanisms, chronic alveolar hypoventilation is the prominent one. It is produced by a loss of sensitivity of peripheral chemoreceptors to hypoxia (increment in ventilation to 8% FiO_2: 12% among patients with PHAE, 46% in controls). This depression of ventilation during the awake state is more marked during sleep with the subsequent lowering of O_2 saturation. Another factor is the reduction of the ventilation-perfusion rate (VA/Q < 0.1) without a real shortcircuit at the alveolar-capillary level, which gets better with hemodilution, cardiac debit (Q 5.5 ± 1.2 to 6.9 ± 1.2 l/min) as well as ventilation (VE 8.5 ± 1.4 to 9.6 ± 1.3 l/min). We should also mention an increment in the alveolar arterial oxygen gradient (Δ A-aO_2) which together with the other mentioned factors gives rise to a progressive hypoxemia an moderate retention of CO_2. The resultant, an abnormally elevated erythrocytosis and hemotocrit that graduallly produce a noxious effect by the alterarion of the pulmonary microcirculation, conforming a vicious cycle: the erythocytosis exerts an action over the hypoxia and this at time stimulates and increases the erythytosis. At the end we analyze the results obtained in an therapeutic trial with bismetilate of almitrina given at different concentrations.

Key words: Altitude, loss of adaptation, chronic mountain sickness, pathological erythrocytosis of altitude, Bolivian Andean Zone, ventilatory regulation, gas exchange, pulmonary circulation, treatment of Monge´s desease.

INTRODUCCIÓN

En el año 1928, Carlos Monge Medrano, ilustre médico peruano, principal investigador de la biopatología andina de la época, describió por primera vez la Enfermedad Crónica de la Montaña, señalando que se presentaba en nativos residentes o en migrantes de la costa con larga permanencia en la altura, definiendo sus principales características clínicas y enfatizando su carácter de tipo eritrémico en su histórica publicación *La enfermedad de los Andes* (34) aporte que bien valió la designación de este cuadro con su nombre.

Desde entonces se conoce la enfermedad de Monge como una entidad nosológica propia de los centros poblados de gran altura, entre cuyos habitantes según las regiones se encuentra un porcentaje variable de personas que han perdido su tolerancia a la hipoxia desarrollando una serie de signos y síntomas, en algunos casos severos, constituyendo una verdadera patología regional con sus repercusiones lógicas, no sólo sobre la salud de los habitantes, sino también sobre su rendimiento en la vida cotidiana.

La vida humana en regiones altas, es un tema que, aparte de sus implicaciones en el campo de la medicina, especialmente en el dominio de la fisiología, la clínica y la salud pública, tiene repercuciones biológicas y socioeconómicas sobre una gran parte de la población del mundo.

CENTROS URBANOS EN ALTURA, PROBLEMÁTICA DE LOS FACTORES AMBIENTALES

En el caso de Bolivia la población total de 6.344.396 habitantes (28), se distribuye en tres zonas geográficas: 1) La zona andina, que comprende la cordillera occidental, el altiplano y la cordillera oriental; 2) La zona subandina que comprende los valles altos y tierras semitropicales (Yungas), situadas en los torrentes contrafuertes de la cordillera; 3) Las zonas de tierras bajas, o llanos tropicales que comprende la mayor parte del territorio y que se extiende hasta la región amazónica.

Es justamente en la zona andina, más precisamente en el altiplano, valles altos y parte de la cordillera, donde se concentra un 46% por ciento de la población de todo el país. Estos centros urbanos o rurales, geográfica y físicamente, están definidos biológicamente como de gran altura, pues se sitúan entre los 3.000 a 5.500 metros sobre el nivel del mar (La Paz, altura media: 3.600 m., mina Chorolque 4.850 m., planta Apacheta 5.022 m., Empresa Emicla 5.500 m).

La Paz es la capital política, sede del gobierno, con una población de 1.115.403 habitantes (28) que se desplazan entre el altiplano y un valle alto. Su topografía que de hecho es muy particular, está caracterizada por importantes variaciones de altura y como consecuencia, también de la presión barométrica (Fig. 1).

La distribución de sus barrios tiene un gradiente que oscila entre 4.000 m. (PB 462 mmHg) y 3.233 m. (PB 520 mmHg) sometiendo a sus habitantes a condiciones de hipoxia, en muchos casos intermitente, que sin lugar a dudas tiene consecuencias biológicas ciertamente importantes, dentro de un verdadero "laboratorio natural", cuyo habitat tiene influencia sobre las costumbres y la salud de las personas expuestas.

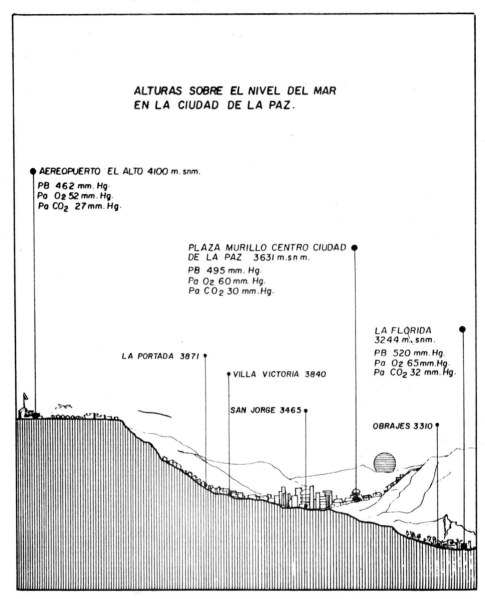

ALTURAS SOBRE EL NIVEL DEL MAR EN LA CIUDAD DE LA PAZ.

AEREOPUERTO EL ALTO 4100 m.snm.
PB 462 mm.Hg.
Pa O_2 52 mm.Hg.
Pa CO_2 27 mm.Hg.

PLAZA MURILLO CENTRO CIUDAD DE LA PAZ 3631 m.sn m.
PB 495 mm. Hg.
Pa O_2 60 mm. Hg.
Pa CO_2 30 mm.Hg.

LA FLORIDA 3244 m. snm.
PB 520 mm. Hg.
Pa O_2 65mm.Hg.
Pa CO_2 32 mm.Hg.

LA PORTADA 3871

VILLA VICTORIA 3840

SAN JORGE 3465

OBRAJES 3310

Fig. 1 - Perfil topográfico de la ciudad de La Paz y sus diferentes barrios. Se puede apreciar el gradiente de altura y los diferentes parámetros a partir de los cambios de presión barométrica.

El término "habitat" resume muy bien el complejo problema del estudio de la adaptación a un medio y, a propósito de la altura, se debe considerar un conjunto bien definido de factores físicos, cada uno de los cuales juega un rol más o menos importante en los procesos biológicos de acomodación, aclimitación o adaptación y la consiguiente homeostasis resultante. Estos factores motivan detalles particulares en cada caso:

- Desde Paul Bert (6), sabemos que la presión barométrica (PB) es considerada como el factor determinante desde el punto de vista biológico; con ella disminuye la presión parcial de oxígeno del aire ambiente a medida que la altura aumenta.

- Especialmente en invierno, las variaciones de temperatura ambiente en el curso de un mismo día son muy significativas.

- En la misma forma la sequedad del aire, con aumento moderado del grado de humedad, en las estaciones de lluvia.

- Una mayor cantidad de radiaciones solares no ionizantes; especialmente de las radiaciones ultravioletas, cuya influencia en razón de la disminución de la capa de ozono (29) es analizada con dedicación por sus efectos secundarios.

Este conjunto de variables físicas, representan lo que Bernard & Ruffié, definieron como la Ecología Humana (5) que a su vez considera tres tipos de clima: el físico, el biológico y el social, donde la adición de respuestas o las modificaciones de estos diversos parámetros, constituyen los caracteres generales de una adaptación.

El elemento de mayor influencia para el hombre, es la disminución de la presión barométrica, pues la hipoxia ambiental que produce constituye un fenómeno natural contra el cual la moderna tecnología de *confort*, no está en condiciones de ofrecer una solución práctica como sucede en los climas demasiado fríos o acondicionar el aire en climas tropicales. Por esta razón, es conveniente fijar los límites fisiológicos de la altura tomando como base los valores de la presión parcial del oxígeno en sangre arterial (PaO_2). Sin embargo este concepto fisiológico no es precisamente proporcional a la elevación terrestre pues, por una parte, la presión atmosférica no tiene una relación linear con la altura física; por otra, el contenido de sangre en oxígeno no depende exclusivamente de su concentración en el aire ambiente (11) (Fig. 2).

En el alcance de estos límites, se pueden distinguir tres niveles según el valor de la presión parcial de oxígeno de la sangre arterial (2), partiendo del principio de que la PaO_2 normal a nivel del mar es de 95 mmHg. Hasta los 70 mm Hg, las modificaciones de la presión parcial de oxígeno en aire ambiente, en relación con la altura, tienen poca influencia sobre la cantidad de oxígeno de la sangre arterial; entre 70 y 40 mmHg, la influencia de la presión parcial de oxígeno es cada vez mayor.

Por debajo de 40 mmHg, el contenido de oxígeno de la sangre arterial disminuye de una manera evidente, y más o menos constante, según las modificaciones, aún ligeras de la presión parcial del oxígeno en el aire ambiente.

El primer nivel corresponde a regiones cuyos valles no sobrepasan 3.000 metros. En ellos las manifestaciones sobre el transporte de oxígeno no tienen consecuencias notables; es precisamente en el segundo nivel, entre 70 y 40 mm Hg de PaO_2, donde se sitúan la mayoría de las poblaciones andinas dispersas entre los valles altos, altiplano y la cordillera de los Andes propiamente dicha, lugar en el que se encuentran los centros de explotación minera.

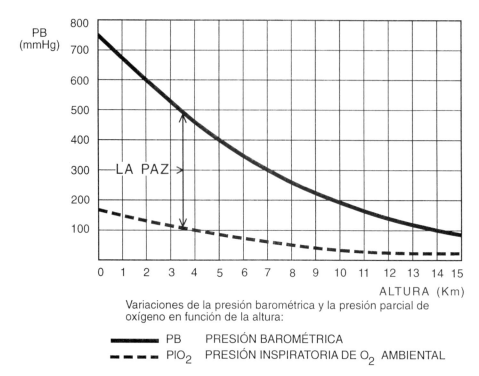

Fig. 2 - **Variaciones de la presión barométrica y de la presión parcial de oxígeno ambiental en función de la altura, puntos correspondientes a la ciudad de La Paz.**

En el tercer nivel, la oxigenación tisular presenta presiones muy bajas (alturas superiores a 5.000 m.), y desde un punto de vista fisiológico, es difícil y muy sacrificado el establecimiento de poblaciones permanentes (minas de azufre en el sudoeste de Bolivia).

Analizados todos estos elementos dentro del concepto de "aclimatación natural" (20) y teniendo en cuenta los probables factores genéticos (14), (25), podríamos afirmar que la mayor parte del grupo humano residente permanente de la altura, constituye una entidad biológica perfectamente adaptada a su habitat. Sin embargo, un pequeño porcentaje de esta población pierde su capacidad de adaptación a la baja tensión de oxígeno del ambiente en que vive, desarrollando paulatinamente la Enfermedad de Monge o Eritrocitosis Patológica de Altura (EPA), cuyas manifestaciones clínicas giran en torno a una disminución progresiva de la PaO_2 con el consiguiente incremento del número de eritrocitos y de la hemoglobina por encima de los valores considerados como normales al nivel correspondiente de altura.

RELACIÓN CAUSAL ENTRE HIPOXEMIA Y HEMATOCRITO

Después de la descripción original de Carlos Monge M., muchos otros autores contribuyeron, en diferentes aspectos, a un mejor conocimiento de esta enfermedad. El profesor Alberto Hurtado en su tiempo y basado en el criterio eritrémico que se le dio en un principio, hizo una descripción de las características hematológicas en el año 1942 (19); él mismo, más tarde, buscó la explicación etiopatogénica mencionando la existencia de una hipoventilación como factor principal de hipoxemia (20). Posteriormente se hicieron estudios de variada orientación, tanto en el campo clínico como etiopatogénico (45; 35; 32; 10; 24), estudios sobre la regulación ventilatoria (26; 25; 47) y su relación con el intercambio a nivel de LCR (41); los cambios anatomopatológicos fueron descritos en clásicos trabajos (3; 18) las modificaciones cardiovasculares y hemodinámicas de la circulación pulmonar (40) y un completo estudio de seguimiento clínico-cardiológico (31; 38).

En el Instituto Boliviano de Biología de Altura, situado a 3.600 m. de altura, en medio de la población de La Paz, cotidianamente recibimos solicitudes de atención de pacientes cada vez más jóvenes, que nos muestran la importancia de los estudios de profundización, tratando de establecer en cada caso una explicación fisiopatológica del mal.

Entre los años 1980 y 1991, estos pacientes representaron el 7.47% de los estudiados en el Departamento Respiratorio; los porcentajes entre la población son un tanto menores: en 1981 entre 600 trabajadores estudiados encontramos un porcentaje de 5.2 % de estos casos (44).

Podríamos afirmar que los mecanismos, casi siempre respiratorios, que parecen intervenir en la enfermedad no siempre son los mismos y en cada caso existe más de un factor a tomarse en cuenta para la evaluación final.

El concepto generalmente adoptado para explicar este cuadro, es el desarrollo de una hipoventilación alveolar crónica que está directamente en relación con la hiposensibilidad de los quimioreceptores periféricos a la hipoxia y a la hipercápnea; la hipoxia tisular estimularía la secreción de eritropoyetina, dando como consecuencia la eritrocitosis (20).

La constatación frecuente de la Eritrocitosis Patológica de Altura en personas jóvenes, casi siempre varones, de menos de 30 años, hipóxicos aunque sólo moderadamente hipercápnicos, nos lleva a revisar las hipótesis fisiopatológicas según las cuales: 1) La edad sería un factor determinante en la poliglobulia de altura; y 2) Que la hipoxia está ligada únicamente a una hipoventilación crónica.

En una revisión practicada (17) estudiamos 81 pacientes con esta enfermedad; entre ellos únicamente había una mujer. El exámen clínico y radiológico estableció que todos eran indemnes de lesiones cardiacas o pulmonares; sin embargo su recuento globular y el hematocrito eran superiores a los 6.000.000/dl y 57% respectivamente. Este valor constituye el límite superior del Ht normal en La Paz (media ± 3 D.S) (21). Los signos y síntomas anotados son variables, siendo los más frecuentes las cefaleas, cianosis, disnea, somnolencia o diferentes grados de insomnio, transtornos tróficos digitales, signos clínicos e imágenes radiológicas de hipertensión arterial pulmonar, desaturación oxihemoglobínica e hipoxemia arterial. En pocos casos hubo una hipercápnea acentuada con acidosis respiratoria; en los enfermos con hematocrito superior a 74% los vértigos, la pérdida de la memoria y los adormecimientos de los miembros son frecuentes, en muchos casos las cefaleas son intensas con disnea de reposo, ortopnea, edemas distales y claudicación intermitente.

Una interrogante que es necesario esclarecer se refiere a la edad en que comenzaría el proceso de intolerancia a la hipoxia. ¿Cual es la época de la vida en que el organismo empieza a franquear la frontera hacia la enfermedad? En la revisión mencionada los 81 enfermos tenían edades que fluctuaban entre 15 a 70 años; la Fig. 3 muestra que el mayor porcentaje se encuentra a los 50 años. Este dato sin duda es relativo, pues únicamente contempla los casos que se ven obligados a consultar, a veces por síntomas generales (cefaleas, cansancio fácil, color de la piel); en las personas jóvenes con eritrocitosis patológica (y probablemente en algunos niños), los síntomas no pueden ser evidenciados como en una persona adulta, pues forman parte de su vida misma. En un estudio interesante, Sime encontró que la depresión ventilatoria ya era indiscutible a los 4 años (42), por lo tanto se hace necesario difundir entre los pediatras la necesidad de realizar estudios funcionales completos en niños con signología sospechosa.

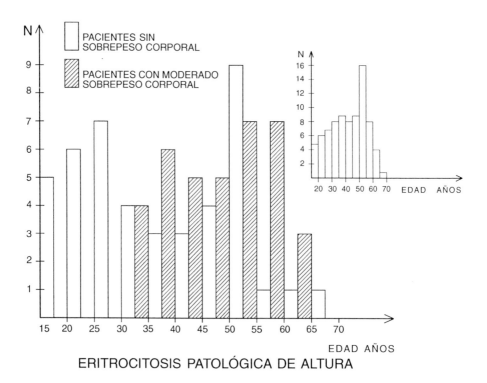

Fig. 3 - **Histogramas que muestran el número de pacientes por edades. A la derecha, el histograma de edad de la población total.**

	GRUPO A EDAD < 35 a. n = 22	GRUPO B EDAD > 35 a. n = 22	GRUPO C c/SOBRE PESO n = 37	GRUPO D CONTROL n = 17
Hematocrito	63.6 ± 5.8	64.3 ± 5.9	65.4 ± 6.4	52 ± 1.5
Pa O_2 (mmHg)	52 ± 6.0	46.7 ± 5.2	46.3 ± 4.5	61.8 ± 1.1
Pa CO_2 (mmHg)	33 ± 3.7	33 ± 3.7	34.6 ± 3.7	30.9 ± 0.7
pH	7.40 ± 0.03	7.39 ± 0.03	7.39 ± 0.03	7.40 ± 0.02
CO3H (m mol/l)	20 ± 1.8	19.9 ± 1.9	20.6 ± 1.8	18.5 ± 0.3

TABLA 1 - Valores de gasometría arterial y hematocrito en los tres grupos de pacientes con eritrocitosis (n=81) y el grupo control (n=17).

En la Tabla 1 se reunen las medias y desviaciones standard del hematocrito, la PaO_2, la $PaCO_2$ el pH y la concentración de bicarbonatos, tanto de los pacientes (Grupos A, B y C) como del grupo control (Grupo D). En este último no hubo ninguna correlación entre PaO_2 ni $PaCO_2$ y la edad; sin embargo entre los pacientes, la PaO_2 es más elevada en los de menor edad (p<0, 01, en test de t no apareado) aunque es más baja que la del grupo control.

Así, realizada la comparación de los grupos por edades encontramos que la PaO_2 es significativamente más baja en los pacientes con Enfermedad de Monge (p<0, 001); las medias de $PaCO_2$ aunque poco diferentes del valor normal (± 2, 3 mm Hg ± 3, 7 mmHg) son significativamente elevadas (p<0, 01). Las cifras correspondientes a la serie control, tienen desviaciones standard menores que las series patológicas, lo que, sobre el plan estadístico, nos llevó a realizar una comparación de las medias de los grupos patológicos con relación al valor medio de la serie control y no así un test de t de comparación entre las medias de ambos grupos. Dentro del plan biológico, esta dispersión relativamente importante de los valores obtenidos entre los grupos patológicos nos lleva a buscar la o las causas de esta variabilidad.

Los otros parámetros obtenidos por exploración funcional respiratoria, es decir: espirometría, curva flujo-volúmen, compliance pulmonar, resistencias bronquiales y trabajo ventilatorio fueron normales. Es necesario remarcar el hallazgo constante de una baja ventilación alveolar en todos los casos, con un consumo de oxígeno normal o levemente elevado en reposo.

El valor de hematocrito ha sido escogido de preferencia al de la concentración de hemoglobina o el recuento globular; en el caso de los enfermos con EPA es importante, pues este valor condiciona la microcirculación capilar (15). En la concepción de Monge & Whittembury (36), la edad tiene un rol fundamental en el aumento de la eritrocitosis en los pacientes que van perdiendo su adaptación a la vida en altura; de esta manera la PaO_2, disminuiría en función de los años. Esta hipótesis es difícil aceptarla si consideramos la forma de la curva de disociación de la hemoglobina y de los mecanismos mediante los cuales se desarrolla una hipoxemia en el hombre anciano (49). Algunas publicaciones sobre la eritrocitosis fisiológica (16) también se encuentran en contraposición a los datos que al respecto publicaron Whittembury & Monge (52). En un estudio longitudinal Arnaud (4) toma en cuenta especialmente el origen étnico y sobre 1.328 personas no encuentra una correlación que permita sostener el efecto de la edad sobre la desadaptación.

En los pacientes que padecen una EPA, es evidente que con el paso del tiempo la hipoventilación alveolar y la hipoxia crónica agravan la eritrocitosis produciendo un efecto nocivo en forma gradual, pues el aumento del hematocrito podría, por sí mismo, conducir a una hipoxia por alteración de la microcirculación pulmonar. Si esta hipótesis es verificada se trataría entonces del punto de partida de un círculo vicioso: la eritrocitosis ejerce una acción sobre la hipoxia y ésta a su vez estimula y aumenta la eritrocitosis. Veamos algunos argumentos que apoyarían esta hipótesis fisiopatológica:

- Una distribución no uniforme del hematocrito en los capilares pulmonares podría provocar una disminución del rendimiento del sistema de intercambio gaseoso, es decir un aumento del gradiente alvéolo-capilar en O_2 (7; 53); otras experiencias realizadas sobre la microcirculación sostienen esta teoría (6).

- Un segundo argumento experimental se puede deducir del hecho que la hemodilución aumenta la PaO_2 en los enfermos con EPA (8; 30) aún cuando teóricamente la sangría debería producir una disminución de la PaO_2, a $PaCO_2$ y relación ventilación-perfusión constantes (51).

- El tercer argumento puede extraerse de la presente revisión. En el grupo de pacientes menores de 35 años la correlación entre la hipoxia arterial y la edad es mala, mientras que aquella realizada con el hematocrito es en extremo significativa. En este grupo, un enfermo tenía 20 años, un hematocrito de 81% y una PaO_2 de 43 mmHg (La Paz: PaO_2 60 mm.Hg., $PaCO_2$ 30 mm.Hg.)

RESPUESTA VENTILATORIA A LA HIPOXIA

Desde hace mucho tiempo se ha establecido que los nativos de altura poseen una sensibilidad disminuida a la hipoxia; ésta fue objeto de una cuantificación mediante tests especiales (9). Actualmente se admite incluso que su respuesta ventilatoria es menor comparada con la que se observa en los nativos del nivel del mar recién llegados a la misma zona o altura; esta afirmación procede de estudios comparativos efectuados en habitantes de los Andes (27; 47; 41; 21), y también en gente del Himalaya (25). Otros estudios han mostrado que esta hiposensibilidad se mantiene en los nativos de altura aún después de una estadía prolongada a nivel del mar (26).

Los mecanismos íntimos de esta diferencia entre los residentes permanentes de altura y los nativos del nivel del mar aclimatados, todavía son objeto de estudios experimentales, sin embargo algunos hechos son probables:

- Que la hipoxemia durante un período importante en la edad temprana de la vida extrauterina diera lugar a una alteración en el desarrollo de la actividad quimiorefleja.

- Que una permanencia prolongada en condiciones de hipoxia de altura conduzca a una desensibilización de los receptores periféricos, produciendo un efecto negativo y mayor hipoxia.

- Que esta menor respuesta a la hipoxia podría tener un orígen genético.

- Que en los pacientes con Eritrocitosis Patológica de Altura, se mantiene una hipoventilación inadecuada, aún en condiciones de acidosis por hipercápnea.

El caso es que los pacientes con EPA, muestran cifras de ventilación de reposo manifiestamente bajas en vigilia, registrándose una ausencia casi total de respuesta al estímulo hipóxico; en ellos existe diferentes grados de retención de anhidrido carbónico. Así hipoxemia e hipercápnea crónicas se traducen paulatinamente en un cortejo de manifestaciones orgánicas sin que haya sido detectada, ni clínica, ni radiológicamente una causa cardiopulmonar.

Por lo tanto nos pareció que en todos estos casos era necesario lograr, en la medida de lo posible, un estudio sistemático de la regulación ventilatoria mediante la inhalación de una mezcla gaseosa hipóxica standard (FIO_2 8%), adoptando el test según la técnica de Dejours (9). Para ello hacemos uso de una cadena electrónica de pletismografía corporal total, que nos permite obtener una colección de respuestas inmediatas analizadas por programa especial en una computadora (HP 9825 A). Una vez que el paciente está familiarizado con el sistema electrónico, se verifica la regularidad de su ventilación dentro del pletismógrafo, observando las cifras consecutivas de su volumen corriente que aparecen en la pantalla analógico-digital (correspondientes a señales de un neumotacógrafo), las que son integradas electrónicamente permitiendo registrar variaciones, aún pequeñas, de la ventilación.

El paciente respira a través de una válvula unidireccional con el lado inspiratorio conectado a una llave de 3 vías, la misma que facilita la inhalación de la mezcla gaseosa hipóxica sin que el paciente se dé cuenta.

Al final la respuesta ventilatoria seleccionada por la computadora se expresa en l/min BTPS, con su correspondiente porcentaje de variación en relación a la VE obtenida antes de la administración de la mezcla hipóxica.

Con la metodología descrita, y en forma comparativa, estudiamos la quimiosensibilidad ventilatoria a la hipoxia en 2 grupos de personas, en cada una de las cuales se practicaron 5 tests consecutivos, cuyas respuestas fueron automáticamente seleccionadas:

1) Grupo A de control, compuesto por 88 varones sanos;

2) Grupo B, pacientes con eritrocitosis patológica de altura (EPA), igualmente varones, cuyo número fue de 75.

	EDAD	PESO Kg	TALLA cm	Hb/dl gr.	Ht %	GLÓBULOS ROJOS mm^3
GRUPO EPA n = 75	29 ± 7	65 ± 8.4	168 ± 7.5	21.6 ± 1.5	66 ± 4.3	6.914.758 ± 538
GRUPO NORMALES n = 88	30 ± 7.9	62.2 ± 8.3	167 ± 5.9	16.7 ± 0.7	53 ± 2.2	5.418.000 ± 495

TABLA 2 - **Datos biométricos y de hematología en los dos grupos de estudio, pudiéndose advertir la media de edad, relativamente joven del grupo de pacientes.**

Los datos biométricos y hematológicos se encuentran en las Tabla 2.

Normalmente el test permite observar un aumento transitorio de la ventilación como consecuencia de la inhalación, involuntaria y desapercibida, de una mezcla hipóxica durante 10 segundos que representan unos 3 a 4 ciclos ventilatorios.

RESULTADOS

El promedio de la respuesta después de la inhalación de la mezcla hipóxica, representa un aumento de un 46% del valor de referencia de la ventilación en reposo del grupo A o de control (PaO$_2$ = 59.8 ± 1.4 mm/Hg); por el contrario el valor de respuesta en los pacientes con EPA alcanza únicamente 12% del valor de referencia (PaO$_2$ = 51.2 ± 6.0 mm/Hg).

Es preciso remarcar que casi de una manera uniforme la respuesta es menor en los pacientes, ello se aprecia en la escasa desviación standard (± 0.7%); aspecto no observado en el grupo control, en el que debido a respuestas individuales diferentes, se puede constatar un cierto grado de dispersión (± 11.7 %).

Teniendo en cuenta el tiempo de inhalación, podemos suponer que la presión alveolar de O$_2$ (PAO$_2$) llega a ser muy baja, consiguientemente pretendemos haber alcanzado un umbral suficiente para el estímulo hipóxico a nivel de los quimioreceptores, como para obtener una respuesta representativa de la actividad refleja periférica (Figs. 4 y 5).

En las personas normales podemos observar una respuesta similar a la descrita por otros autores para la sensibilidad ventilatoria en residentes permanentes; en los pacientes con EPA la respuesta es parecida a lo que ocurre en pacientes pulmonares hipóxicos crónicos con eritrocitosis secundaria (12) en los cuales parece evidente la acción negativa de la hipoxia sobre los quimioreceptores en función del tiempo.

Desde hace mucho se conoce que la sensibilidad al CO$_2$ tambien se encuentra disminuída en los residentes permanentes de altura comparados con los recién llegados y aclimatados (27). En el caso de los pacientes con

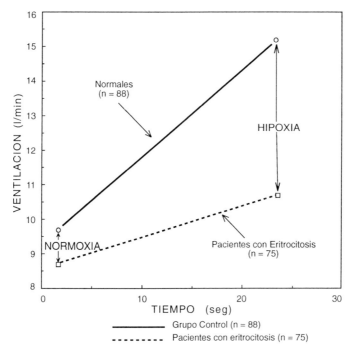

Fig. 4 - Respuesta ventilatoria a la hipoxia (FIO$_2$=8%) en función del tiempo de respuesta.VE: ventilación minuto en litros.

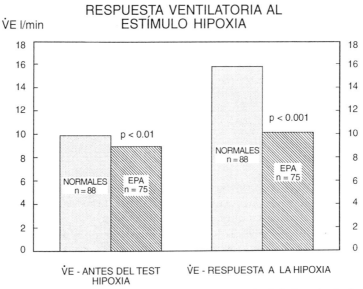

Fig. 5 - Representación gráfica de la respuesta ventilatoria.A la izquierda los valores de la ventilación (VE) antes de la inhalación de la mezcla hipóxica (FIO$_2$=8%). A la derecha los valores incrementados como respuesta.

EPA, la sensibilidad es mucho menor aún, y la respuesta como para las personas normales depende de la concentración de bicarbonatos (H-CO3̄) del líquido cefalorraquídeo (41).

Analizando la mayoría de las investigaciones realizadas hasta el presente, se puede admitir que esta hiposensibilidad ventilatoria es factor fundamental dentro del conjunto de causas posibles que convergen hacia una explicación etiopatogénica del síndrome clínico que determina la Enfermedad de Monge.

Lo cierto es que en este cuadro resaltan una hipoxemia arterial progresiva acompañada de un hematocrito elevado a veces extremo, que en muchos casos no puede ser explicado por el sólo hecho de una disminución de la PaO_2 de vigilia.

Basados en ésta interrogante, hemos realizado investigaciones dirigidas a cuantificar el efecto de la depresión ventilatoria durante el sueño, que en estos pacientes es muy profunda, tratando de explicar esta discordancia en el paciente despierto.

Lo importante fue lograr un registro contínuo de la ventilación y la saturación oxihemoglobínica durante el sueño (39); el estudio además permitió examinar las variaciones de las ondas de un electroencefalograma y un electrocardiograma junto a las variaciones que pudiera experimentar la presión arterial sistémica.

La conclusión fundamental de este estudio es que los pacientes con EPA manifiestan episodios de respiración periódica (RP) con mucho más profundidad y frecuencia que las personas normales. En ocasiones se llegan a registrar apneas sostenidas, las que pueden alcanzar hasta un minuto de duración, determinando oscilaciones de la saturación oxihemoglobínica (SaO_2) con un número aproximado de 18 a 61 por hora, provocando caídas simultáneas del porcentaje de saturación que, entre una y otra pausa ventilatoria descienden sus valores entre 75 y 30%, con una sucesión mas evidente entre la 1 y 4 de la mañana (La Paz: SaO_2: 90%) (21).

Pudimos observar igualmente que la severidad de la desaturación oxihemoglobínica en los pacientes con EPA, es independiente del tiempo de padecimiento ó antiguedad de la enfermedad, de la magnitud del hematrocrito, la duración de la respiración periódica durante el sueño ó la amplitud de las oscilaciones de la SaO_2 (37).

CIRCULACIÓN PULMONAR E INTERCAMBIO GASEOSO

Un capítulo todavía mal conocido de la Enfermedad de Monge es el relativo a la circulación pulmonar y sus variables inmediatas, como la relación ventilación - perfusión ($\dot{V}A/\dot{Q}$) ó el gradiente alvéolo-arterial de oxígeno (A-aO_2). Como es de suponer, una ventilación global disminuida provoca una alteración de este gradiente; existen estudios que demuestran que en los pacientes con EPA el mismo se encuentra aumentado en relación a las personas normales (10; 22; 33). Este fenómeno puede tener su explicación en la existencia de un corto circuito ó en una mala relación ventilación-perfusión.

Otros autores (24) después de excluir los pacientes con enfermedad bronco-pulmonar, no encuentran alteración del gradiente alvéolo-arterial en pacientes con EPA; a través de sondas radioactivas en las zonas altas y bajas pulmonares de 14 pacientes con EPA, en La Paz, Ergueta y Col (10) encontraron una disminución en la perfusión de la parte apical de ambos pulmones, factor probablemente causal de un incremento en el espacio muerto fisiológico y de hipoxemia arterial.

Con estos antecedentes, desarrollamos un estudio multidisciplinario (30) con el propósito de analizar los mecanismos responsables de la hipoxemia en un grupo pequeño de pacientes con EPA (n=8) que aceptaron la prueba de un cateterismo cardíaco, permitiéndonos determinar el gradiente alvéolo-arterial ideal de O_2 (Ai-aO_2) y sus componentes *i.e.* shunt intrapulmonar verdadero, relación $\dot{V}A/\dot{Q}$ alterada, desequilibrio en la difusión del O_2 al final del componente alvéolo-capilar y los cortocircuitos post-pulmonares, fueron estudiados a través de medidas de la ventilación alveolar (VA), la perfusión (Q) y los factores de la distribución intrapulmonar en función de la relación $\dot{V}A/\dot{Q}$; se empleó la técnica de eliminación de gases inertes (50). Además la contribución de la eritrocitosis a la mala relación $\dot{V}A/\dot{Q}$ fue evaluada comparando estos parámetros antes y después de una sangría con reposición isovolémica. En este reducido grupo de pacientes oriundos de La Paz y El Alto (3600 y 4000 m), los exámenes clínico-radiológicos, de laboratorio y electrocardiográfico, descartaron compromiso cardio-pulmonar; a pesar de ello mostraron una hipoxia acentuada (PaO_2 = 45.6 + 5.6 mm Hg) y un hematocrito elevado (Ht=65 + 6.6 %).

En todos ellos se practicaron exámenes funcionales respiratorios de rutina, mostrando valores de volúmenes pulmonares, tanto estáticos como dinámicos, dentro de límites normales (CV/CV Teórica= 102 + 9%, índice de permeabilidad bronquial = 75, 3 + 6.8%).

El cateter utilizado para obtener los parámetros hemodinámicos fue un Swan Ganz 7-F; la posición correcta del mismo en la arteria pulmonar fue controlada a través de un amplificador de imagen fluoroscópica en circuito cerrado (TELCO); a partir de ese punto, todas las otras medidas fueron posibles. Un control osciloscópico permanente del ECG fue efectuado durante la prueba y los valores del débito cardíaco fueron establecidos por termodilución (Edwars Lab.).

La medida de la relación $\dot{V}A/\dot{Q}$ por la técnica de los gases inertes múltiples (Etano, Ciclopropano, Halotano, Éter, Acetona y SF6) analizados por cromatografía según la metodología de Wagner (50) permite obtener valores muy precisos aún cuando el procedimiento es largo y de mucha agudeza técnica (13).

El proceso de la hemodilución consistió en extraer entre 13 a 18.4% del volumen sanguíneo, asumiendo que éste corresponde a 8% de peso corporal; simultáneamente se procedió a la reposición de líquido mediante la perfusión entibiada de Dextran 40 con 5% de Sorbitol, sustancia conocida por sus propiedades expansoras plasmáticas. A partir de este momento otras medidas fueron hechas con la reducción del hematocrito de 66 + 7 a 55 + 6, 6.

Con este estudio concluimos que antes de la hemodilución, la baja relación ventilación perfusión ($\dot{V}A/\dot{Q}$ < 0.1), sin un verdadero shunt, contribuye con 11.6 + 5% al flujo total de sangre, siendo esta alteración una de las causas de hipoxemia; otro factor constituye la hipoventilación alveolar con PO_2 venosa mezclada (P$\bar{v}O_2$) baja, sin que exista una modificación en la capacidad de difusión alvéolo-capilar.

Después de la hemodilución, el gasto cardíaco y la ventilación aumentan significativamente (Q de 5.5. ± 1.2. a 6.9 + 1.2 l/m, VE de 8.5 ± 1.4 a 9.6 ± 1.3 l/m).

La presión arterial pulmonar (Pāp) que antes de la hemodilución mostraba cifras elevadas con relación a los valores establecidos para la altura de La Paz (Pāp = 22.7 mmHg) (1), desciende, aunque no significativamente (Tabla 3).

VALORES MEDIOS DE RESPUESTA A LA HEMODILUCIÓN

	$\dot{VE}$ l/min	$\dot{Q}$ l/min	Pa O_2 mm Hg	Pa CO_2 mm Hg	pHa	Pap mm Hg	Fc Lat/min	Pcp mm Hg
ANTES	8.5+1.3	5.5+1.2	45.6+5.6	35.5+4.6	7.43+0.04	27.4+10.1	67.6+7.9	5.2+2.8
DESPUÉS	9.6+1.3	6.9+1.2	46.6+5.2	35.3+5.4	7.44+0.04	25.4+8.2	73+7.1	3.1+3.6

TABLA 3- Valores medios registrados por los pacientes con eritrocitosis (n=8), antes y después de la hemodilución.

A pesar de estas variaciones, las presiones arteriales y venosas de oxígeno no se modificaron favorablemente; sin embargo la relación $\dot{VA}/\dot{Q}$ mejora significativamente.

Según estos resultados la hipoxemia observada en pacientes con Eritrocitosis Patológica de Altura parecería deberse a un aumento del flujo sanguíneo de perfusión en zonas pobremente ventiladas, pero sin que exista un corto circuito verdadero, intra o extrapulmonar. La hipoventilación alveolar así como la baja PO_2 de sangre venosa mezcada ($P\bar{v}O_2$) también contribuirían a la hipoxia arterial de estos enfermos.

EFECTOS TERAPÉUTICOS

Si bien existe una serie de investigaciones médicas en los diversos campos de estudio que puede generar la Eritrocitosis Patológica de Altura, la situación es diferente si analizamos lo que pudo realizarse en relación a las posibilidades terapéuticas para estos pacientes; nuestra preocupación es lógica pues los servicios médicos de los departamentos de La Paz, Oruro y Potosí (46), cotidianamente reciben un número creciente de consultas.

Habitualmente parecería ser que la recomendación de cambiar de residencia hacia una zona mas baja es la regla final de un seguimiento clínico y de laboratorio de estos pacientes; esta determinación es demasiado vertical y no todos están en condiciones de cumplirla.

Algunos ensayos han sido realizados en base a los elementos fisiopatológicos ya descritos. Conocemos que la depresión ventilatoria en estos pacientes es mucho más pronunciada durante el sueño que en estado de vigilia, sin que exista una insuficiencia respiratoria global crónica; es decir los casos que evidencian una retención de CO_2 son poco frecuentes a excepción de los más graves, así la hipercápnea es moderada ó está ausente.

En algunos centros, se practica rutinariamente la sangría; este procedimiento paliativo es realmente transitorio; el uso de estimulantes respiratorios tiene un resultado variable. La medroxiprogesterona da buenos resultados (23), pero con efectos secundarios poco aceptables por los pacientes; por todo ello escogimos el bismesilato de almitrina, pues su acción está especialmente vinculada a una estimulación de los quimioreceptores aórticos y carotideos.

Nuestro estudio (48) evalúa la acción de la almitrina:

a) En 40 pacientes cuyo hematocrito (66, 8%) supera los valores normales de La Paz (21), la almitrina fue administrada por vía oral, a la dosis de 3 mg/Kg^{-1} peso para un primer estudio destinado a observar el efecto del medicamento a las 3 horas de su administración. Los resultados obtenidos muestran un aumento significativo de la PaO_2 ($\pm$ 3.5. mm Hg), del pH y de la frecuencia respiratoria, con reducción de la $PaCO_2$ (-3mm Hg) (Fig.6). A pesar de un incremento de la ventilación, éste no fue estadísticamente significativo.

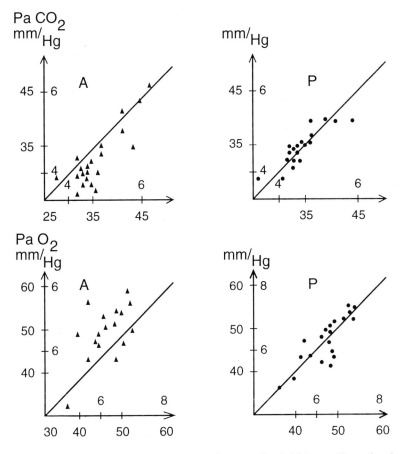

Fig 6 - Gráficas que muestran el efecto en fase aguda del bismesilato de almitrina (3mg Kg/peso) sobre la PaO_2 y la $PaCO_2$. Los valores de respuesta al medicamento se representan en función de los valores antes de la administración del mismo.

b) En la 2a. etapa del estudio se administró 1, 5 mg/Kg peso del producto a 12 pacientes durante 4 semanas. En este período fueron medidos semanalmente: la ventilación (V̇E), el consumo de oxígeno (V̇O$_2$), la producción de anhidrido carbónico (V̇CO$_2$), el hematocrito y la gasometría arterial.

Al cabo se pudo constatar una disminución del hematocrito (-3.5%). Los otros parámetros tuvieron muy poca variación; es probable que la mejoría de estos pacientes con la administración de bismesilato de almitrina tenga su razón en una mejoría de la ventilación, especialmente durante el sueño. Por otro lado se ha descrito una acción favorable sobre la relación ventilación-perfusión por acción de esta sustancia (43).

REFERENCIAS

1. ANTEZANA, G. 1988. *Circulación pulmonar en grandes alturas*. IBBA. Libro Bodas de Plata Imp.Master: 52-60.

2. ANTEZANA, G., PAZ ZAMORA, M. & VARGAS, E. 1987. Aclimatación a la altura. UNESCO *El Correo* No. 6-87. 8-11.

3. ARIAS STELLA, J., KRUGER, H. & RECAVARREN, S. 1971. Chronic Mountain Sickness Pathology and Definition. *In*: Ciba Foundation Symposium, *High Altitude Physiology. Cardiac and Respiratory Aspects*. London: 31-40.

4. ARNAUD, J. 1982. Haematocrit and age in man at high altitude. *Coll. Antropol.* Vol 6 (2): 223-224.

5. BERNARD, J. & RUFFIE, J. 1966. *Hématologie géographique* Tome I. Masson: Ecologie Humaine: .

6. BERT, P. 1878. *Barometric Pressure: 1943 Research in Experimental Physiology*. Translated by M.A. Hitchcock and R.A. Hitchcock. Ohio: College Book Co., Columbus: .

7. BRISCOE, W.A. 1959. A method for dealing with data concerning uneven ventilation of the lung and its effects on blood gas transfer. *J. Appl. Physiol.* 14: 291-298.

8. CRUZ, J. C., DÍAZ, C., MARTICORENA, E. & HILARIO, V. 1979. Phlebotomy improves pulmonary gaz exchange in chronic mountain polycythemia. *Respiration* 38: 305-313.

9. DEJOURS, P. 1962. Chemoreflexes in breathing. *Physiol. Rev.* 42: 335-358

10. ERGUETA, J., SPIELVOGEL, H. & CUDKOWICZ, L. 1971. Cardiorespiratory studies in Monge's Syndrome. *Respiration* 28: 485-517.

11. EVRARD, E. 1975. *Précis de Medecine Aeronautique et Spatiale*. Maloine Editor.

12. FLENLEY, D.C., COOKE, N.J., KING, A.J., LEITCH, A.G. & BRASH, H.M. 1973. The hipoxic drive to breathing during exercise in normal man and in hypoxic patients with chronic bronchitis and emphysema. *Bull. Physio-path. Respir.* vol. 9 (3): 689-691.

13. FORSTER, R.E. 1964. Diffusion of gases. *In*: *Handbook of Physiology. Respiration*. Washington DC: Am. Physiol. Soc., sect 3, vol. I chap. 33: 839-872.

14. FRISANCHO, R. 1991. *Human Adaptation, a Functional Interpretation*. Ann Arbor: The University of Michigan Press: XXXp.

15. FUNG, Y.C. 1973. Stochastic flow in capillary blood vessels. *Microvasc. Res.* 5: 34-48.

16. GONZÁLES G., HUM, N. & GUERRA GARCÍA, R. 1978. Relación del hematocrito con la edad en varones de Huancayo (3.200 m.) y Cerro de Pasco (4.200 m.). *In*: *Actas de las Primeras Jornadas de Medicina y Cirugía de la Altura*. Lima: Gráfica Pacific Press.

17. GUENARD, H., VARGAS, E., VILLENA, M. & CARRAS, P.M. 1984. Hypoxémie et Hématocrite dans la polyglobulie pathologique d'altitude. *Bull. Eur. Physiopathol. Respir.* 20: 319-324.

18. HEATH, D. & REID WILLIAMS, D. 1981. *Man at high altitude.* Edinburgh: Churchill-Livingstone:

19. HURTADO, A. 1942. Chronic mountain sickness. *J. Am. Med. Assoc.* 120: 1278.

20. HURTADO, A. 1960. Some clinical aspects of life at high altitudes. *Ann. Internal. Med.* 53: 247.

21. IBBA -LIBRO BODAS DE PLATA. 1988. *Fisiología de la adaptación respiratoria a la vida en altura*: 22-51.

22. KREUZER, F., TENNEY, S.M., MITHOEFER, J.C. & REMMERS, J. 1964. Alveolar-arterial oxygen gradient in Andean natives at high altitude. *J. Appl. Physiol.* 19: 13-16.

23. KRYGER, M., MC CULLOUGH, R.E., COLLINS, D., SCOGGIN, C.H., WEIL, J. & GROVER R. 1978. Treatment of excessive polycythemia of high altitude with respiratory stimulant drugs. *Am. Rev. Respir. Dis.* 117: 455-464.

24. KRYGER, M., MC CULLOUGH, R., DOEKEL, R., WEIL, J.V. & GROVER, R.F. 1978. Excessive polycythemia of high altitude: role of ventilatory drive and lung disease. *Am. Rev. Resp. DIS.* 118: 659-666.

25. LAHIRI S., KAO F., VELASQUEZ T., MARTINEZ C. PEZZIA W. 1969. Irreversible blunted respiratory sensitivity to hypoxia in high altitude natives. *Respir. Physiol.,* 6, 360-374.

26. LEFRANCOIS, R., GAUTIER, H. & PASQUIS, P. 1968. Ventilatory oxigen drive in acute and chronic hypoxia. *Respir. Physiol.* 4: 217-228.

27. LEFRANCOIS, R., VARGAS, E., HELLOT, M.F., PASQUIS, P. & DENIS, PH. 1978. *Interaction of humoral ventilatory. Stimuliat high altitude.* New York: Plenum Press.

28. LUPO, J.L. 1992. *Informe sobre el Censo Nacional de Población y Vivienda.* Lima: Publicación INE.

29. MADDOX, J. 1987. The great ozone controversy. *Nature* 239: 101.

30. MANIER, G., GUENARD, H., CASTAING, Y., VARENE, N. & VARGAS, E. 1988. Pulmonary gas exchange in Andean natives with excessive polycythemia-effect of hemodilution. *J. Appl. Physiol.* 65 (5): 2107-2117.

31. MARTICORENA, E., SEVERINO, J., GAMBOA, R., SIME, F., PEÑALOZA, D.Y. & DÍAZ, C. 1974. Volumen cardíaco en el nativo normal de la altura, en el portador de soroche crónico y en el individuo normal del nivel del mar. *Acta Médica Peruana*:

32. MERINO, C. 1950. Studies on blood formation and destruccion in the polycythemia of high altitude. *Blood* 5: 5 1.

33. MITHOEFER, J.C., REMMERS, J.E., ZUBIETA, G. & MITHOEFER, M.C. 1972. Pulmonary gas exchange in Andean natives at high altitude. *Respir. Physiol.* 15: 182-189.

34. MONGE-M., C. 1928. *La Enfermedad de los Andes (Síndromes Eritrémicos)* Lima: Anales de la Facultad de Médicina, 11: 1-314.

35. MONGE-M., C. & MONGE C., C. 1966. *High Altitude Diseases Mechanism and management.* Springfield: Charles C. Thomas, Publ. III: pp 1-97.

36. MONGE-C., C. & WHITTEMBURY, J. 1982. Chronic mountain sickness and physiopathology of hypoxemic polycythemia. *In*: J.R. Sutton et al eds., *Hypoxia: man at altitude.* New York: Thiene-Stratton: 51-56.

37. NORMAND, H., VARGAS, E., BODOCHAR, J., BENOIT, O. & RAYNAUD, J. 1992. Sleep Apneas in High Altitude Residents (3.600 m.). *In: Physiology abstracts of sport and mountain International Scientific. Congress.* France: Chamonix, B 53: 36.

38. PEÑALOZA, D. 1969. Corazón Pulmonar Crónico por desadaptación a la altura. Mal de Montaña Crónico. Tesis Doc. UPCH Lima.

39. RAYNAUD, J., VILLENA, M., FLORES, C., BORDACHAR, J., NORMAND, H., BAILLIARD, O., BENOIT, O. & DURAND, J. 1989. Periodicity in breathing and PaO$_2$ during sleep in normal and polycythemic highlanders at 3.600 m. *In: Abstracts of sixth international Hypoxia Symposim*. Canadá: Chateau lake Louise: .

40. ROTTA, A. 1962. Enfermedad de Monge (Mal de Montaña Crónico). *Rev. Perú Cardiol.* 9: 57.

41. SEVERINGHAUS, J.V., BAINTON, C.R. & CARCELEN, A. 1966. Respiratory insensitivity to hypoxia in chronically hypoxic man. *Respir. Physiol.* 1: 308-334.

42. SIME, F. 1973. Ventilación humana en hipoxia crónica. Etiopatogenia de la Enfermedad de Monge o desadaptación crónica a la altura. Tesis Doctoral. (UPCH) Lima.

43. SIMONNEAU, G., DENJEAN, A., RAFFESTIN, B., MAYNIARD, O., LAURENT, S., MEIGNAN & HARF, A. 1981. Improved pulmonary gas exchange caused by almitrine. *Amer. Rev. Resp. Dis.* 123 (suppl), 88 (abstract).

44. SPIELVOGEL, H., VARGAS, E., PAZ ZAMORA, M., HAAS, J., BEARD, J., DAIGH GILLIAN TUFTS & CUDKOWICZ, L. 1981. Poliglobulia y Ejercicio Muscular. *Gaceta del Tórax* 48 Vol XII - No. 4-6-11

45. TALBOT, J.H. & DILL, B.M. 1936. Clinical observations at high altitude. Observation on six healthy persons living at 17.500 feet and a report of one case of chronic mountain sickness. *Ann J.* 5. 5 192: 626.

46. VARGAS, E., VÁSQUEZ, R., VILLENA, M., VIDEA,   & VIDAURRE, M. 1978. Estudio de la función respiratoria en personas residentes en Chorolque (4.800 m.d.a.). *In: Informe encuesta en la población de Chorolque*. La Paz: Imp. UMSA: .

47. VARGAS, E. & VILLENA, M. 1989. La vie humaine en haute altitude: Mythes et réalités. *Bull. Soc. Path. Ex.* 82: 701-719.

48. VILLENA, M., VARGAS, E., GUENARD, H., NALLAR, N., TELLEZ, W. & SPIELVOGEL, H. 1985. Etude en double insu de l'effet de l' almitrine sur les malades porteus de polyglobulie pathologique d'altitude. *Bull Eur. Physiopathol. Resp.* 21: 165-170.

49. WAGNER, P.D., LARAVUSO, R.B., UHL, R.R. & WEST, J.B. 1974. Continuos distributions of ventilation-perfusion ratios in normal subjets breathing air and 100% O$_2$. *J. Clin. Invest.* 54: 54-68.

50. WAGNER, P.D., SALTZMAN, H.A. & WEST, J.B. 1974. Measurement of continuous distribution of ventilation-perfusion ratio: theory. *J. App. Physiol.* 36: 588-599.

51. WEST, J.B. 1969. Ventilation-perfusion inequality and overall gas exchange in computer models of the lung. *Respir. Physiol.* 7: 88-110.

52. WHITTEMBURY, J. & MONGE C., C. 1972. High altitude, hematocrit and age. *Nature* 238: 278-279.

53. YOUNG, I.H. & WAGNER, P.D. 1979. Effect of intrapulmonary hematocrit mal-distribution on O$_2$, CO$_2$ and inert gas exchange. *J. Appl. Physiol.* 46: 240-248.

LA ENFERMEDAD DE MONGE
ENFOQUE MULTIFACTORIAL

Fabiola León-Velarde

Resumen

Se presenta un modelo, basado en un estudio epidemiológico, que enfoca multifactorialmente la enfermedad de Monge. En este modelo se cuantifican, tanto las variables involucradas en su etiopatogenia (saturación de oxígeno, concentración de hemoglobina), las intervinientes (edad, enfermedades respiratorias comunes, peso corporal, tiempo de permanencia en la altura) como otras asociadas a la enfermedad (rasgos depresivos, actividad laboral, consumo de coca, práctica de deportes). El análisis estadístico toma como punto central a la hemoglobina (variable dependiente), por ser ésta, cuando se encuentra elevada por encima de los valores normales para la altura de residencia, el signo preponderante de la enfermedad de Monge. Las variables candidato se empiezan a contrastar luego unas con otras en base a criterios fisiológicos para la selección y organización de las variables dentro del modelo. Se concluye, en base al análisis de los factores involucrados en la elevación de la concentración de hemoglobina y en la aparición de síntomas y signos de la enfermedad, que ésta no solo es una enfermedad multisistémica, sino también multifactorial, donde el delicado equilibrio que el hombre ha establecido con su ambiente hipóxico, se rompe cuando se le demanda adicionales esfuerzos (exceso de trabajo, ser minero, y más aún, perforista), se le modifica, se deteriora o recarga (aumento de peso, problemas respiratorios comunes), o simplemente envejece sometido, de manera permanente, a una hipoxia crónica severa.

Palabras claves: Hipoxia, altura, Andes, mal de montaña crónico, enfermedad de Monge, policitemia, saturación de oxígeno, enfermedad respiratoria.

Résumé

Ce travail présente un modèle basé sur une étude épidémiologique qui met l'accent de façon multifactorielle sur la maladie de Monge. On quantifie, dans ce domaine, aussi bien les variables impiquées dans sa physiopathologie (saturation de l'oxygène, concentration de l'hémoglobine), les intervenants (âge, maladies respiratoires communes, poids du corps, temps de séjour en altitude), que celles associées à la maladie (caractéristiques dépressives, type de travail, consommation de coca, pratique de sports). L'hémoglobine constitue le point central de l'analyse statistique (variable dépendante), celle-là étant, quand elle se trouve au-dessus des valeurs normales pour l'altitude de séjour, le signe prépondérant de la maladie de Monge. Les variables sélectionnées commencent à se contraster ensuite les unes avec les autres sur la base de critères physiologiques pour la sélection et l'organisation des variables dans le modèle. Sur la base de l'analyse des facteurs mis en cause dans l'élévation de la concentration d'hémoglobine et dans l'apparition de symptomes et signes de la maladie, l'article conclut que celle-ci n'est pas seulement une maladie multisystémique, mais aussi factorielle, où l'équilibre délicat que l'homme établit avec son milieu hypoxique est rompu quand on lui demande des efforts supplémentaires (excès de travail, travail comme mineur, et surtout comme mineur de fonds), quand on le modifie, quand il se détériore ou quand il s'alourdit (hausse de poids, problèmes respiratoires communs) ou simplement quand il vieillit soumis, de façon permanente, à une hypoxie chronique sévère.

Mots clés : Hypoxie, altitude, Andes, mal des montagnes chronique, maladie de Monge, polycythémie, saturation d'oxygène, maladie respiratoire.

Summary

A model for a multifactorial approach to Monge's disease is presented. It quantifies the variables involved in the etiopathogenesis (oxygen saturation, hemoglobin concentration) as well as variables consired intervenient (age, common respiratory disorders, body weight, time of residence at high altitude) or those associated with the disease (depressive symptoms, labor activity, coca leaf use, sports practice). The statistical analysis takes hemoglobin as its central point (independent variable), because it is the preponderant finding of Monge's disease when its concentration raises above the normal limits for the altitude of residence. The selected variables are contrasted one to each other on the basis of physiological criteria in order to select and organize them inside the model. It is concluded from the analysis of the factors involved in the elevation of hemoglobin concentration and in the appearence of symptoms and signs of the disease, that this is not only a multisystem clinical condition but also a multifactorial illness. It represents a situation in which the delicate balance between man and his hypoxic environment obtained through millenia of selection is broken by the aging process and when additional demands like excessive work, mining activity, especially drilling work, are added, and associated to conditions like overweight and common respiratory disorders.

Key words: Hypoxia, high altiitude, Andes, chronic mountain sickness, Monge's disease, polycythemia, oxygen saturation, respiratory disease.

La enfermedad de Monge o mal de montaña crónico, inicialmente llamada Enfermedad de los Andes, fue descrita en 1925 por el Dr. Carlos Monge Medrano en un nativo de la ciudad de Cerro de Pasco (Pasco, Perú; 4,340 m) como "...el conjunto de síndromes eritrémicos que se desarrolla en el organismo como consecuencia de la inadaptación o desadaptación del hombre a la vida en las grandes alturas..."(30; 31). Los sujetos afectados, usualmente hombres adultos, presentan por lo general síntomas primordialmente neuropsíquicos, tales como cefalea, mareo, somnolencia, insomnio, nerviosismo, fatiga física y mental, dificultades en el control del movimiento, alteraciones de la memoria, y tendencia a la depresión; además de inapetencia, dolores musculares, osteocopos o articulares, zumbidos de oídos y sensación de quemazón en las manos y pies. En casos avanzados el enfermo presenta síntomas de cor pulmonale secundario a la acentuación de la hipertensión pulmonar, pudiendo presentar también accidentes vasculares en el cerebro u otro órgano afectado

(31; 32; 33; 18; 19; 35; 37; 38; 1; 50). Un aumento del número de glóbulos rojos, de la concentración de la hemoglobina y del hematocrito, como signo preponderante, acompañan al cuadro clínico. Estas cifras se encuentran por encima de aquellas que corresponden a la respuesta fisiológica normal para la altura de residencia (eritremia o eritrocitosis excesiva) (31; 32; 35). Monge-M. notó que los enfermos se curaban al bajar a nivel del mar y que la enfermedad regresaba si el enfermo volvía a la altura; consideró esta entidad como propia de quienes viven en la altura y la diferenció claramente del soroche o mal de montaña agudo, que se presenta en quienes recién llegan a la altura.

El factor común hallado en los enfermos estudiados es la hipoventilación; la hipoxemia generada por esta, sería la causa del síndrome eritrémico (23; 8; 17; 50). Sorensen & Severinghaus (46) señalan que la exposición a hipoxia crónica durante los primeros 2 años de vida atenúa irreversiblemente la respuesta refleja a la hipoxia aguda mediada por los quimiorreceptores periféricos. De hecho, Severinghaus *et al.* (43) y Velásquez (48), encuentran en los nativos de altura adultos una desensibilización generalizada de la respuesta. Sin embargo, esta desensibilización de la respuesta ventilatoria a la exposición a la hipoxia no parece ser la causa de la eritremia excesiva, pues se sabe, que si bien todos los nativos se encuentran desensibilizados, no todos presentan eritremia excesiva para la altura de residencia, ni mal de montaña crónico. No obstante, si bien no se descarta a la hipoventilación primaria como causa de la eritremia excesiva en ausencia de enfermedad pulmonar, Heath (15) y Monge-C. (1971; comunicación personal) cuestionan esta proposición. Postulan que todos los casos de enfermedad de Monge tendrían algún grado de disfunción respiratoria, los detectados como hipoventiladores primarios, presentarían también disfunciones pulmonares, pero estas habrían pasado inadvertidas. Hecht & Mc Clement (16) proponen asimismo, que algunos casos de enfermedad de Monge, serían el resultado de perturbaciones en el intercambio gaseoso respiratorio y en la relación ventilación/perfusión. Estas perturbaciones tendrían como base, enfermedades pulmonares intrínsecas, demasiado leves para mostrar signos o síntomas a nivel del mar.

De cualquier modo, primaria o secundaria la disfunción pulmonar, se acepta hasta hoy como explicación fisiopatológica para la aparición de la enfermedad de Monge, la secuencia de eventos: hipoventilación, hipoxemia, eritremia excesiva. A este concepto, se han agregado posteriormente factores agravantes de la enfermedad. Whittembury & Monge (49; 27) y Sime *et al.* (45) postulan a la edad como uno de ellos; en la altura, la normal disminución de la ventilación pulmonar que acompaña a la edad sería suficiente para reducir la presión parcial de oxígeno en la sangre arterial (PaO_2) y generar la eritremia. Los casos extremos de la triple correlación ventilación y hematocrito en función de la edad, señalada por estos autores, estarían representados por los enfermos con mal de montaña crónico (44; 45). Como corroboración a este estudio longitudinal, y en base a estudios epidemiológicos de tipo transversal nuestro grupo de trabajo ha encontrado que en 2890 mineros de la ciudad de Cerro de Pasco (4300 m) la prevalencia de eritrocitosis excesiva

(Hb > 21.3 g/dl) aumenta y que la capacidad vital disminuye con la edad (29; 2; 26). Otro de los factores descritos como agravantes para la enfermedad es la acentuación de la hipoventilación que ocurre durante el sueño, que, al producir una mayor desaturación arterial aceleraría el proceso eritrémico (22; 24; 44).

Si bien la enfermedad de Monge fue descrita por primera vez en el Perú, con el transcurso del tiempo, esta se ha encontrado y estudiado en otros países con regiones montañosas como en Bolivia (8), Estados Unidos (16; 21), Tibet (52; 36) y China (17). Estos estudios, y otros sobre eritremia de la altura sugieren que las modificaciones en el género de vida podrían ser causales de la desadaptación. Por ejemplo, Pei *et al.* (36) señalan que si bien en el Tibet el mal de montaña crónico no es común entre los pobladores tibetanos, si lo es entre la población china inmigrante. En Estados Unidos, en las minas de Leadville, Colorado (3,100 m), también se han reportado casos de mal de montaña crónico, a pesar de la moderada altura en la que se encuentra la ciudad (21). En La Paz (Bolivia), la eritremia es mayor que en poblaciones que llevan un estilo de vida rural (28). En la ciudad minera de Chuquicamata, en Chile, a solo 2,800 m., la media de concentración de hemoglobina es superior a aquella encontrada en la población nativa del altiplano chileno a 4,100 m. (40; 39). Y Frisancho, comparando las concentraciones de hemoglobina de varias poblaciones mineras con poblaciones rurales a diversas alturas en los Andes y los Himalayas, mostró que las primeras tenían concentraciones de hemoglobina más elevadas para cada altura de residencia estudiada (12). Esta diferencia podría interpretarse como una mejor capacidad del nativo del Altiplano de adaptarse a su medio, pero es también posible que el régimen de vida, la alimentación, el hábito de fumar, el sedentarismo y la contaminación urbanas, podrían ser causas suficientes para producir una disminución de la función pulmonar que conduzca a la elevación de las cifras de hemoglobina (50).

Tradicionalmente, los aspectos arriba mencionados, no han sido tomados en cuenta para el estudio de la enfermedad de Monge, la discusión ha estado centrada más bien, en la existencia de las dos formas de la enfermedad: mal de montaña crónico primario, no asociada a perturbación pulmonar o cardiovascular alguna, y secundario a enfermedad pulmonar; no obstante, puede verse que conforme se comparan poblaciones, empiezan a aparecer otras variables, todavía poco conocidas, que podrían estar involucradas en la aparición de la enfermedad de Monge. En este artículo, se han incluído variables candidato, buscando cuantificar, y analizar de una forma integral, el efecto de los factores agravantes del mal; se intenta demostrar, que, además de la hipoventilación primaria o secundaria a una disfunción respiratoria existen otras variables intervinientes, como el tiempo de residencia en la altura, los viajes a zonas más bajas, el peso corporal, el tipo de trabajo entre otras, que median directa o indirectamente en el proceso de desadaptación a la vida en las grandes alturas, *i. e.*, en la aparición de la enfermedad de Monge.

METODOLOGÍA

Los datos provienen de estudios epidemiológicos llevados a cabo en el campamento minero de Cerro de Pasco, de un total entre 213 a 378 residentes de la ciudad, entre mineros y no mineros; si bien esta era una pequeña ciudad minera cuando la enfermedad fue descrita por primera vez, ahora cuenta con aproximadamente 75,000 habitantes. En estos estudios, el jefe de familia respondía a una encuesta, que tenía como objetivo obtener información sobre la edad, ocupación, hábitos de consumo (alcohol, coca, tabaco), así como sobre sus principales problemas de salud, poniendo énfasis en los asociados a la enfermedad de Monge y a los problemas respiratorios.

Como los signos y síntomas de la enfermedad de Monge han sido bien definidos (31), se los pudo traducir en 10 preguntas, las que con valores mínimos de 10 y máximos de 20 compusieron el puntaje de la enfermedad de Monge o mal de montaña crónico (pMMC) (Arregui & León-Velarde, en preparación). Asimismo, como en el cuadro general de la enfermedad, los rasgos depresivos son bastante frecuentes, se realizó una encuesta independiente, tanto para evaluar los rasgos depresivos de la población en estudio, como para determinar su asociación con el mal de montaña crónico. Se hicieron 14 de las 20 preguntas de la escala de Zung para la medición de la depresión. En su versión original la escala consta de 20 preguntas con cuatro respuestas posibles que van de 'nunca o casi nunca' a 'siempre o casi siempre'. De estas preguntas se descartaron seis, algunas, para evitar interferencias de índole orgánico, y otras, para simplificar y hacer más comprensible la encuesta a los pobladores andinos. La encuesta quedó entonces reducida a 14 preguntas con tres posibles respuestas: 'no', 'sí, a veces' y 'sí, por lo general o con frecuencia'. El cálculo del puntaje se hizo en base a lo contestado por los encuestados, cada pregunta con sus tres posibles respuestas, recibió un puntaje (de 1 a 3), la suma de éstos correspondía al puntaje de depresión (pDep).

Los problemas respiratorios detectados se dividieron en enfermedades agudas altas (*e.g.*, faringitis) o bajas (*e.g.*, neumonía) y en crónicas altas (*e.g.*, sinusitis) o bajas (*e.g.*, asma) según una guía detallada de examen clínico. Cabe la aclaración que la metodología empleada no pretendía detectar casos de enfermedades específicas como por ejemplo neumoconiosis, sino evaluar los problemas respiratorios crónicos bajos más comunes en su conjunto. La frecuencia de problemas respiratorios fue de 37% para la población encuestada siendo las enfermedades crónicas bajas las más prevalentes.

En caso que la persona encuestada resultara evocada por la encuesta como un sujeto candidato, se le pesaba, medía, se le determinaban sus presiones arteriales sistólica y diastólica, su valor de concentración de hemoglobina, de saturación de oxigeno y de flujo expiratorio máximo. La hemoglobina (Hb -g/dl) se determinó por el método de la azidohemoglobina (Hemocue -inc), la saturación de oxígeno (SatO$_2$ -%) mediante un pulso-oxímetro (Nellcor -inc) y el flujo expiratorio máximo (FEM -ml/min/talla) con un espirómetro. La Hb y la SatO$_2$ se realizaron por duplicado, el FEM, por triplicado, tomando la lectura más alta de las tres, lectura que se corregía adicionando el 6.6% por 100 torr de caída de la presión barométrica (47).

Las variables independientes, intervinientes y asociadas se escogieron inicialmente entre algunas variables fisiológicas, clínicas, laborales y culturales posibles de acuerdo al peso relativo (considerado inicialmente de manera subjetiva) que pudieran tener en el desencadenamiento de la eritrocitosis excesiva (variable dependiente). Esta ha sido definida como dos desviaciones estandar a la derecha de la distribución normal para la población joven [(Hb > 21.3 g/dl; (2)]. Posteriormente, las variables independientes, intervinientes y asociadas fueron ubicadas de acuerdo al modelo fisiológico y a su peso estadístico real en un modelo explicativo.

Las variables independientes candidato fueron, la saturación de oxígeno (SatO$_2$) y el flujo expiratorio máximo (FEM). La disminución de éstas, actuaría directamente produciendo la hipoxemia, la eritrocitosis excesiva (EE), y consecuentemente elevando el pMMC. Las variables intervinientes, la edad, el peso, las enfermedades respiratorias crónicas bajas (ERCB), y los viajes a zonas más bajas (-Talt); esta última utilizada como reflejo de la disminución del tiempo de permanencia real en la altura de residencia. Las variables intervinientes actuarían directamente sobre las variables independientes, y de manera indirecta, sobre las dependientes. Las variables asociadas escogidas fueron, los rasgos depresivos (pDep), la actividad laboral (ser minero o no minero, ser perforista o realizar otra labor dentro de la mina), el consumo de coca y la práctica de deportes.

Los resultados fueron procesados mediante el paquete estadístico SPSS Inc. SPSS/PC+ V2. Para las variables contínuas se determinaron la media, la mediana, la variancia y la desviación estandar. Para el análisis de las variables discretas se utilizó el test de Xi Cuadrado, corregido por Yates. La comparación y el valor de la significancia entre las variables contínuas se realizó mediante análisis de variancia, regresiones simples y múltiples.

EL MODELO EXPLICATIVO

El modelo acá presentado tiene como objetivo explicar el peso relativo de las variables fisiológicas, clínicas, laborales y culturales que van a desencadenar en unos casos, y coadyuvar en otros, la aparición del mal de montaña crónico expresado como pMMC (Fig. 1). El análisis estadístico toma como punto central a la hemoglobina (variable dependiente). Se tomó a esta variable como expresión de la enfermedad, no solo por ser el signo determinante de la misma, sino también, en base a los hallazgos experimentales y clínicos, en los que se demuestra claramente la desaparición de los síntomas (42; 41) y mejoría global del transporte de oxígeno (6; 51) cuando la hemoglobina y el hematocrito disminuyen. Las variables candidato se empiezan a contrastar unas con otras en base a criterios fisiológicos y clínicos para la selección y organización de las variables dentro del modelo. Se asume asociación directa entre dos variables cuando la regresión múltiple resulta altamente significativa luego de la eliminación selectiva de las variables intervinientes.

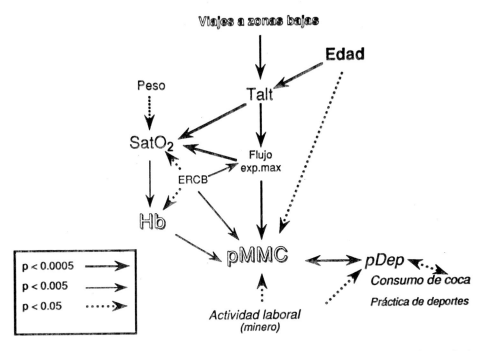

Fig. 1 - Modelo explicativo del mal de montaña crónico como enfermedad multifactorial: pMMC, puntaje de mal de montaña crónico; Hb, concentración de hemoglobina; pDep, puntaje de depresión; ERCB, enfermedad respiratoria crónica baja; SatO$_2$, saturación de O$_2$; Talt, tiempo de residencia permanente en la altura.

LA DISMINUCIÓN DE LA SATURACIÓN DE OXÍGENO Y SUS VARIABLES INTERVINIENTES

Dado que una hipoxemia sanguínea se traducirá directamente en una menor SatO$_2$ se seleccionaron las variables que pudiesen estar afectándola, obteniéndose las siguientes ecuaciones de regresión múltiple:

$$SatO_2 = 63.43 + 0.094*Edad + 0.13*FEM + 0.23*(-Talt)$$

                    (NS)   (NS)   (p=0.04)

Ecuaciones parciales:

$$SatO_2 = 88.39 - 0.094*Edad \qquad (p=0.0000)$$

$$SatO_2 = 78.66 + 0.018*FEM \qquad (p=0.0003)$$

$$FEM = 424.8 - 2.31*Edad \qquad (p=0.0000)$$

$$SatO_2 = 72.21 + 6.29*(-Talt) \qquad (p=0.023)$$

Cuando el peso corporal se incorpora en el análisis (p=0.012) y la variable viajes a zonas más bajas (-Talt) se desprecia, por el efecto que sobre la SatO$_2$ tiene el ausentarse de la altura, *i.e.* reoxigenarse en zonas bajas, el FEM adquiere significancia, y la SatO$_2$ depende ahora tanto del peso como del FEM.

$$SatO_2 = 86.32 - 0.11*Edad + 0.26*FEM - 0.23*Peso$$

$$(NS) \qquad (p=0.0001) \quad (p=0.0006)$$

Los valores de $SatO_2$ entre los que viajan frecuentemente a zonas más bajas y los que no lo hacen nunca, pone en evidencia el peso de esta variable sobre la $SatO_2$ y sobre el FEM. Los que viajan frecuentemente presentan una $SatO_2$ de 84.5%(±4.3) y un FEM de 328.0ml/min(±51.6), mientras que los que nunca han abandonado Cerro de Pasco tienen una media de $SatO_2$ de 79.3%(±7.0), y una media de FEM de 291.6ml/min(±65.2) (p<0.002 y 0.014 respectivamente).

Del análisis de las ecuaciones multivariables en las que la $SatO_2$ es la variable independiente puede verse, que si bien la edad no adquiere significancia estadística en ninguna de las dos ecuaciones, y el flujo expiratorio pierde peso en la segunda, cuando se considera -Talt, estas variables se encuentran correlacionadas con la $SatO_2$ en las ecuaciones parciales. Con la edad disminuyen tanto la Sat O_2 como el FEM. Entre los 20 y 60 años hay una reducción de 33% en el FEM y un 5% en la $SatO_2$. Adicionalmente, se encontró que los sujetos con ERCB tenían una $SatO_2$ de 82.8%(±5.5), mientras que los que no fueron detectados como enfermos crónicos mostraban una $SatO_2$ de 84.7%(±4.5) (p<0.03). Evidentemente, si existe una disminución de la FEM con la edad o con la presencia de ERCB, ésta traerá consigo un incremento de la hipoxemia. El aumento de peso, al generar una hipoventilación aunque moderada, en la altura, disminuirá adicionalmente la saturación de oxígeno en sangre.

LA CONCENTRACIÓN DE HEMOGLOBINA Y EL PMMC

La ecuación de regresión múltiple de la concentración de hemoglobina teniendo en cuenta las variables con las cuales podría encontrarse asociada fisiológicamente fue:

$$Hb = 234.7 - 0.21*SatO_2 - 0.0024*FEM - 0.0005*Edad + 0.14*pMMC$$

$$(p=0.0034) \qquad (NS) \qquad (NS) \qquad (p=0.044)$$

A su vez, la ecuación de regresión múltiple para el pMMC con las variables que lo podrían estar afectando queda definida como:

$$pMMC = 10.69 - 0.02*SatO_2 + 0.18*Edad + 0.15*pDep - 0.11*FEM$$

$$(NS) \qquad (0.02) \qquad (0.0001) \qquad (NS)$$

Ecuaciones parciales:

$$pMMC = 14.96 + 0.060*Edad \qquad (p=0.0005)$$

$$pMMC = 22.95 - 0.014*FEM \qquad (p=0.0007)$$

$$pDep = 18.72 + 0.350*pMMC \qquad (p=0.0000)$$

$$pDep = 28.39 - 0.055*Peso \qquad (p=0.0320)$$

$$Hb = 140.50 + 0.761*Peso \qquad (p=0.0000)$$

La edad (variable interviniente), si bien afecta la $SatO_2$ y el FEM, tiene un efecto aparentemente despreciable sobre la Hb. El efecto de la edad en la Hb aparece más bien como aumento en la prevalencia (% de sujetos con EE) a medida que aumenta la edad (29). También puede verse el efecto de la edad a través de la $SatO_2$ cuando se compara la $SatO_2$ para individuos entre 20-29 años (85.4%±4.5) con la de personas mayores de 50 años (82.0%±4.1) (p<0.002). La disminución de la $SatO_2$ (variable independiente), sí aumenta directa y apreciablemente la concentración de hemoglobina. Cuando la saturación disminuye, la concentración de hemoglobina aumenta, aparece la eritrocitosis y los síntomas y signos asociados al MMC aumentan. Como aparece en el modelo, la edad, el FEM y el peso, estarían actuando a través de la disminución de la saturación de oxígeno. Como el hecho de tener mayor tiempo de vida en la altura está relacionado a un mayor FEM, el -Talt, también se encuentra relacionado al pMMC a través de este. Así, las personas que han permanecido durante toda su vida en la altura presentan un pMMC de 18.3(±4.4), mientras que las que han viajado con frecuencia a zonas bajas (-Talt) presentan un pMMC de 16.7(±3.6) (p<0.04).

Como asociaciones importantes se encontraron: la ocupación de minero en lo general, y la de perforista en lo particular, la práctica de deportes, y el consumo de coca. El ser minero o perforista, se encontró asociado a un mayor pMMC. Los mineros y perforistas tuvieron puntajes de 18.2(±4.1) y 19.7(±4.8) respectivamente y los no mineros, una media de 17.5(±3.9) (p<0.03). El ser perforista, se encuentra también asociado a un mayor pDep, los perforistas tienen un pDep de 26.5(±3.8), mientras que los que se dedican a otras labores en el tajo abierto de la mina muestran un pDep de 24.4(±4.0) (p<0.03). La actividad física altamente desgastadora del minero en general, y del perforador minero en particular, aceleraría tanto la aparición de los síntomas y signos asociados al MMC como la aparición de rasgos depresivos. Por el contrario, una mayor actividad física se encuentra asociada a un menor pDep; las personas que practican deportes tienen un pDep de 24.5(±3.7), mientras que las que no suelen hacer deporte muestran un pDep de 26.5(±4.1) (p<0.0001). El consumo de coca se encontró también asociado a los rasgos depresivos, mostrando un pDep de 25.5(±3.7) los individuos que refirieron consumir coca y un pDep de 24.5(±3.9) (p< 0.02) los que declararon no hacerlo.

El análisis desarrollado nos permite concluir que nos encontramos ante un proceso sumamente complejo donde la fisiología, la geografía humana y la salud ocupacional se encuentran íntimamente relacionadas. La fisiología de la adaptación a la altura determina las pautas que estarán dadas por las diferentes modificaciones fisiológicas en distintos sistemas del organismo, la geografía humana define los límites de la distribución de los grupos humanos en las grandes alturas y la salud ocupacional agrega nuevas "agresiones" ambientales a un ambiente de por sí ya bastante adverso. El delicado equilibrio del hombre con su ambiente, logrado a través de milenios, se rompe cuando se le demanda adicionales esfuerzos (exceso de trabajo, ser minero, y más aún, perforista), se le modifica, se deteriora o recarga (aumento de peso, problemas respiratorios comunes), o simplemente envejece sometido, de manera permanente, a una hipoxia crónica severa.

CONSIDERACIONES FINALES

A fines de la Colonia y comienzos de la República el trabajo minero era llevado a cabo por un semiproletariado sumamente móvil más campesino que obrero (5; 20), que proporcionaba la mano de obra. Al respecto algunos investigadores han sugerido que la razón de esta gran movilidad era acortar los periodos en las labores mineras, pues el prolongarlas provocaría enfermedades "profesionales". Las salidas periódicas al campo eran en este sentido, un mecanismo necesario para preservar la salud de los trabajadores (25; 4). A mediados y fines del siglo XIX se produce un cambio lento en la geografía migratoria, y finalmente a partir del presente siglo, sin abandonar todavía el sistema de las migraciones periódicas de retorno al campo, se empieza a conformar una población minera más estable (10; 3). Desde la década de los años 30 la disminución de la migración, se muestra más claramente: el trabajador minero deja su doble condición de campesino agrícola de zonas bajas y minero de grandes alturas para convertirse en un poblador estable de las minas a gran altura (4; 2). Con el establecimiento permanente de estos campamentos mineros se generan necesidades de tipo urbano que inducen a un grupo humano no minero a instalarse en los alrededores de los yacimientos. De esta manera se crean ciudades en los más inhóspitos lugares de la cordillera de los Andes y así, tanto el poblador minero como el no minero fijan su residencia permanente en alturas "habitadas, más no necesariamente habitables" (34), sometiéndose a una situación biomédica particular no prevista en el pasado: la exposición permanente a las grandes alturas, *i.e.* a una hipoxia crónica ambiental severa. Pero estas poblaciones, no sólo están expuestas en forma permanente al estresor hipóxico, sino que además han sufrido paulatinamente cambios en sus estilos de vida y de trabajo tradicionales. Tales condiciones, han provocado graves desventajas para la salud de la población en cuestión, pues han exigido al máximo su capacidad adaptativa a la altura, y han producido la ruptura de su patrón cultural primario. Este patrón ha sido sustituído por un modelo de vida propio de las ciudades industrializadas, donde la dieta, el alcohol y el género de vida en general, distan mucho de la vida del campesino altoandino. Estos presores permanentes coadyuvan a la quiebra del delicado equilibrio que implica la adaptación del hombre a su ambiente.

El hombre, a diferencia de los animales genéticamente adaptados a vivir en las grandes alturas, no posee un armamentario genético humano propio de la altura (7; 9); las flebotomías, que disminuyen los síntomas del mal de montaña crónico, y mejoran el rendimiento general del individuo (6; 51; 42; 41), y las características hematológicas, respiratorias, cardio-vasculares, del hombre andino que revierten en su mayoría a nivel de mar, y que pueden ser adquiridas practicamente en su totalidad antes del desarrollo (11; 13; 14), apuntan también hacia una aclimatación más que hacia una adaptación genética a su ambiente. No obstante, es evidente, que el hombre andino ha logrado conquistar su ambiente bajo condiciones de vida tradicionales; más, cuando confluyen desarrollo urbano a grandes alturas, con la consecuente hipoxia crónica permanente, y el estresor laboral, aparece el riesgo de la enfermedad de Monge, que, de una entidad clínica discreta que afecta a unos pocos individuos, pasa a ser la expresión de un proceso de pérdida de adaptación a la altura de la población altoandina.

REFERENCIAS

1. ARIAS-STELLA, J., KRÜGER, H. & RECAVARREN, S. 1973. Pathology of Chronic Mountain Sickness. *Thorax* 28: 70-708.

2. ARREGUI, A., LEÓN-VELARDE, F. & VALCÁRCEL, M. 1990. *Salud y Minería. El riesgo del Mal de Montaña Crónico entre mineros de Cerro de Pasco.* Lima: ADEC-ATC/Mosca Azul: 127p.

3. BONILLA, H. 1974. *El Minero de los Andes.* Lima: Instituto de Estudios Peruanos: 89p.

4. CONTRERAS, C. 1988. *Mineros y Campesinos en los Andes.* Lima: Instituto de Estudios Peruanos: 155p.

5. COTLEAR, D. 1979. *El sistema de enganche a principios del siglo XX. Una versión diferente.* Memoria. Lima: Pontificia Universidad Católica del Perú.

6. CRUZ, J.C., DÍAZ, C., MARTICORENA, E. & HILARIO, V. 1979. Phlebotomy improves pulmonary gas exchange in Chronic Mountain Polycythemia. *Respiration* 38: 30-313.

7. CRUZ-COKE, R., CRISTOFFANINI, A.P., ASPILLAGA, M. & BIANCANI, F. 1966. Evolutionary forces in human population in an environmental gradient in Arica, Chile. *Human Bio.* 38: 42-38.

8. ERGUETA, J., SPIELVOGEL, H. & CUDKOWICZ, L. 1971. Cardio-respiratory studies in chronic mountain sickness (Monge's syndrome). *Respiration* 28: 485-517.

9. FERREL, R.E., BERTIN, T., BARTON, S., ROTHAMMER, F. & SCHULL, W. J. 1980. A multinational Andean genetic and health program. Gene frequencies and rare variants of 20 serum protein and erythrocyte enzymes systems. *American J. Human Genet.* 32: 92-102.

10. FLORES, A. 1974. *Los Mineros de la Cerro de Pasco. 1900-1930.* Lima: Departamento de Ciencias Sociales de la Universidad Católica: 142p.

11. FRISANCHO, A.R. 1969. Human growth and pulmonary function of a high altitude Peruvian Quechua population. *Human Biol.* 41: 365-379.

12. FRISANCHO, A.R. 1988. Origins of differences in hemoglobin concentration between Himalayan and Andean populations. *Resp. Physiol.* 72: 13-8.

13. FRISANCHO, A.R., MARTÍNEZ, C., VELÁSQUEZ, M.T., SÁNCHEZ, J. & MONTOYE, H. 1973a. Influence of developmental adaptation on aerobic capacity at high altitude. J. Appl. Physiol. 34: 176-180.

14. FRISANCHO, A.R., VELÁSQUEZ, M.T. & SÁNCHEZ, J. 1973b. Influence of developmental adaptation on lung function at high altitude. *Human Biol.* 45: 583-594.

15. HEATH, D. 1971. Cor pulmonale in chronic mountain sickness: present concept of Monge's disease in High Altitude Physiology: Cardiac and Respiratory Aspects. *In*: R. Porter & J. Knight (eds.) *A Ciba Foundation Symposium*. Edinburgh and London: Churchill Livingstone: 52.

16. HECHT, H.H. & McCLEMENT, J.H. 1958. A case of "chronic mountain sickness" in the United States. *Amer. J. Med*. 25: 470-477.

17. HU, X.C., GU, Z.Z., NING, X.H., ZHOU, C.F., LIN, H.Y., FENG, Z.M., CHEN, Z.Z. & PAN, T.C. 1981. The role of respiratory function in the pathogenesis of severe hypoxemia in chronic mountain sickness. *In*: Gordon & Breach Science (ed.) *Geological and Ecological Studies of Qinghai-Xizang Plateau*. New York: 1427-1432.

18. HURTADO, A. 1942. Chronic mountain sickness. *JAMA* 120: 1278-82.

19. HURTADO, A. 1955. Pathological aspects of life at high altitudes. *Military Medicine* 117: 272-84.

20. KRUIJT, D. & VELLINGA, M. 1987. *La Cerro y el Proletariado Minero-Metalúrgico*. Lima: ADEC-ATC, Industrial Gráfica S.A.: 160p.

21. KRYGER, M. & GROVER, R.F. 1983. Chronic mountain sickness. *Semin. Resp. Med*. 5: 164-168.

22. KRYGER, M., GLAS, R., JACKSON, D.L., McCULLOUGH, R.E., SCOGGIN, C.H., GROVER, R.F. & WEIL, J.V. 1978a. Impaired oxygenation during sleep in excessive polycythemia of high altitude: improvement with respiratory stimulation. *Sleep (NY)* 1: 3-17.

23. KRYGER, M., McCULLOUGH, R., DOEKEL, R., COLLINS, D., WEIL, J.V. & GROVER, R.F. 1978b. Excessive polycythemia of high altitude: role of ventilatory drive and lung disease. *Amer. Rev. Resp. Dis*. 118: 659-666.

24. KRYGER, M., WEIL, J.V. & GROVER, R.F. 1978c. Chronic mountain polycythemia: A disorder of the regulation of breathing during sleep? *Chest*. 73: 303-4.

25. KUCZYNSKY, G.M.H. 1945. *Estudios Médico-Sociales en Minas de Puno*. Lima: Ministerio de Salud Pública y Asistencia Social: 98p.

26. LEÓN-VELARDE, F., ARREGUI, A., MONGE-C., C. & RUIZ Y RUIZ, H. Aging at high altitudes and the risk of chronic mountain sickness. *J. Wild. Med*. 4; 183-188.

27. MONGE-C., C. & WHITTEMBURY, J. 1976. Chronic mountain sickness. *Johns Hopkins Med. Jour*. 139: 87-89.

28. MONGE-C., C., BONAVÍA, D., LEÓN-VELARDE, F. & ARREGUI, A. 1990. Adaptations to hypoxia in high altitude populations that reside in Nepal and the Andes. *In*: J. R. Sutton, G. Coates & J. E. Remmers (eds.),*Hypoxia. The Adaptations*. Toronto: BC Decker Inc.: 53-58.

29. MONGE-C., C., LEÓN-VELARDE, F. & ARREGUI, A. 1989. Increasing prevalence of excessive erythrocytosis with age among healthy high-altitude miners (Letter). *New Eng. J. Med*. 321: 1271.

30. MONGE-M., C. 1925. Sobre un caso de enfermedad de Váquez. Comunicación presentada a la Academia Nacional de Medicina: 1-7. Lima.

31. MONGE-M., C. 1928. La enfermedad de las Andes (Síndromes eritrémicos). *Anales de la Facultad de Medicina (Lima)* 11: 1-314.

32. MONGE-M., C. 1942. Life in the Andes and chronic mountain sickness. *Science (Washington DC)* 95: 79-84.

33. MONGE-M., C., 1943. Chronic mountain sickness. *Physiol. Rev*. 23: 166-184.

34. MONGE-M., C., 1948. *Acclimatization in the Andes*. Baltimore: John Hopkins Press: pp 1-148.

35. MONGE-M., C., & MONGE-C., C. 1966. *High Altitude Diseases. Mechanims and Management*. Springfield: Charles C. Thomas: pp 1-97.

36. PEI, S.X., CHEN, X.J., SI REN, B.Z., LIU, Y.H., CHENG, X S., HARRIS, E.M., ANAND, I.S. & HARRIS, P.C. 1989. Chronic mountain sickness in Tibet. *Q. Journal of Medicine* 71: 555-574.

37. PEÑALOZA, D. & SIME, F. 1971. Chronic cor pulmonale due to loss of altitude acclimatization (chronic mountain sickness). *American Journal of Medicine* 50: 728-743.

38. PEÑALOZA, D., SIME, F. & RUIZ, L. 1971. Cor pulmonale in chronic mountain sickness: present concept of Monge's disease. *In:* edited by R. Porter & J. Knight, *High Altitude Physiology: Cardiac and Respiratory Aspects.* Edinburgh: Churchill Livingstone: 41-60.

39. SANTOLAYA, R. 1983. Aclimatación al medio de altura: un proceso integral. *In:* *El Norte Grande de Chile.* Seminario Latinoamericano. Asentamientos humanos y desarrollo en ecosistemas áridos, anexo-5; Santiago.

40. SANTOLAYA, R., ARAYA, J., VECCHIOLA, A., PRIETO, R., RAMÍREZ, R. M. & ALCAYAGA, R. 1981. Hematocrito, hemoglobina y presión de oxígeno arterial en 270 hombres y 266 mujeres sanas y residentes de altura (2,800 m.) *Revista Médica del Hospital Roy H. Glover* 1: 17-29.

41. SEDANO, O. & ZARAVIA, A. 1988. Hemodilución isovolémica inducida en mal de montaña crónica. Resúmenes de Trabajos Libres. V Congreso Nacional. X Curso Internacional de Medicina Interna. Sociedad Peruana de Medicina Interna, [Resumen 250]; Lima.

42. SEDANO, O., PASTORELLI, J., GÓMEZ, A. & FLORES, V. 1988. "Sangría roja" aislada *vs.* hemodilución isovolémica inducida en mal de montaña crónica. Resúmenes de Trabajos Libres. V Congreso Nacional. X Curso Internacional de Medicina Interna. Sociedad Peruana de Medicina Interna, [Resumen 249]; Lima.

43. SEVERINGHAUS, J.W., BAINTOM, C.R. & CARCELÑN, A. 1966. Respiratory insensitivity to hypoxia in chronically hypoxic man. *Resp. Physiol.* 1: 308.

44. SIME, F. 1973. Ventilacion humana en hipoxia crónica. Etio-patogenia de la enfermedad de Monge o desadaptacion crónica a la altura. Tesis de Doctor, Universidad Peruana Cayetano Heredia, XXXp.

45. SIME, F., MONGE-C., C. & WhiTTEMBURY, J. 1975. Age as a cause of Chronic Mountain Sickness (Monge's disease). *Int. J. Biometeorol.* 19(2): 93-98.

46. SORENSEN, S.C. & SEVERINGHAUS, J.W. 1971. Irreversible respiratory insensitivity to acute hypoxia in man born at high altitude. *J. Appl. Physiol.* 25: 217-222.

47. THOMAS, P.S., HARDING, R.M. & MILLEDGE, J.S. 1990. Peak expiratory flow at altitude. *Thorax* 45: 620-622.

48. VELÁSQUEZ, T. 1969. Irreversible blunted ventilatory response to hypoxia in high altitude natives. *Resp. Physiol.* 6: 360-368.

49. WHITTEMBURY, J. & MONGE-C., C. 1972. High altitude, haematocrit and age. *Nature (Lond.)* 238: 278-279.

50. WINSLOW, R. & MONGE-C., C. 1987. *Hypoxia, Polycythemia, and Chronic Mountain Sickness.* Baltimore: John Hopkins University Press: xxxp.

51. WINSLOW, R.M., MONGE-C., C., BROWN, E.G., KLEIN, H.G., SARNQUIST, F., WINSLOW, N.J. & McKNEALLY, S.S. 1985. Effects of hemodilution on O_2 transport in high-altitude polycythemia. *J. Appl. Physiol.* 59: 1495-1502.

52. WU, T.Y., ZHANG, Q., CHEN, Q.H., JING, B.S., XU, F.D., LIU, H., DAI, T.F. & WANG, X.Z. 1987. [Twenty-six cases of chronic mountain sickness]. *National Medicine Journal of China* 64: 167-168.

MIGRAINE AND CHRONIC MOUNTAIN SICKNESS: EPIDEMIOLOGICAL STUDIES

Alberto Arregui

Abstract

In epidemiological studies among adult men residing at 4,300 meters, we found 32.2% with migraines, 15.2% with tension-type headaches and 7.2% with other headaches. The frequency of migraines increased with age from 30.1% in the younger age group (20-29 yr) to 36.8% in the group 50-59 yrs. Tension-type headaches also showed this trend. The survey also included measurements of hemoglobin and oxygen saturations levels, and a chronic mountain sickness score calculated from questions of symptoms and signs frequently associated with that disorder. The percentage of men with low oxygen saturation (< 81.5%) increased from 14.5% at age 20-29 to 38.5% at ages 60-69. The frequency of excessive eryhtocytosis (hemoglobin > 213 g/l) increased with age from 15.8% at ages 20-29 to 23.1% at ages 60-69. A high chronic mountain sickness score (> 20, i.e., mean + 2 SD) was found in 5.3% of men in the 20-29 age group and increased to 23.1% in the 60-69 age group. Men with migraine had higher hemoglobin levels and chronic mountain sickness scores than men with no headaches or men with tension-type headaches, thus suggesting that migraine, the most frequent type of headache associated with exposure to chronic hypoxia, is, in addition, the most frequent type of headache associated with the syndrome of chronic mountain sickness.

Key words: Hypoxia, migraine, headache, polycythemia, high altitude, chronic mountain sickness, aging.

Resumen

En estudios epidemiológicos de hombres adultos que viven a 4,300 metros, se han encontrado a 32.5% con migrañas, 15.5% con cefaleas tipo tensionales y a 6.1% con otros tipos de cefaleas. La frecuencia de migrañas incrementa con la edad de 30.1% en el grupo más joven (20-29 años) a 36.8% en el grupo de 50-59 años. Las cefaleas tipo tensionales también muestran esta tendencia. La encuesta epidemiológica también midió niveles de hemoglobina y de saturación de oxígeno, y un puntaje de mal de montaña crónico calculado a partir de preguntas sobre síntomas y signos frecuentemente asociados a este desorden. La frecuencia de hombres con baja saturación de oxígeno (< 81.5%) aumenta con la edad de 14.5% a los 20-29 años hasta 38.5% a los 60-69 años. La frecuencia de eritrocitosis excesiva (hemoglobina > 213 g/l) aumenta con la edad de 15.8% a los 20-29 hasta 23.1% a los 60-69 años. Se encontró puntaje alto de mal de montaña crónico (> 20, i.e., media + 2 DE) en 5.3% de hombres de 20-29 años y un aumento hasta 23.1% en hombres de 60-69 años. Los hombres con migraña tienen niveles de hemoglobina y puntaje de mal de montaña crónico más altos que los de hombres sin cefaleas o con cefaleas tipo tensionales, lo que sugiere que la migraña, el tipo de dolor de cabeza más frecuente entre aquellos expuestos crónicamente a la hipoxia, es, además, el tipo de cefalea que se asocia con más frecuencia al sindrome de mal de montaña crónico.

Palabras claves: Hipoxia, migraña, cefáleas, altura, mal de montaña crónico, envejecimiento.

Résumé

Suite aux études épidémiologiques réalisées chez des hommes adultes vivant à 4300 m d'altitude, on a trouvé 32.5% de cas de migraine, 15.5% de tension s'assimilant à des maux de tête, et 6.1% d'autres types de maux de tête. La fréquence des migraines augmente de 30.1% avec l'âge dans le groupe le plus jeune (20-29 ans) et à 36.8% pour le groupe des 50-59 ans. Les céphalées s'assimilant à des tensions montrent également cette tendance. L'enquête épidémiologique a mesuré également les niveaux d'hémoglobine et de saturation d'oxygène et une quantité de cas atteints du mal des montagnes chronique calculée à partir de questions sur les symptomes et les signes fréquemment associés à ce désordre. La fréquence d'hommes ayant une saturation d'oxygène basse (<81.5%) augmente avec l'âge, de 14.5% chez les 20-29 ans jusqu'à 38.5% chez les 60-69 ans. La fréquence d'érythrocytose excessive (hémoglobine >213g/l) augmente avec l'âge de 15.8% chez les 20-29 ans à 23.1% chez les 60-69 ans. On a trouvé un score élevé de mal des montagnes chronique (>20, i.e., moyenne + 2 DE) chez 5.3% des hommes entre 20 et 29 ans et une augmentation atteignant 23.1% chez les hommes entre 60 et 69 ans. Les hommes atteints de migraine ont des niveaux d'hémoglobine et un score de mal des montagnes chronique plus élevés que chez ceux qui ne souffrent pas de céphalées ou qui ont des céphalées provoquées par la tension, ce qui permet de suggérer que la migraine, le type de maux de tête le plus fréquent chez ceux qui sont exposés de façon chronique à l'hypoxie, est, en outre, le type de céphalée qui s'associe le plus fréquemment au sydrome du mal des montagnes chronique.

Mots clés : Hypoxie, migraine, céphalée, altitude, mal des montagnes chronique, vieillissement.

INTRODUCTION

Our thesis in the last years has been that chronic exposure to the hypoxia of altitudes increases the frequency of chronic mountain sickness (CMS), a syndrome characterized by a variety of symptoms and signs, including headaches (6, 7). In their opportune review of 1966, Monge-M and Monge-C (7) described CMS as «...an insidious disease whose only manifestation for years often is diminished mental and physical capacity. Nervous system symptoms usually dominate the clinical picture ... and are by far the most frequent and varied in nature...» and then go on to state that «...different types of headaches are common; sometimes migraine crises are present.. usually aggravated by exercise... dizziness and vertigo are prominent...

paresthesias may be present: numbness, tingling, aches, pains, commonly felt in hands and feet...». Despite these studies, the frequency of affected individuals was not known. In 1987, with Fabiola León-Velarde, we started epidemiological studies at high altitude in order to have an idea of the magnitude of the problem and published our first results in 1989 (4).

The finding of a high frequency of symptoms associated with CMS in a population residing in the mining town of Cerro de Pasco (4,300 m), led us to question the long term adaptability of man to high altitudes (4). Our pilot neuroepidemiological studies showed a high prevalence of headaches, migraine in particular, in a general population residing at 4,300 meters above sea level when compared with a similar population at sea level (3). However, the types of headaches and their relationship to hemoglobin levels and oxygen saturation, and their possible association to symptoms of CMS were not known. This prompted us to study the frequency and types of headaches among adult high altitude men and their possible association with hemoglobin and oxygen saturation. In addition, we tested the hypothesis that migraine could be the most frequent type of headache in men with symptoms of chronic mountain sickness.

METHODS

In June, 1991, we conducted an epidemiological survey among 475 adult men born or residing for more than 10 years in the mining town of Cerro de Pasco, Perú (total population: 70,000; altitude: 4,300 meters above sea level) followed by a complete medical and neurological examination in the relevant cases. A World Health Organization neuroepidemiological protocol was used (9) and criteria for the diagnosis of headaches were those of the Headache Classification Committee of the International Headache Society (5). When both migraine and tension-type headache coexisted in a person, only the most frequent or disabling type was entered as the diagnosis. The number of headaches per year was also entered and men were divided among those with no headaches, those with less than two headaches per month and those with more than one headache per week. In 379 men, hemoglobin levels were measured in a finger stick blood sample using a portable hemoglobinometer (Hemocue, Inc.) and O_2 saturations were determined in the index finger using a portable flowmeter (Nellcor, Inc.). High hemoglobin was defined as 213 g/l or more (8). Low oxygen saturation was defined as less than 81.5%. In addition, a chronic mountain sickness (CMS) score was developed from the nine most frequent symptoms (excluding headaches) and signs associated with this disorder (6,7) with the following minimum and maximum scores:

	No	Yes	
		Occasional	Frequent
1. Physical tiredness	1	2	3
2. Mental tiredness	1	2	3
3. Feelings of sadness	1	2	3
4. Shortness of breath upon awakening	1	2	3
5. Muscle and/or joint pains	1	2	3
6. Cyanosis of lips, face or hands	1	2	3
7. Venous dilatation in hands or feet	1	2	3
8. Ringing in the ears (tinnitus)	1	2	3
9. Paresthesia in hands or feet	1	2	

Chronic mountain sickness score:

Mean	Std Dev	Minimum	Maximum
14.54	3.32	9.00	26.00

The mean plus two standard deviations, i.e., > 20, was considered as a high chronic mountain sickness (CMS) score.

RESULTS

The percentage of men complaining of frequent symptoms associated with CMS increased with age (Table 1).The prevalence rate for all headaches among adult high altitude men was 54.6%. When looked separately, migraine had a prevalence rate of 32.2%, tension-type was 15.2% and other headaches were 7.1% (Table 2). The frequency of migraines increased steadily with age from 30.4% at ages 20-29 years to 36.5% at ages 50-59 years, and dropped to 34.6% after 60 years of age (Table 2). This trend was also found in tension-type headaches where the episodic type (the most frequent tension-type headache) showed an increase with age between 30 and 60 or more years of age (data not shown).

The percentage of men with oxygen saturations less than 81.5%, hemoglobin concentrations greater than 213 g/l, and CMS scores greater than 20 increased streadily with age. (Table 2), in parallel with the increase in frequent symptoms of CMS and headaches.

Hemoglobin levels and CMS scores were higher in men with migraine when compared to men with tension-type headaches or men without headaches (Table 3). In addition, men with other types of headaches had higher CMS scores than men without headaches.

Table 1. Age-related percentage of men answering «frequent» to questions of symptoms and signs associated with chronic mountain sickness (June 1991).

	Age groups (years)					
	20-29 n=82	30-39 n=137	40-49 n=132	50-59 n=92	60-69 n=32	Total n=475
	%	%	%	%	%	%
Physical tiredness	6.1	15.3	17.4	20.7	31.3	16.4
Mental tiredness	7.3	14.6	12.1	19.6	31.3	14.7
Sad or depressed	11.0	16.1	14.4	27.2	31.3	17.9
Shortness of breath	3.7	5.1	1.5	9.8	18.8	5.7
Muscle aches	6.1	9.5	17.4	22.8	28.1	14.9
Cyanosis	6.1	10.9	6.1	13.0	18.8	9.7
Venous dilatation	9.8	7.3	9.8	17.4	18.8	11.2
Tinnitus	3.7	4.4	9.8	15.2	12.5	8.4
Paresthesia	39.0	43.1	49.2	56.5	62.5	48.0

Table 2. Age-specific frequencies (percentage) of headaches, low oxygen saturation (Sat < 81.5%), high hemoglobin (Hb > 213 g/l) and high chronic mountain sickness scores (> 20) among high altitude men surveyed in June 1991.

	Age groups					
	20-29 n=57	30-39 n=112	40-49 n=110	50-59 n=74	60-69 n=26	Total n=379
	%	%	%	%	%	%
Migraine	30.1	33.1	29.1	36.5	34.5	32.2
Tension-type	15.8	9.8	16.3	17.6	26.9	15.2
Other types	7.1	4.5	10.0	6.8	7.6	7.2
Sat < 81.5%	14.5	12.5	16.4	33.8	38.5	19.9
Hb > 213	15.8	16.1	9.1	17.6	23.1	14.8
CMSSco > 20	5.3	6.3	7.3	12.2	23.1	8.7

Hb: hemoglobin (g/l); Sat: oxygen saturation (%); CMSSco: chronic mountain sickness score (see Methods).

Table 3. Hemoglobin levels, oxygen saturation and chronic mountain sickness scores among high altitude men with different types of headaches compared to high altitude men without headaches.

	No headache n=172	Migraine n=122	Tension-type n=58	Others n=23
Hb(1)	185.1 ± 21.3	196.7 ± 24.3**	187.4 ± 24.7	188.1 ± 23.4
Sat	84.8 ± 4.2	84.0 ± 4.8	83.9 ± 4.7	83.6 ± 4.3
CMS(1)	13.5 ± 2.9	15.8 ± 3.5**	14.6 ± 3.3*	14.9 ± 2.3*

Hb: hemoglobin (g/l); Sat: oxygen saturation (%); CMSSco: chronic mountain sickness score (see Methods).

(1) probability of F=0.000 by analysis of variance.

* $p < 0.05$ when compared to 'no headache'; ** $p < 0.05$ when compared to 'no headache' and to 'tension-type'.

DISCUSSION

The high prevalence of migraine in a general high altitude population chronically exposed to hypoxia has been previously reported (3) and the suggestion was made that low oxygen tensions within the central nervous system may cause migraine by unknown mechanisms. In the studies that we describe here, we find an increasing prevalence of migraine and episodic tension-type headaches with age in adult men, as well as an increasing frequency of symptoms and signs associated with CMS, as previously reported (3, 4). That this may relate to erythrocytosis, which increases with age at high altitudes (8), is suggested by the finding of a higher hemoglobin and CMS scores in men with migraine headaches. A high hemoglobin may cause elevated blood viscosity, which together with a low oxygen saturation, lowers oxygen delivery to the brain — the latter possibly causing the higher frequency of migraine among these men by altering brain neurotransmitters (1, 2). Our results also suggest that migraine, and perhaps episodic tension-type headaches, may be part of the syndrome of loss of adaptation to high altitudes, i.e., chronic mountain sickness. In addition, the presence of an increasing frequency of symptoms ad signs of loss of adaptation with age or time of residence among high altitude men is indicative of the limitations of human adaptation to an environment with low oxygen tensions.

ACKNOWLEDGEMENTS

Fabiola León-Velarde, DSc, has been the co-investigator in these projects. Juan Cabrera. MD, Darwin Vizcarra, MD, Hugo Umeres, MD, Raúl Acosta, MD, Manuel Vargas MD, and Luis Huicho MD participated in the studies. We thank Miguel Campos, MD, for helpful advise in the design of the study, and María Rivera, Rosario Tapia, Victor Yzaguirre and Antonio Espinoza for invaluable help during our field work. The research project was supported by a grant from IDRC-Canada to A. Arregui and F. León-Velarde. The author was a Guggenheim Fellow during completion of this paper.

REFERENCES

1. ARREGUI, A., BARER, G.R. & EMSON, P.C. 1981 Neurochemical studies in chronic hypoxia: substance P, met-enkephalin, GABA and angiotensin-converting enzyme. *Life Sci* 28: 2925-2929.

2. ARREGUI, A. & BARER, G.R. 1980 Chronic hypoxia in rats: alterations of striato-nigral angiotensin-converting enzyme, GABA and glutamic acid decarboxylase. *J Neurochem* 34: 740-743.

3. ARREGUI, A., CABRERA, J., LEÓN-VELARDE, F., PAREDES, S., VIZCARRA, D. & ARBAIZA, D. 1991. High prevalence of migraine in a high altitude population. *Neurology* 41: 1678-80.

4. ARREGUI, A., LEÓN-VELARDE, F., VALCARCEL, M. 1989. *Salud y Minería. Mal de Montaña Crónico entre Mineros de Cerro de Pasco.* Lima: ADEC-ATC/Mosca Azul Editores, pp. 1-127

5. Headache Classification Committee of the International Headache Society. Classification and diagnostic criteria for headache disorders, cranial neuralgias and facial pain, 1988 *Cephalalgia* 8 (Suppl 7): 9-96.

6. MONGE-MEDRANO, C. 1928 La enfermedad de los Andes (sindromes eritremicos). *Anales de la Facultad de Medicina* (Lima) 11: 1-134.

7. MONGE-M, C. & MONGE-C, C. 1966 *High-altitude diseases. Mechanism and Management.* Sprinfield, Illinois: Charles C Thomas: pp. 33-34.

8. MONGE-C, C., LEÓN-VELARDE, F. & ARREGUI, A. 1989 Increasing prevalence of excessive erytrocytosis among healthy high altitude miners (letter). *New Eng J Med*, 321: 1271.

9. OSUNTOKUN, B.O., SCHOENBERG, B.S., NOTTIDGE, V., ADEUJA, A., KALE, O., ADEYEFA, A., BADEMOSI, O. & BOLIS, C.L. 1982 Migraine headache in a rural community in Nigeria: Results of a pilot study. *Neuroepidemiology* 1: 31-39.

V.

ASPECTOS HEMODINÁMICOS, ENDOCRINOLÓGICOS Y BIOQUÍMICOS

CAN THE FETAL LLAMA SUCCESFULLY CLIMB HIGHER THAN MOUNT EVEREST DURING HYPOXIA?

Aníbal J. Llanos, Raquel A. Riquelme, Mauricio I. Espinoza, Cristián R. Gaete, Emilia M. Sanhueza, Gertrudis R. Cabello, Fernando Moraga, Julian T. Parer

Abstract

Fetal cardiorespiratory responses to hypoxemia in species that have evolved at high altitudes are unknown. Because basal organ blood flows in fetal llamas are lower than in fetal sheep, we hypothetized that during hypoxemia the fetal llama could maintain oxygen delivery to vital organs by a proportionally greater increase in blood flow than fetal sheep. We tested this contention by chronically catheterizing 7 fetal llamas and 8 fetal sheep in the last third of gestation. After a post surgical recovery of 1.9 ± 0.4 days in the llamas and 5.9 ± 0.3 days in the sheep, we subjected the fetuses to a 30 min acute hypoxemia by giving the mother a low oxygen gas mixture to breathe, sufficient to drop fetal saturation of hemoglobin to less than 30%. We determined fetal systemic arterial pressure, fetal ventricular output and its distribution (radioactive microspheres), blood oxygen content, and oxygen delivery to the fetal organs. Compared with fetal sheep, in fetal llamas there were no changes in arterial pressure and in brain and adrenal blood flows; the increase of heart blood flow was less prominent, and the decrease in kidneys and spleen blood flows was more marked during hypoxemia. A striking difference between the fetal llama and sheep during hypoxemia was the decrease in oxygen delivery to the brain and a marked drop in oxygen delivery to the kidneys in the fetal llama. These results suggest as a major adaptation to hypoxemia in fetal llamas the ability to reduce oxygen consumption·in almost every organ. These results allow us to hypothetize that tissular rather than circulatory responses are the basic mechanisms in the adaptation to hypoxemia in the fetal llama.

Keys words: Fetal llama, high altitude, hypoxia, cardiac output, oxygen content, oxigen delivery.

Resumen

Las respuestas cardiorespiratorias fetales de especies nativas de altura a la hipoxemia han sido muy poco estudiadas y se desconocen casi totalmente. En base a que el flujo sanguíneo de los fetos de llamas es menor al del feto de oveja, hipotetizamos que durante la hipoxemia el feto de llama puede mantener el aporte de oxígeno a los órganos vitales por un aumento proporcionalmente mayor del flujo sanguíneo que el feto de oveja. Esta proposición fue evaluada en 7 fetos de llamas y en 8 fetos de ovejas cateterizados crónicamente, en el último tercio de la gestación. Luego de la recuperación post quirúrgica, 1.9±0.4 días en las llamas y 5.9±0.3 días en las ovejas, los fetos fueron expuestos a 30 min. de hipoxemia aguda, sometiendo a las madres a una baja concentración de oxígeno, hasta que la saturación de la hemoglobina fetal fuese menor que 30%. Se determinó la presión arterial sistémica fetal, el volumen de eyección ventricular fetal y su distribución (microesferas radioactivas), contenido de oxígeno sanguíneo, y entrega de oxígeno a los órganos fetales. En comparación con los fetos de las ovejas, los de las llamas no muestran cambios en la presión arterial, ni en los flujos cerebral, y de las glándulas suprarrenales; el aumento en el flujo sanguíneo cardíaco fue menos prominente, y la disminución de los flujos sanguíneos renales y del bazo, fueron menos marcados durante la hipoxemia. Una notable diferencia entre los fetos de llama y de oveja durante la hipoxemia, fue la disminución de la entrega de oxígeno al cerebro y a los riñones en el feto de llama. Los resultados sugieren que la capacidad del feto de llama de disminuir el consumo de oxígeno en casi todos sus órganos sería su mejor estrategia de adaptación a la hipoxemia. Estos resultados nos permiten postular a las respuestas tisulares, más bien que las circulatorias, como mecanismos básicos de adaptación a la hipoxemia.

Palabras claves: Feto de llama, grandes altitudes, hipoxia, gasto cardíaco, contenido de oxígeno.

Résumé

Les réponses cardiorespiratoires fétales à l'hypoxémie parmi les espèces nées en altitude ont été très peu étudiées et sont pratiquement inconnues. Sachant que le flux sanguin des foetus de lamas est moindre que celui du foetus de mouton, nous lançons l'hypothèse que, au cours de l'hypoxémie, le foetus de lama peut maintenir l'apport d'oxygène aux organes vitaux grâce à une augmentation du flux sanguin proportionellement supérieure à celui du foetus de mouton. Cette hypothèse fut vérifiée sur 7 foetus de lamas et 8 de moutons cathétérisés de façon chronique, au cours du dernier tiers de la gestation. Pendant la récupération post-opératoire, 1.9±0.4 jours chez le lama et 5.9±0.3 jours chez le mouton, les foetus ont été exposés à 30 minutes d'hypoxie aiguë, en soumettant les mères à une faible concentration d'oxygène, jusquà ce que la saturation de l'hémoglobine fétale soit inférieure à 30%. On a déterminé la pression artérielle systémique fétale, le volume de l'éjection ventriculaire fétale et sa distribution (micro sphéres radioactives), contenu de l'oxygène sanguin et distribution de l'oxygène aux organes fétaux. En comparaison avec les foetus de moutons, ceux de lamas ne montrent pas de changements dans la pression artérielle, ni dans le flux cérébral, ni dans les glandes sur rénales; l'augmentation dans le flux sanguin cardiaque fut moins proéminent et la distribution des flux sanguins rénaux et de la rate, furent moins marqués durant l'hypoxémie. Au cours de celle-ci, on a remarqué une différence notable entre les foetus de mouton et de lama, constatant chez ce dernier une diminution de la distribution d'oxygène au cerveau et aux reins. Les résultats suggèrent que la capacité du foetus de lama de diminuer la consommation d'oxygène dans presque tous les organes serait sa meilleure stratégie d'adaptation à l'hypoméxie. Ces résultats nous permettent de postuler que ce seraient les réponses tissulaires plutôt que les circulatoires qui constitueraient les mécanismes de base de l'adaptation à l'hypoxémie.

Mots clés : Foetus de lama, haute altitude, hypoxie, débit cardiaque, contenu d'oxygène, apport d'oxygène.

Fetal cardiorespiratory responses to hypoxemia have been extensively studied in the sheep, species that has evolved in low altitudes. In term fetal sheep arterial blood pressure increases, heart rate decreases, and there is a redistribution of combined ventricular output during hypoxemia (4, 5). This redistribution favors the heart, brain and adrenal glands, maintaining umbilical blood flow and cardiac output, while blood flow to the gut, kidneys and carcass decreases (4).

Fetal cardiorespiratory responses to hypoxemia in species that have evolved in high altitudes are virtually unknown. In term fetal llamas, combined ventricular output and blood flow to all organs except the adrenal glands are severalfold lowerthan in term fetal sheep during basal conditions (2), suggesting an enhanced oxygen extraction by the tissues in the fetal llama in order to maintain an oxygen consumption comparable to that of the fetal sheep. We hypothesized that because the blood flows are low during normoxemia, the fetal llama may be able to maintain oxygen delivery to certain organs such as the heart, brain and adrenal glands, by a greater augmentation of blood flows during hypoxemia than those seen in fetal sheep. We tested this hypothesis by comparing fetal cardiorespiratory responses to a similar degree of hypoxemia in catheterized fetal llamas and sheep.

MATERIALS AND METHODS

Seven pregnant llamas (weight 80 to 100 kg) were obtained from shepherds from the altiplano (Parinacota and surroundings, 4, 400 meters above sea level). The llamas were born and raised in the altiplano and brought to Santiago (586 meters above sea level). Pregnant llamas were operated from one to five weeks after their arrival to Santiago. The fetuses weighed 5264 ± 658 g (mean ± SEM) at the time of the study. Although the gestational age was uncertain, we considered that the fetuses were in the last third of gestation according to fetal weight. Gestation is 335 to 360 days in the llama (8).

Eight time-mated pregnant sheep of mixed breed (weight 50 to 70 kg) between 120 and 133 days of gestation (term is 145 days) were obtained from local suppliers. The sheep were born and raised in Santiago and the fetuses weighed 3172 ± 296 g at the time of the study.

We have recently developed the experimental preparation of chronically catheterized fetal llama (2). The fetal preparation of fetal sheep was similar to that of the llamas and has been described previously (15) (Fig. 1).

Fetal arterial blood pressure, fetal venous pressure, and amniotic fluid pressure were measured continuously and recorded on a polygraph. Fetal vascular pressures were corrected using amniotic pressure as zero reference. Heart rate was determined from the tracing of pulsatile blood pressure.

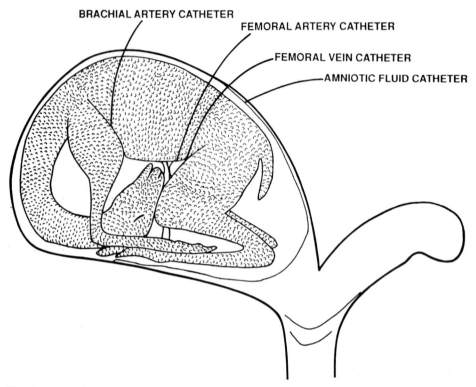

Fig. 1 - Fetal llama experimental preparation.

Carbon dioxide tension and pH were measured with Radiometer electrodes at 39° C. Percent saturation of hemoglobin and hemoglobin concentration were measured with a OSM2 Hemoximeter. Oxygen content and capacity were calculated as described previously (2). Fetal combined ventricular output and organ blood flows were determined by injection of 15 um diameter radionuclide-labelled microspheres (57Co and 65Zn) into the inferior vena cava while obtaining reference samples from the descending and ascending aorta (10). Oxygen delivery was calculated as described previously (2).

Prior to the commencement of the experiment, llamas were allowed to recover from surgery from 1 to 4 days (mean 1.9 ± 0.4 days), while sheep were allowed to recover from 5 to 7 days (mean 5.9 ± 0.3 days). The sheep experiments were conducted first, and we intended using the same protocol for llamas. However, the fragility of the fetal llama preparation precluded us from doing so.

After a baseline period of 20 minutes, hypoxemia was induced by giving the maternal llama or ewe a low oxygen gas mixture to breathe (9 l/min air, 15-20 l/min N2) from a plastic bag placed over the head. The hypoxemia was sufficient to drop fetal descending aortic hemoglobin saturation to less than 30%. Fetal descending aortic blood pH, PCO2, hemoglobin concentration and percent saturation of hemoglobin were measured -20 and 0 min before, and 10 and 20 min after the induction of hypoxemia. Fetal combined ventricular output and its distribution was measured at 0 minutes and between 15 and 20 minutes during hypoxemia.

Changes in the measured variables during the experiment were tested for statistical significance using the paired sample t test or the Wilcoxon paired sample test. Comparisons between llama and sheep variables were done by using single factor analysis of variance. A difference was considered significant when the p value was less than 0.05 (9). The values given in tables, figures and text are expressed as means ± SEM.

RESULTS

Fetal cardiorespiratory variables

Basal values of heart rate, pH and hemoglobin saturation were lower and hemoglobin concentration and oxygen capacity were higher in fetal llamas than in fetal sheep. During hypoxemia, hemoglobin saturation and oxygen content decreased to similar values in fetal llamas and sheep. Also, fetal heart rate decreased during hypoxemia in both species. Arterial blood pressure increased and descending aortic pH decreased in fetal sheep but not in fetal llamas. During hypoxemia, heart rate, arterial blood pressure, and PCO2 were lower, and hemoglobin concentration and oxygen capacity were higher in fetal llamas than fetal sheep (Table 1).

TABLE 1 - Effect of acute hypoxemia on fetal cardiorespiratory variables.

	Llama		Sheep	
	Basal	Hypoxemia	Basal	Hypoxemia
Fetal heart rate (1 x min $^{-1}$)	121 ± 6	96 ± 8[a]	157 ± 6[b]	127 ± 7[a, c]
Arterial blood pressure (mmHg)	54 ± 5	56 ± 3	52 ± 6	65 ± 2[a, c]
Descending Aorta:				
pH (U)	7.33 ± 0.01	7.29 ± 0.04	7.39 ± 0.07[b]	7.28 ± 0.02[a]
pCO2 (mmHg)	39.1 ± 1.7	31.2 ± 1.5[a]	42.4 ± 1.2	41.4 ± 3[c]
Hemoglobin concentration (g x dl -1)	15.5 ± 1	17.1 ± 0.9	11.6 ± 0.9[b]	12.9 ± 1[c]
Hemoglobin saturation (%)	46 ± 3	25 ± 3[a]	59 ± 3 b	24.0 ± 2[a]
02 Content (ml x dl -1)	9.1 ± 0.7	5.4 ± 0.8[a]	9.1 ± 0.7	4.2 ± 0.3[a]
O2 Capacity (ml x dl -1)	20.5 ± 0.9	22.5 ± 1.1	15.6 ± 1.2[b]	17.3 ± 1.3[c]

Values are means ± SEM for 7 fetal llamas and 8 fetal sheep. [a]: p<0.05 basal *vs* hypoxemia; [b]: p<0.05 basal llama *vs* basal sheep; [c]: p<0.05 hypoxemic llama *vs* hypoxemic sheep.

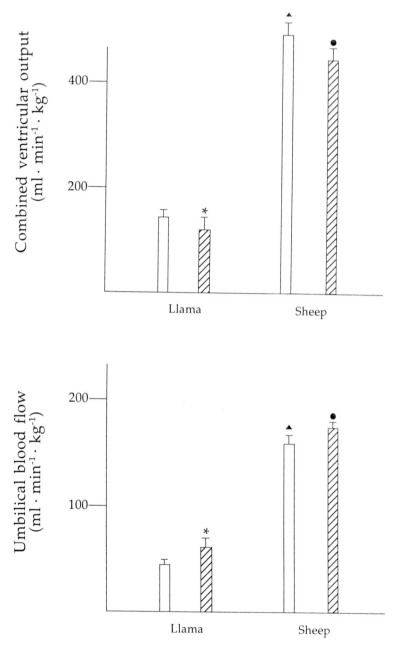

Fig. 2 - Effect of acute hypoxemia on fetal combined ventricular output and umbilical blood flow. Bars are mean ± SEM for 7 fetal llamas and 8 fetal sheep. Open bars are basal values and hatched bars are values during hypoxemia. * p<0.05 basal *vs* hypoxemia; ▲ p< 0.05 basal llama *vs* basal sheep;● p<0.05 hypoxemic llama *vs* hypoxemic sheep.

Fetal combined ventricular output and its distribution

Basal fetal combined ventricular output and umbilical blood flow in fetal llamas were less than one third of those of fetal sheep (Fig. 2). Basal heart, brain, kidney, gut and carcass blood flows in fetal llamas were less than 55% of those of fetal sheep (Fig. 3, 4, 5). Exceptions were the adrenal glands, spleen, and liver, which had similar basal values in fetal llamas and sheep (Fig. 3, 4, 5).

During hypoxemia, combined ventricular output decreased in fetal llamas, without changes in fetal sheep (Fig. 2). Umbilical blood flow did not change significantly in the fetal llamas and sheep (Fig. 2). Blood flows to the heart, brain, and adrenal glands increased in fetal sheep, whereas only heart blood flow increased in fetal llamas during hypoxemia (Fig. 3).

Blood flows to the kidneys, gut, carcass, spleen and liver decreased in fetal sheep during hypoxemia (Fig. 4, 5). The same was observed in fetal llamas, except in the gut, where the 50% decrease of blood flow did not

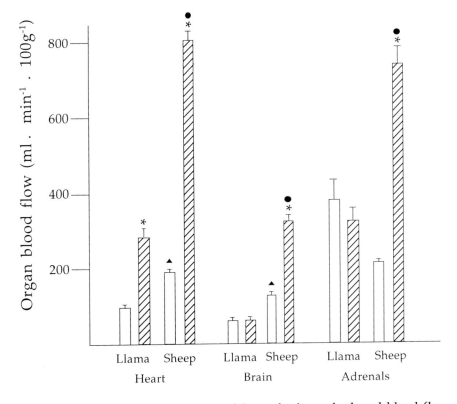

Fig. 3 - Effect of acute hypoxemia on fetal heart, brain, and adrenal blood flows. Bars are mean ± SEM for 7 fetal llamas and 8 fetal sheep. Open bars are basal blood flows and hatched bars are blood flows during hypoxemia. * p<0.05 basal *vs* hypoxemia; ▲ p<0.05 basal llama *vs* basal sheep; ● p<0.05 hypoxemic llama *vs* hypoxemic sheep.

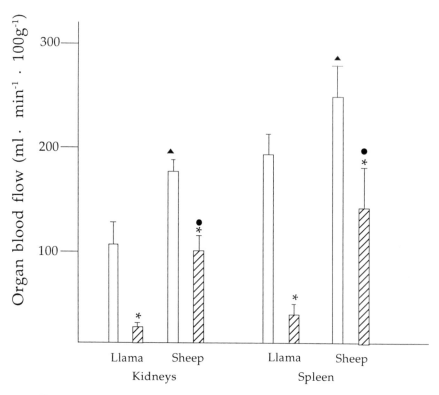

Fig. 4 - Effect of acute hypoxemia on fetal kidney and spleen blood flows. Bars are
mean ± SEM for 7 fetal llamas and 8 fetal sheep. Open bars are basal blood
flows and hatched bars are blood flows during hypoxemia.   * $p<0.05$ basal *vs*
hypoxemia; ▲ $p<0.05$ basal llama*vs* basal sheep; ● $p<0.05$ hypoxemic llama *vs*
hypoxemic sheep.

reach statistical significance. The magnitude of the decrease of blood flow
was comparable in the carcass, gut and liver in llamas and sheep (about 50%
of basal), but it was more marked in the kidneys and spleen in the llamas
(14% of basal) than in sheep (50% of basal). All blood flows, with the exception
of the liver, were lower in fetal llamas than in fetal sheep during hypoxemia
(Fig. 3, 4, 5).

Basally, heart, brain, kidneys and gut oxygen delivery were lower in
fetal llamas than in fetal sheep (Table 2). During hypoxemia, fetal llamas
maintained their heart and decreased their brain, kidneys, liver and spleen
oxygen deliveries (Table 2). Sheep fetuses increased their heart, maintained
their brain and decreased their kidneys, gut, liver, spleen and carcass oxygen
deliveries. Fetal llama oxygen delivery to the heart and brain during hypoxemia
was lower than in fetal sheep.

Our results demonstrate that the cardiorespiratory responses to a similar
degree of hypoxemia in the fetal llama are not comparable to those of the
fetal sheep. In contrast to our expectation, brain and adrenal blood flows

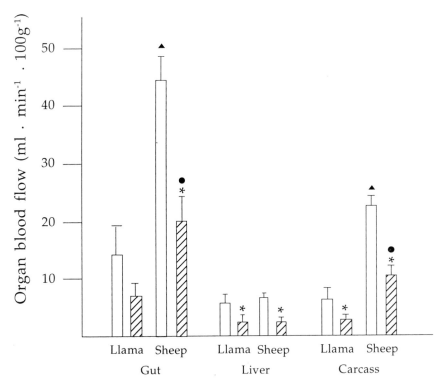

Fig. 5 - Effect of acute hypoxemia on fetal gut, liver, and carcass blood flows. Bars are mean ± SEM for 7 fetal llamas and 8 fetal sheep. Open bars are basal blood flows and hatched bars are blood flows during hypoxemia. * p<0.05 basal *vs* hypoxemia; ▲ p< 0.05 basal llama *vs* basal sheep;● p<0.05 hypoxemic llama *vs* hypoxemic sheep.

did not increase during hypoxemia in the fetal llama, and the increase in heart blood flow was less marked than in fetal sheep. Moreover, arterial blood pressure did not increase and there was a more marked decrease in kidney and spleen blood flows in the fetal llama than in the fetal sheep.

DISCUSSION

A striking difference between fetal llamas and sheep is the decrease in oxygen delivery to the brain during hypoxemia in the fetal llama. In fetal sheep, brain oxygen delivery during hypoxemia is maintained by an increase of brain blood flow. This did not occur in the fetal llama, resulting in the decrease of brain oxygen delivery. The lack of a hypoxemic vasodilatation in llama fetuses may reflect a higher sensitivity of cerebral vessels to arterial carbon dioxide tension. Since mean P_{CO_2} during hypoxemia decreased in fetal llamas, this drop may have opposed cerebral vessels dilatation. However, in two of the llama fetuses the P_{CO_2} was maintained during hypoxemia, and no increase of brain blood flow was observed.

Table 2 - Effect of acute hypoxemia on organ oxygen delivery in the fetus.

	Llama		Sheep	
	Basal	Hypoxemia	Basal	Hypoxemia
Heart	10.3 ± 1.4	12.4 ± 2.8	18.5 ± 2.1^b	$33.4 \pm 2.1^{a,\,c}$
Brain	7.2 ± 1.5	3.1 ± 0.7^a	15.0 ± 1^b	14.5 ± 1.0^c
Adrenal	30.9 ± 9.7	18.1 ± 5.1	20.5 ± 2.8	32.2 ± 6.1
Kidneys	7.7 ± 1.1	0.9 ± 0.3^a	14.5 ± 1.1^b	3.9 ± 0.8^a
Gut	0.9 ± 0.3	0.3 ± 0.1	4.1 ± 0.5^b	1.1 ± 0.2^a
Spleen	16.1 ± 3.6	0.9 ± 0.02^a	22.4 ± 4.0	5.1 ± 1.7^a
Liver	0.6 ± 0.2	0.1 ± 0.03^a	0.6 ± 0.1	0.1 ± 0.02^a
Carcass	0.6 ± 0.2	0.2 ± 0.04^a	2.0 ± 0.7	0.5 ± 0.1^a

Values are means $\pm$ SEM (in ml/ min x 100 g) for 7 fetal llamas and 8 fetal sheep. [a]: $p<0.05$ basal vs hypoxemia; [b]: $p<0.05$ basal llama vs basal sheep; [c]: $p<0.05$ hypoxemic llama vs hypoxemic sheep.

The lack of increase of brain blood flow during hypoxemia could make the llama brain more vulnerable to hypoxemia, unless there is either an increase in fractional oxygen extraction, $i.\ e.$, a widening of the difference in arteriovenous oxygen concentration that maintains brain oxygen consumption, or an ability to reduce brain oxygen consumption without damage to brain cells during hypoxemia. An increase in fractional oxygen extraction without changes in brain oxygen consumption is not probable since arterial oxygen content during hypoxemia is so low that, maintaining oxygen consumption would require a drop of vein oxygen content to practically zero, which is very unlikely. On the other hand, reduction of brain oxygen consumption during severe hypoxemia has been documented in fetal sheep, although the impact of this decrease on brain cell viability has not yet been fully explored (6).

Of the three organs whose blood flows increased during hypoxemia in the fetal sheep, the heart was the only one that increased blood flow in the fetal llama. However, the fetal llama increased heart blood flow only by 167% compared with a 326% increase in the sheep. Cardiac work estimated from the blood pressure-heart rate product is decreased in fetal llamas during hypoxemia, so the smaller increase of heart blood flow could reflect a lower metabolic demand by the hypoxic llama heart.

During hypoxemia, there was a marked decrease of kidney and spleen blood flows to 14% of baseline in the fetal llama, while it decreased to 54% in the fetal sheep. The decrease of kidney blood flow in fetal llamas was associated with a marked decrease of kidney oxygen delivery, that is probably insufficient to maintain kidney oxygen consumption. Kidney oxygen delivery during hypoxemia in the llama was 0.7 mlO$_2$ x min -1 x 100 g -1 , and kidney oxygen consumption in fetal sheep is approximately 2.5 mlO$_2$ x min -1 x 100 g -1   (16). Fetal llama kidney may be similar to that of the seal during diving, where a complete cessation of kidney blood flow and thus a complete arrest of oxidative metabolism, have been reported (11). It has been proposed that the kidneys of the seal during diving compensate for reduced ATP-dependent ion pumping capacity either by reducing the density of functional channels per square unit of cell membrane surface in proportion to the decline of metabolic rate, or by maintaining low channel density all the time, so they are not compromised by the drop of ion pumping capacity (11). In any case, the net effect would be the maintenance of the ratio of leak rate to pumping rate at unity, even during metabolic arrest. It is not known whether these mechanisms are present in the kidney or other fetal llama organs.

Basal cardiac output and its distribution of these 7 fetal llama are about 24% higher that those previously reported (2). We believe that performing the measurements almost 2 days following surgery compared with 7 hours after surgery can explain these differences. During hypoxemia, the cardiac output and organ blood flows were considerably lower in fetal llamas than in fetal sheep, with the exception of the liver. The magnitude of the differences in blood flows between fetal llamas and sheep is such that we do not believe that could be explained by the differences in the recovery time after surgery. Moreover, in a group of fetal sheep studied five hours after surgery, the umbilical blood flow was 144 ml x min -1 x kg -1, still 2.5 times higher than our basal umbilical blood flow in the fetal llama (3).

The low cardiac output measured in fetal llamas both basally and during hypoxemia, makes it difficult to understand how the fetal llama obtains its oxygenation. If we assume that basal oxygen consumption in the fetal llama is close to that of the fetal sheep, the fetal llama having an umbilical blood flow of only a third of that of the fetal sheep, then the difference in oxygen content between the umbilical vein and artery must be very large in the llama. We do not find a lower oxygen content in the umbilical artery in the fetal llama so the venous-arterial oxygen difference has to be widened by a higher oxygen content in the umbilical vein. However, in recent measurements performed during surgery, the umbilical venous-umbilical arterial O$_2$ content difference was 4.1 ± 0.6 mlO$_2$ x dl -1 (n=4, mean ± SEM), which is very close to the O$_2$ content difference reported in fetal sheep early after surgery (3). Using these values and an umbilical blood flow of 57 ml x min -1 x kg -1, the fetal llama oxygen consumption would be 2.3 ± 0.3 ml 02 x min -1 x kg -1, only one half that of fetal sheep (3).

Fetal sheep adapt to hypoxemia by reducing oxygen consumption (14), by increasing anaerobic metabolism in some tissues (13), and by maintaining oxygen uptake in vital organs (7, 12). In addition to these responses a greater oxygen extraction by the fetal llama tissues is suggested. This mechanism is present in the adult llama, who is able to maintain a normal oxygen uptake despite low blood flow and oxygen delivery to the tissues (1). However, as we noted above, a greater oxygen extraction by the tissues is limited by the already low arterial oxygen content during hypoxemia, suggesting that a major adaptive mechanism to hypoxemia could be a decrease in oxygen consumption in almost every organ of the body.

In conclusion, our results allow us to hypothesize that highly developed tissular, cellular and molecular responses rather than systemic responses are more prominent in the adaptation to hypoxemia in the fetal llama than in the fetal sheep. These differences between fetal llamas and fetal sheep to face of hypoxemia may be the reflection of the environment where the evolution of each species took place, at high altitudes for the llama and at the lowlands for the sheep. Finally, these results support the idea that during hypoxia, the fetal llama can succesfully climb higher than Mount Everest.

AKNOWLEDGMENTS

This work was supported by the Grant 89-1080, Fondo Nacional de Ciencia y Tecnología (FONDECYT), Chile.

We thank Mr. Carlos Muñoz, Mr. Francisco Barahona, and Mr. Daniel Prado for their skillful technical assistance.

REFERENCES

1. BANCHERO, N., GROVER, R.F. & WILL, J.A. 1971. Oxygen transport in the llama. *Resp Physiol* 13: 102-115.

2. BENAVIDES, C.E., PÉREZ, R., ESPINOZA, M., CABELLO, G. RIQUELME, R., PARER, J.T. & LLANOS A.J. 1989. Cardiorespiratory functions in the fetal llama. *Resp Physiol* 75: 327- 334.

3. BLOCK, B.S., PARER, J.T., LLANOS, A.J. & COURT, D.J. 1989. Effects of ridotrine and fetal oxygenation after in utero fetal surgery in sheep. *Biol Neonate* 56: 94-100.

4. COHN, H.E., SACKS, E.J., HEYMANN, M.A. & RUDOLPH, A.M. 1974. Cardiovascular responses to hypoxemia and acidemia in fetal lambs. *Am J Obst Gynecol* 120: 817- 824.

5. COURT, D.J., PARER, J.T., BLOCK, B.S.B. & LLANOS, A.J. 1984. Effects of beta-adrenergic blockade on blood flow distribution during hypoxemia in fetal sheep. *Jour Develop Physiol* 6: 349-358.

6. FIELD, D.R., PARER, J.T., AUSLANDER, R.A., CHECK, D.B., BAKER, W. & JOHNSON, J. 1990. Cerebral oxygen consumption during asphyxia in fetal sheep. *Jour Develop Physiol* 14: 131-137.

7. FISHER, D.J., HEYMANN, M.A. & RUDOLPH, M.A. 1982. Fetal myocardial oxygen and carbohydrate consumption during acutely induced hypoxemia. *Amer J Physiol* 242: H657- H661.

8. FOWLER, M.E. 1989. Medicine and Surgery of South American Camelids: Llama, Alpaca, Vicuña, Guanaco. Ames, Iowa: Iowa State University Press. pp 126-127.

9. GLANTZ, S.A. 1981. Primer of Biostatistics. New York: McGraw-Hill, Inc., pp 71-77 and 302-310.

10. HEYMANN, M.A., PAYNE, B.D., HOFFMAN, J.I.E. & RUDOLPH, A.M. 1977. Blood flow measurements with radionuclide-labeled particules. *Prog Cardiovasc Dis* 20: 55-79.

11. HOCHACHKA, P.W. & GUPPY, M. 1987. Metabolic Arrest and the Control of Biological Time. Cambridge, Massachusetts: Harvard University Press. pp 45-56.

12. JONES, JR., M.D., SHELDON, R.E., PEETERS, L.L., MESCHIA, G., BATTAGLIA, F.C. & MAKOWSKI, E.L. 1977. Fetal cerebral oxygen consumption at different levels of oxygenation. *J Appl Physiol* 43:1080-1084.

13. MANN, L. 1970. Effects of hypoxia on umbilical circulation and fetal metabolism. *Amer J Physiol* 218: 1453-1458.

14. PARER, J.T. 1980. The effect of acute maternal hypoxia on fetal oxygenation and the umbilical circulation in the sheep. *Eur J Obst Gyneco Repro Biol* 10: 125-136.

15. PÉREZ, R., ESPINOZA, M., RIQUELME, R., PARER, J.T. & LLANOS, A.J. 1989. Arginine vasopressin mediates cardiovascular responses to hypoxemia in fetal sheep. *Amer J Physiol* 256: R1011-R1018.

16. RUDOLPH, A.M. 1984 Oxygenation in the fetus and neonate. A perspective. *Semin Perinatol* 8: 158-167.

ALGUNAS CARACTERÍSTICAS DEL EMBARAZO Y DEL RECIÉN NACIDO EN LA ALTURA

Gustavo F. Gonzáles, Roger Guerra-García

Resumen

En este reporte se presentan datos referentes a las características hormonales durante el embarazo en la altura, así como aspectos relacionados a la endocrinología y antropometría del recién nacido en la altura en comparación con lo observado a nivel del mar.

La progesterona sérica es similar en el embarazo en la altura y a nivel del mar, mientras que la prolactina sérica es menor en el embarazo en la altura. La insulina y la IGF-I en suero son menores en las gestantes a término de la altura. La incidencia de diabetes gestacional fue de 5.8% en la altura inferior que a nivel del mar (8.7%). Igualmente la incidencia de macrosomía fetal fue menor en la altura que a nivel del mar.

Existe una relación inversa entre el peso al nacer y la altitud de residencia, y entre edad gestacional al parto y altitud. Cuando se compara la antropometría de los recién nacidos a término a nivel del mar y de la altura no se encuentran diferencias significativas. Esto sugiere que el menor peso en la altura se debe a que los niños nacen más tempranamente. La incidencia de partos a pre-término fue de 12% en la altura en relación al 4% observado a nivel del mar.

No se observaron diferencias entre los niveles basales de hormonas en el recién nacido de altura y de nivel del mar.

Se concluye que la altura acelera el parto, y que esto determina el bajo peso al nacer y el mayor índice de prematuridad.

Palabras claves: Altura, embarazo, progesterona, insulina.

Résumé

Ce travail présente des informations sur les caractéristiques hormonales durant la grossesse en altitude, ainsi que sur les aspects endocrinologiques et anthropométriques du nouveau né en altitude, en comparaison avec ce que l'on peut observer au niveau de la mer.

La progestérone sérique est identique pour la grossesse en altitude et au niveau de la mer, tandis que la prolactine sérique est moindre pour la grossesse en altitude. L'insuline et l'IGF-I sérique se trouvent en quantité plus réduite dans les cas de grossesses à terme en altitude. L'incidence des diabètes dans les cas de gestation fut de 5,8% en altitude, alors qu'elle fut de 8,7% au niveau de la mer. De même, l'incidence de la macrosomie fétale est moindre en altitude qu'au niveau de la mer.

Il y a une relation inverse entre le poids de naisssance et l'altitude de résidence, et entre l'âge de la parturiente et l'altitude. Quand on compare l'anthropométrie des nouveaux nés à terme au niveau de la mer et en altitude, on ne trouve pas de différence significative. Ceci laisse entendre qu'un poids plus faible en altitude est dû à ce que les enfants naissent prématurement. La fréquence des accouchements prématurés fut de 12% en altitude alors qu'elle était de 4% au niveau de la mer.

On n'a pas constaté de différence dans les niveaux de base des hormones chez le nouveau né en altitude et au niveau de la mer.

La conclusion est que l'altitude accélère l'accouchement, ce qui détermine un faible poids à la naissance et un plus fort pourcentage d'accouchements prématurés.

Mots clés : Altitude, grossesse, progestérone, insuline.

Abstract

The report presents data related to hormonal characteristics during pregnancy at high altitude compared with those at sea level, and also anthropometric and endocrinological aspects of newborn at high altitude.

Serum progesterone is similar during pregnancy at sea level and at high altitude, whereas serum prolactin levels are lower at high altitude. Serum insulin and IGF-I are lower in pregnant women at delivery. Incidence of diabetes during pregnancy is 5.8% at high altitude, a value lower than at sea level (8.7%). Incidence of fetal macrosomy is lower at high altitude than at sea level.

There is an inverse relationship between birthweight and altitude of residence, and between gestational age at delivery and altitude of residence. When newborns at term are compared at sea level and at high altitude no differences were observed in anthropometric parameters. This suggests that low birthweight at high altitude is due to the fact that children born earlier than at sea level. The incidence of newborns at pre-term was 12% at high altitude and 4% at sea level.

No differences were observed in basal hormone levels in newborn at sea level and at high altitude.

It is concluded that high altitude accelerates the delivery and this is determining the low birthweight and the high incidence of prematurity observed in these populations.

Key words: Altitude, pregnancy, progesterone, insulin.

INTRODUCCIÓN

La elevada Tasa Global de Fecundidad que se observa en las poblaciones de la altura, que en promedio llega a 6 hijos por mujer (17), refleja un hecho singular, de que las mujeres nativas de la altura puedan mantener un embarazo y tener un parto a pesar de las condiciones adversas del medio ambiente. Para llegar a esta situación, el organismo ha debido desarrollar una serie de mecanismos de adaptación que han permitido el mantenimiento de la fertilidad.

Esta aseveración se basa en las observaciones iniciales del Padre Antonio de la Calancha (3) quien refiere que el primer español que tuvo un hijo en las alturas del Potosí (4500 m) ocurrió 53 años después que los españoles llegaran a esa ciudad, mientras que los nativos de la zona se reproducían normalmente.

En 1971 Guerra-García publicó en la Revista de Ginecología y Obstetricia (Lima, Perú) «Estudios sobre la gestación y el recién nacido en la altura» donde se tratan tópicos relacionados a la placenta (22, 32, 33), la oxigenación, equilibrio ácido-básico de la madre y feto durante el parto en la altura (35), y la bioquímica de la sangre materna y del cordón umbilical (20, 24).

En el presente capítulo vamos a describir algunas variables hormonales que normalmente cambian durante el embarazo, así como aspectos hormonales y antropométricos del recién nacido y de la placenta en la altura.

LUGARES DE ESTUDIO

Los estudios que a continuación describiremos se han llevado a cabo en las siguientes ciudades del Perú:

Lima a 150 m

Huancayo a 3280 m

Cusco a 3400 m

Puno a 3800 m

La Oroya a 3800 m

Cerro de Pasco a 4340 m

ESTUDIOS ENDOCRINOS DEL EMBARAZO EN LA ALTURA

Progesterona durante el embarazo en la altura

Durante las primeras semanas del embarazo la progesterona es sintetizada por el cuerpo lúteo; esto ocurre hasta la novena semana de embarazo, momento en el cual se establece la producción placentaria de la hormona.

La progesterona es sintetizada por la placenta principalmente a partir del colesterol materno. La secreción de progesterona resulta vital para el mantenimiento del embarazo, aunque no ha sido establecido con claridad su modo de acción. Probablemente bloquea los mecanismos de contracción uterina que puedan acelerar el parto.

La progesterona se va incrementando durante la progresión del embarazo y es proporcional a la masa placentaria, por lo que el estado funcional del feto tiene poca influencia sobre la secreción de la hormona.

La producción de esteroides a partir del colesterol requiere de oxígeno, por lo que se ha planteado que en condiciones de hipoxia como la que viven los pobladores de la altura, ésta pueda influenciar en la biosíntesis de esteroides. Así, se han determinado los niveles de progesterona sérica durante el embarazo en la altura y se los han comparado con los observados a nivel del mar.

Se han estudiado 60 mujeres embarazadas nativas de Lima (150 m) y 60 mujeres embarazadas nativas de Cerro de Pasco (4340 m). La progesterona fue medida por radioinmunoensayo.

No se encontraron diferencias significativas en los niveles de progesterona sérica entre Lima y altura (1er trimestre: 34.02 ± 9.68 ng/ml y 32.59 ± 9.73 ng/ml; 2do trimestre:105.15 ± 16.37 ng/ml y 76.31 ± 8.50 ng/ml; 3er trimestre: 109.19 ± 14.96 ng/ml y 160.15 ± 21.09 ng/ml; $\bar{x} \pm$ ES) (16).

Estrógenos durante el embarazo en la altura

El feto y la placenta conforman una unidad metabólica y funcional, y participan notablemente en la biosíntesis, catabolismo, transporte y excreción de esteroides por los compartimientos materno, placentario y fetal.

Los estrógenos son la estrona, el estradiol y el estriol. El estradiol es el estrógeno predominante en la mujer adulta, y la estrona se forma a partir de la dehidroepiandrosterona sulfato; su formación es activa en el tejido adiposo. Tanto la madre como el feto proveen de la dehidroepiandrosterona sulfato, que en la placenta se transforma en dehidroepiandrosterona y ésta a su vez en androstenediona y testosterona, quienes por acción de una aromatasa se convierten en estrona y estradiol respectivamente. La excreción urinaria de estrona y estradiol al final del embarazo son menores en la altura de La Oroya (3800m) (31), y de Cerro de Pasco (4340 m) (37) que a nivel del mar.

El estriol es el estrógeno cuantitativamente más importante en el embarazo. La placenta provee al feto con la 17-hidroxipregnenolona sulfato que se convierte en la dehidroepiandrosterona, que puede hidroxilarse en posición 16 y que es llevada a la placenta para convertirse en estriol. La estrona y el estradiol producidos en la placenta pueden llegar al feto y por 16 alfa hidroxilación convertirse en 16 alfa-dehidroepiandrosterona, que es transportada a la placenta donde se aromatiza y se transforma en estriol.

Durante el embarazo en la altura se observa una menor excreción urinaria de estriol tanto en La Oroya a 3800 m (31) como en Cerro de Pasco a 4340 m (37); sin embargo el estriol en sangre materna y en líquido amniótico fueron similares en Lima (150 m) y Cerro de Pasco (4340 m). El hecho de encontrar menor excreción urinaria de estriol con niveles venosos maternos y de líquido amniótico similares a nivel del mar y la altura, sugiere que existe una menor tasa de excreción urinaria de este esteroide en la altura.

Excreción Urinaria de Gonadotrofina Coriónica Humana (hCG)

No se han encontrado diferencias en la excreción urinaria de hCG en mujeres embarazadas de Lima (150 m), La Oroya (3800 m) y Cerro de Pasco (4340 m) (34, 31).

Prolactina durante el embarazo y puerperio en la altura

Se han estudiado 60 mujeres embarazadas nativas de Lima (150 m) y 60 mujeres embarazadas nativas de Cerro de Pasco (4340 m) y 40 mujeres durante el puerperio. La prolactina fue medida por radioinmunoensayo utilizando reactivos proporcionados por la OMS.

Los niveles de prolactina fueron significativamente menores en la altura (Tabla 1) en cada uno de los trimestres de gestación estudiados (16).

Tabla 1 - Prolactina en suero de mujeres con ciclos menstruales normales, en el embarazo y puerperio en Lima (150 m) y Cerro de Pasco (4340 m).

Grupo	Lima 150 m	Cerro de Pasco 4340 m
No gestante	160.4 ± 16.5 18	60.72 ± 7.0* 18
Gestante Primer Trimestre	1206.2 ± 241.3 18	386.50 ± 65.5* 20
Gestante Segundo Trimestre	2494.7 ± 248.3 19	1424.00 ± 194.4* 18
Gestante Tercer Trimestre	3770.0 ± 285.3 20	2362.00 ± 275.3* 20
Puerperio	1356.6 ± 207.9 19	970.05 ± 185.1 20

Los datos son el promedio ± ES (mUI/ml). *P<0.01 con respecto a lo observado a nivel del mar. El número de sujetos se encuentra debajo de los datos.

Niveles de Insulina y Factores de Crecimiento Insulino Símiles I y II (IGF-I, IGF-II) en Gestantes a Término del Nivel del Mar y Altura

Existen reportes de que la resistencia a la insulina es menor durante la gestación a término. En tal sentido se ha tratado de establecer en qué medida la vida en las grandes alturas modifica este comportamiento observado en gestantes a nivel del mar. Así, Cipriani y col. (2) han estudiado a 10 jóvenes con gestación a término de Lima (150 msnm) y de La Oroya (3700 m) de paridad similar, determinándose por radioinmunoensayo los niveles séricos de insulina, Insulin-Like Growth factor I (IGF-I) y II (IGF-II) antes del parto. Los resultados demuestran menores niveles de insulina y de IGF-I en la altura (Tabla 2).

Se encontró relación lineal entre el nivel de insulina e IGF-I materno y el peso del producto, sólo en la altura, r= 0.77 p<.0025 y r=0.38 p< 0.05. No hubo relación entre los niveles de Insulina e IGF-I, en ambas altitudes, sugiriendo que estos dos compuestos se regulan independientemente.

La gestación a término en la altura cursa con menores niveles de insulina, indicativo de una menor resistencia y con valores menores de IGF-I. Ambas hormonas correlacionan con el peso del producto sólo en la altura.

Tabla 2 - Niveles de insulina, IGF-I e IGF-II en gestantes a término a nivel del mar y en la altura.

	Lima (N=10)	La Oroya (N=10)	p
Edad	23.3 ± 3.6	22.4 ± 3.7	
Gestación (s)	39.4 ± 0.9	38.5 ± 1.2	.05
Peso (Kg)	51.8 ± 5.2	54.3 ± 5.1	
Talla (m)	1.55 ± 0.05	1.52 ± 0.05	
Peso ganado	8.6 ± 2.9	11.5 ± 5.2	
Insulina uU/ml	23.5 ± 14.4	12.0 ± 6.9	.025
IGF-I ng/ml	274 ± 182.4	78.9 ± 42.9	.005
IGF-II ng/ml	282 ± 104.7	203.5 ± 101.4	

Los datos son el promedio ± ES.

Fuente: 2.

Este último dato es interesante puesto que la IGF-I (somatomedina C) es un efector biológico de la hormona del crecimiento, y como es conocido la hormona del crecimiento está incrementada en varones pero no en mujeres de la altura (11), lo cual sugiere que hay una menor respuesta o resistencia a la acción de la hormona del crecimiento en la altura.

Prevalencia de Diabetes Gestacional en la Altura

Estudios previos realizados en nuestro Instituto señalan que la frecuencia de Diabetes Mellitus tipo I y tipo II es sumamente rara en la población andina de las grandes alturas.

Se han reportado niveles bajos de glicemia en el hombre andino, habiéndose postulado factores étnicos, dietéticos y metabólicos para explicar estos hallazgos. Las mujeres no gestantes nativas de Cerro de Pasco (4340 m) ante la administración intravenosa de glucosa (40 ml al 50%) presentan una respuesta similar en su forma a la observada a nivel del mar, pero con menores valores absolutos. Durante el embarazo a nivel del mar se modifica la curva, siendo las glicemias a las 0, 15 y 60 minutos menores que en no gestantes. En la gestación en la altura no se modificó la curva observada en no gestantes (1). Poco se conoce acerca de la diabetes gestacional en la mujer andina y se postula que la frecuencia de este tipo de diabetes debe ser también infrecuente en la altura.

Para demostrar esta hipótesis se ha estudiado 51 gestantes de bajo riesgo obstétrico, nativas y residentes de la altura (Cusco, 3400 m) entre 24 y 28 semanas de gestación, quienes fueron sometidas a una ingesta de 50 gramos de glucosa anhidra, administrada independiente del estado post-prandial, determinándose a la hora, la glicemia capilar mediante un reflectómetro. Considerando como sospechosa de diabetes gestacional cuando los niveles de glicemia fueron > 140 mg/dl. Sólo 3 gestantes presentaron estas cifras (5.8%), y por lo tanto fueron consideradas para el diagnóstico definitivo de diabetes gestacional mediante el test de tolerancia a la glucosa con 100 g.

Esta frecuencia resulta inferior a la reportada en mujeres de Lima (8.7%) utilizando el mismo método. Estos resultados corroboran la hipótesis de la singularidad de las distintas formas de Diabetes Mellitus en la población andina que habita en las grandes alturas, característica que amerita de mayores investigaciones (26).

ESTUDIOS DE RECIÉN NACIDOS DE GESTANTES DE ALTURA

Estudios Hormonales

Se han estudiado 48 recién nacidos de Cerro de Pasco (4340 m) y 13 de Lima (150 m) midiéndose sus niveles hormonales en sangre de cordón umbilical. Los niveles de Hormona del Crecimiento, tiroxina, tri-iodotironina, cortisol y corticosterona son similares a nivel del mar y en la altura; de esto se deduce que las características endocrinas observadas en el adulto de la altura se adquieren posteriormente (18).

En recién nacidos con circular de cordón y con sufrimiento fetal, tanto la concentración del cortisol como de la corticosterona fueron significativamente más altas, modificándose la relación entre ambas de 8.6/1 en normales de altura a 5.2/1 en circular de cordón y 5.4/1 en sufrimiento fetal (19).

Estudios antropométricos

Numerosos estudios reportan un menor peso al nacer en la altura(8) (Tabla 3).

La mayoría de estos estudios se han realizado en épocas diferentes, lo cual dificulta su comparación con los datos obtenidos a nivel del mar, teniendo en cuenta que el peso y talla del recién nacido varía a través del tiempo, cuando mejoran las condiciones de vida de una población, fenómeno que se denomina incremento secular (5); a pesar de ello, tal cual puede apreciarse en la tabla 3, el peso del recién nacido es menor conforme aumenta la altitud.

Tabla 3 - Peso corporal del Recién nacido a diferentes altitudes en el Perú.

Altitud m	Localidad	N	Peso (g)	Año
150	Lima	100	3297±511	1961
		100	3540±550	1962
		88	3311±479	1967
		25	3567±433	1984
3280	Huancayo	20	3247±355	1984
3416	Cusco	80	3092±457	1967
3800	La Oroya	186	3039±420	1961
4340	C. Pasco	100	2730±350	1963
			2770	1972
		60	2929±+382	1987

Existen una serie de factores que pueden explicar la diferencia de peso hallados en estos estudios, entre los cuales destacan la etnicidad, el nivel socioeconómico, la edad gestacional y el sexo de las poblaciones estudiadas.

Se ha demostrado que los varones nacidos a nivel del mar, pero hijos de madres de altura son de menor peso que aquellos hijos de madres de Lima (5). En buena proporción de casos los limeños hijos de madres de altura son de menor nivel sieconómico que los limeños hijos de limeños. Las poblaciones de nivel socioeconómico alto tienen hijos de mayor peso que aquellos de nivel bajo; asimismo el peso del recién nacido varón es mayor que el de mujeres, de lo cual resulta que la mayor o menor contribución de cada uno de estos factores va a modificar el peso y talla del recién nacido.

Passano (27) es el autor peruano que ha estudiado el mayor número de nacimientos en la altura de Puno (3800 m). En sus resultados se observa que sólo el 63.74% de los partos son a término; el estudio del peso, talla, apgar del recién nacido concuerdan con los hallazgos señalados a nivel del mar; el tipo de placenta es mayor que a nivel del mar.

Hass y col (21) evaluaron la influencia de la etnicidad y del sexo sobre el peso y la talla del recién nacido en La Paz (3600 m), Bolivia, comparándolos con aquellos de Santa Cruz (400 m), Bolivia, encontrando que los varones en la altura tienen una menor talla y peso que los de baja altitud, mientras que en las mujeres no se observa estas diferencias. Un fenómeno similar ha sido observado a nivel del mar donde los varones hijos de madres de altura son de menor talla y peso que los hijos de madres a nivel del mar, mientras que las mujeres, independiente de la procedencia materna, son de la misma talla y peso (5, 9).

El dimorfismo sexual está basado en la diferente ecosensibilidad frente a las situaciones ambientales. Ante las situaciones adversas consideradas moderadas, el que se afecta negativamente es el varón, mientras que estos cambios no influyen en la mujer (9). En este caso el dimorfismo sexual se reduce. En situaciones adversas severas, se afectan tanto el varón como la mujer por lo tanto el dimorfismo sexual se mantiene.

En situaciones adversas moderadas como puede observarse en la altura, el dimorfismo sexual se reduce. Así, el dimorfismo sexual del peso al nacer que se observa a nivel del mar no se observa, tal como se ha demostrado para La Paz (3300 m) en Bolivia (21), y para Cerro de Pasco (4340 m) en Perú (13). Esto indica que la altura tiene un mayor efecto sobre los varones que sobre las mujeres, lo cual ha sido confirmado previamente en una serie de reportes sobre función endocrina (6).

Estos hallazgos apoyan la hipótesis de que el sexo femenino tiene una mayor capacidad de resistencia frente a factores adversos, tales como malnutrición, enfermedad o la vida en las grandes alturas.

Re-evaluando los resultados por sexo encontramos que el recién nacido varón a 3300 m de altura en el Perú presenta menor talla, peso, longitud de miembros inferiores y distancia interpupilar (5), no encontrándose diferencias en la grasa subcutánea del triceps y subescapular, perímetro cefálico y torácico, distancia intermamilar, longitud de miembro superior, longitud de la mano, y longitud del pie. Los datos claramente indican que en varones recién nacidos de altura hay un 9.8% de reducción del peso corporal y un 2.5% en la talla, sin modificación en el contenido de grasa, de lo que resultaría que el menor peso podría ser debido a la menor talla y/o menor contenido de agua en el organismo del individuo de altura.

En las mujeres recién nacidas de altura no se observan diferencias en la talla, peso, grasa subcutánea del triceps ni subescapular.

Tiempo de Gestación en la altura

Es evidente que el peso promedio de los recién nacidos es menor en la altura que a nivel del mar. Sobrevilla y col (35) han postulado que en la altura se encuentra un incremento de la tasa de recién nacidos a término de peso bajo. Sobre esta base hemos decidido evaluar esta hipótesis desarrollando diversos diseños experimentales y re-analizando los datos existentes en la literatura.

En alturas por encima de 4000 m se ha demostrado que la talla y peso del recién nacido de ambos sexos son menores que a nivel del mar, mientras que el perímetro cefálico y torácico fueron similares. La talla en las mujeres nacidas a 4340 m fue menor que en varones (P<0.01). La edad gestacional al parto en la altura es de 1 a 2 semanas menor que a nivel del mar (Tabla 4). Esto se ha observado repetidamente en diversos estudios como puede apreciarse en la tabla 5.

Tabla 4 - Antropometría del Recién nacido a nivel del mar y en Cerro de Pasco (4340 m).

Variable	Lima		C. Pasco	
	Varones	Mujeres	Varones	Mujeres
Peso (gr)	3238±61	3218±66	2891±51*	2799±50*
Talla (cm)	50.5±0.3	50.0±0.3	49.5±0.2*	48.5±0.2*
P. Cefálico (cm)	34.0±0.2	33.6±0.2	34.7±0.2	34.4±0.2
P. Torácico (cm)	33.6±+0.2	33.4±0.3	33.6±0.3	33.3±0.3
Edad gestacional (sem)	39.9±0.2	39.8±0.2	38.7±0.2*	37.8±0.4*

*P<0.01 con respecto a Lima (150 m). Los datos son el promedio ± ES.

En la tabla 5 se observa que la edad gestacional al parto es menor conforme aumenta la altitud de residencia; del mismo modo el índice de maduración de Farr es menor en la altura (31, 35), indicando que el nacimiento en la altura está ocurriendo antes que a nivel del mar. Esto se corrobora con el hallazgo de que el 12% de los embarazos en Cerro de Pasco ocurren antes de las 37 semanas en relación al 4% observado en Lima (13).

Cuando se compara el peso y la talla de los recién nacidos con 40 semanas de gestación no se encuentran diferencias entre Lima (150 m) y Cerro de Pasco (4340 m) (Tabla 6). El análisis de covarianza demuestra que para edades gestacionales menores de 38 semanas, a igualdad de edad gestacional, el peso del feto es menor en la altura y la talla del feto es similar en ambas alturas. De 38 a 42 semanas, a igualdad de edad gestacional, no hay diferencias en la talla y peso entre Lima y Cerro de Pasco (4340 m). Nuestros resultados demuestran que la velocidad de aumento del peso corporal es menor en la altura hasta las 37 semanas de gestación y mayor a partir de las 38 semanas (15). Estos datos indican que la altura no estaría afectando el crecimiento del feto intrautero sino que existiría un menor peso y talla al nacer porque en la altura el parto está ocurriendo más tempranamente que a nivel del mar. Este hallazgo es de importancia pues estaría modificando criterios antiguos de un menor crecimiento durante la vida intrauterina en la altura.

Tabla 5 - Edad gestacional al parto e Indice de Maduración del recién nacido a nivel del mar y en la altura.

Lugar	Altura m	Edad Gestacional sem	Indice de Maduración U	Fuente
Lima	150	39.91 ± 0.37	34.54 ± 0.64	(35)
	150		34.90 ± 0.50	(31)
	150	39.40 ± 0.90		(2)
	150	39.90 ± 0.2		(8)
Cusco	3400	39		(4)
La Oroya	3800		33.10 ± 0.70*	(31)
	3800	39.20 ± 0.18		(38)
	3800	38.50 ± 1.20*		(2)
C. Pasco	4340	39.80 ± 0.42	32.46 ± 0.63*	(35)
	4340	38.20 ± 0.30*		(8)

Tabla 6 - Antropometría del recién nacido a término (40 semanas) a nivel del mar y en la altura (4340 m).

Variable	Lima		Cerro de Pasco	
	Varones	Mujeres	Varones	Mujeres
Peso (gr)	3206±118	3149±106	2977±57	2986±96
Talla (cm)	50.4±0.5	49.1±0.6	49.8±0.3	49.2±0.4

Los datos son el promedio ± error standard. No se encontraron diferencias entre ninguno de los grupos de comparación.

Macrosomía Fetal: Efecto de la Edad materna

A nivel del mar se ha demostrado que el alto peso al nacer (> 4000 g) aumenta con la edad materna. No se ha descrito cual es la situación en la altura, donde en promedio los niños nacen con menor peso que a nivel del mar. Para tal efecto se han estudiado los partos ocurridos durante 1 año en el Hospital Arzobispo Loayza y los ocurridos de 1982 a 1985 en el Hospital Daniel A. Carrión de Cerro de Pasco a 4340 m de altitud.

Tanto en Lima como en Cerro de Pasco se han encontrado partos hasta los 46 años de edad. En el grupo control (< 30 años) la incidencia de alto peso al nacer fue de 2.91% en Lima y 0.8% en Cerro de Pasco, siendo 3.6 veces mayor en Lima que en Cerro de Pasco. En el grupo de mujeres añosas (> 35 años) fue de 9.97% en Lima y de 2.6% en Cerro de Pasco, siendo 3.8 veces mayor en Lima que en Cerro de Pasco. Tanto en Lima como en Cerro de Pasco el incremento de la incidencia de alto peso al nacer por efecto de la edad materna es la misma (3.30 veces en Cerro de Pasco y 3.40 veces en Lima).

Se concluye que la altitud *per se* no modifica la influencia de la edad materna tardía sobre la incidencia del alto peso al nacer. La menor incidencia de hijos de alto peso al nacer en la altura está en relación a la menor incidencia de diabetes mellitus en la altura (14).

ESTUDIOS DE RECIÉN NACIDOS DE GESTANTES AÑOSAS DE CERRO DE PASCO

Se ha demostrado que la edad materna al nacer el hijo tiene importancia tanto para la supervivencia como para el desarrollo futuro del hijo (9). El sexo del recién nacido es importante en el pronóstico de la supervivencia y desarrollo futuro, cuando las condiciones ambientales son moderadamente deprimidas, siendo el sexo masculino el más desfavorecido (10, 12).

La vida en las grandes alturas es otra situación que afecta a los individuos encontrándose en condiciones de bajo nivel socioeconómico un menor peso y talla.

Estas tres condiciones: edad materna tardía, nivel socioeconómico bajo y vida en las grandes alturas pueden coexistir en una buena proporción de nuestra población. Por tal motivo se han estudiado las gestaciones y partos de mujeres añosas provenientes de una población socioeconómica baja de Cerro de Pasco (4340 m) tratando de determinar si existen diferencias de acuerdo al sexo del producto en las complicaciones del embarazo, el parto y del recién nacido (13).

Antropometría

No se observaron diferencias en el peso, talla, perímetro cefálico, y perímetro torácico al nacer en relación a la edad materna (madres añosas vs madres no añosas) en Cerro de Pasco (4340 m) (Tabla 7).

Tabla 7 - Antropometría de los recién nacidos de Cerro de Pasco (4340 m) según edad materna.

Parámetro	Edad Materna			
	< 35 años		> 35 años	
	niños	niñas	niños	niñas
Peso (Kg)	2920.4±49.4	2767.7±49.4*	3046.3±70.1	2896.6±56.1
	60	60	54	44
Talla (cm)	49.6±0.2	48.4±0.3*	49.2±0.3	49.0±0.3
	56	55	52	42
P. Cefálico (cm)	35.2±0.2	34.8±0.2	34.7±0.3	34.8±0.3
	56	55	28	30
P.Torácico (cm)	33.8±0.3	33.1±0.4	34.0±0.3	34.4±0.3
	43	36	34	30
E.Gestacional	38.7±0.2	37.9±0.3*	38.6±0.2	38.4± 0.2
(semanas)	60	60	54	44

*P<0.05 con respecto a los varones. Los datos son el promedio ± ES. Debajo de los datos se encuentra el número de sujetos.

Es interesante notar que la edad gestacional promedio oscila entre 37.9 y 38.7 semanas en todos los grupos estudiados, valores por debajo de lo que se observa en poblaciones a nivel del mar.

Indice de masculinidad

Las madres primíparas menores de 35 años produjeron 14 varones por 15 mujeres, mientras que entre mujeres añosas fue de 2 varones por ninguna mujer. Esta observación es diferente a lo reportado a nivel del mar donde en las primíparas añosas existe una mayor incidencia de hijas mujeres que de varones (7)

Recién nacidos de bajo peso

La incidencia de recién nacidos a término, pequeño para su edad gestacional en Cerro de Pasco es de 9.8%, y en madres añosas es de 5.6%. Estos valores son similares a lo observado a nivel del mar en Lima 8.9% y 11.3% respectivamente, y en Iquitos en la Selva del Perú, 5.2% y 8.6% respectivamente (39).

Recién Nacidos a Pre-Término

La incidencia de pre-términos (< 37 semanas) fue de 11.3% en mujeres menores de 35 años y 13% en hijos de madres añosas de Cerro de Pasco sin diferencia significativa (13). Este valor se encuentra por encima a lo observado en una población de la selva del Perú, donde el embarazo a pre-término fue del 6.9% en madres de 20-34 años y 2.9% en madres añosas (39), y a lo observado en Lima, de 4% en madres no añosas y 8% en madres añosas (12). Estos resultados están en corcondancia con el menor promedio de edad gestacional observado en la población de Cerro de Pasco a 4340 m de altura. Sería importante conocer cuál es el grado de madurez fetal en estos recién nacidos a «Pre-Término» en la altura.

Asfixia neonatal

La asfixia neonatal en Cerro de Pasco (4340 m) ocurre en el 25% de los recién nacidos. Este valor está muy por encima al 6.7% encontrado a nivel del mar, en un hospital público (12). Este alto porcentaje es incluso mayor al porcentaje de recién nacidos de bajo peso y de recién nacidos a pre-término, por lo cual estos factores no explicarían totalmente el 25% encontrado. No es posible, con los datos disponibles, sugerir un efecto de la hipoxia de altura como causal de esta mayor incidencia, ni si esta mayor incidencia está asociada a la mayor tasa de mortalidad infantil observada en poblaciones de altura. En Puno a 3800 m de altura también se ha observado una alta tasa de asfixia neonatal que bordea el 14% (27).

Obitos fetales

A nivel del mar se han observado las siguientes tasas de óbitos fetales masculinos, 3.72% en el Hospital Cayetano Heredia (10), 3.5% en el Hospital Loayza (12), y 3.0% en el Hospital Édgardo Rebagliati (9), mientras que en Cerro de Pasco a 4340 m fue de 9.2% en hijos de madres añosas (13).

El Lima el número de óbitos fetales masculinos de madres añosas es 7 veces mayor que de madres menores de 35 años, mientras que en la altura se supera notablemente esta cifra; esto sugiere que la supervivencia del feto masculino a condiciones adversas como la producida por la edad materna tardía es menor en la altura que a nivel del mar.

LA PLACENTA EN LAS GRANDES ALTURAS

Los estudios sobre la placenta de altura revelan cambios estructurales a nivel de las microvellosidades sinciciales con un incremento en el área de intercambio gaseoso (30).

En un estudio realizado en Cerro de Pasco (4340 m) se encontró que el peso de la placenta es similar tanto si el recién nacido es varón como si es mujer (657.7+22.2 g y 627.2±14.4 g, respectivamente). No se encontró diferencias en el peso de la placenta por la edad materna, ni por el número de gestaciones (653.2±24.34 g para primíparas y 664.2±36.4 g para multíparas) (30).

El peso de la placenta correlaciona significativamente con el peso del recién nacido (r=0.61), la talla del recién nacido (r=0.54) y con la edad gestacional (r=0.52). Cuando se correlacionó el peso de la placenta con el peso del recién nacido para edades gestacionales de 39-41 semanas se encontró una correlación de r=0.59 con una ecuación de regresión similar que cuando se incluye la población total (Edad Gestacional: 23-42 semanas), lo cual significa que el peso de la placenta correlaciona más con el peso del recién nacido que con la edad gestacional.

No se encontró correlación lineal entre el peso de la placenta y el peso o talla materna, cuando la edad gestacional fue de 39-41 semanas (r=0.28 y 0.19 respectivamente, P:NS).

El coeficiente placentario (Peso de la placenta/peso del recién nacido) fue en Cerro de Pasco de 0.225±0.032 (Promedio + Desviación standard), para un peso del recién nacido de 2907.86±157.21 g (promedio ± error standard). Este coeficiente placentario es mayor que lo observado a nivel del mar, y aumenta conforme se incrementa la altitud de residencia (33, 29) (Tabla 8)

Tabla 8 - Coeficiente placentario en relación a la altura de residencia.

Lugar	Altitud m	Coeficiente Placentario
Lima	150	0.149
La Oroya	3800	0.162
C. Pasco	4340	0.225

Fuente: 23, 29.

Según nuestros datos el peso placentario en la altura es mayor que a nivel del mar desde las 23 semanas de gestación, y que la velocidad de crecimiento en el peso corporal es similar que la velocidad de crecimiento en el peso placentario, de tal manera que el coeficiente placentario no varía con el peso corporal para edades gestacionales de 23 a 42 semanas (r=0.27. P:NS). Este comportamiento es diferente a lo que reporta la literatura para poblaciones a nivel del mar, donde el peso corporal crece a mayor velocidad que el peso placentario, de tal forma que el coeficiente placentario disminuye con la edad gestacional, de 0.24 para un peso corporal de 1020 g a 0.14 para un peso corporal de 3360 g (28), mientras que en Cerro de Pasco (4340 m) para el mismo rango de peso corporal, el coeficiente placentario varía de 0.25 a 0.22.

Existen factores que pueden afectar el peso del recién nacido sin afectar el peso placentario, entre los que se encuentra el hábito de fumar (25). En nuestro caso se observa un patrón diferente donde se afecta el peso placentario sin afectar el peso del feto, lo cual sugiere que el estímulo hipóxico pueda ser responsable de esta situación. El mayor peso resultaría de un mecanismo compensatorio para favorecer la mejor oxigenación del feto en la altura, favoreciendo los fenómenos de intercambio de gases y de metabolitos entre la madre y el feto en la altura.

REFERENCIAS

1. CALDERÓN, R., LLERENA, L.A., MUNIVE, L., KRUGER, F. 1966. Brief notes and comments: intravenous glucose tolerance test in pregnancy in women living in chronic hypoxia. *Diabetes* 15: 130-132

2. CIPRIANI, E., VILLENA, J., ROE, C., MARTINA, M. & ARAUCO, O. 1992. *Niveles de Insulina y Factores de Crecimiento Insulino Símiles I y II (IGF-I, IGF-II) en Gestantes a Término del Nivel del Mar y Altura.* IV Congreso Peruano de Endocrinología. Resumen 5.

3. DE LA CALANCHA, A. 1639. *Crónica Moralizadora de la Orden de San Agustín.* Barcelona.

4. DUEÑAS, Y., BARRETO, R. & BONILLA, L. 1992. Curva de crecimiento intrauterino en una población a 3400 m. *Acta Andina* 1: 27

5. FALEN, J., ZAPATA, J., KLEIN, E., YTAHASHI, M. & DEL ÁGUILA, C. 1985. Antropometría del recién nacido a nivel del mar y de la altura. *Acta Médica Peruana* 12: 58-63.

6. GONZÁLES, G.F. 1983. Endocrinología en las grandes alturas. *Revista de la ANBIOP,* Lima. 2: 9-66

7. GONZÁLES, G.F. 1985. Selección del sexo por la edad materna. *Acta Médica Peruana* 12: 33-39.

8. GONZÁLES, G.F. 1987. Crecimiento y desarrollo somático en la altura. *Diagnóstico* 19: 50-58

9. GONZÁLES, G.F. & CASTILLO, J. 1985. Dimorfismo sexual de las complicaciones del recién nacido y del escolar, hijos de madres añosas. *Acta Médica Peruana* 12: 44-53

10. GONZÁLES, G.F., CARRILLO, C. & GONZÁLEZ DEL RIEGO, M. 1985. El sexo del hijo de la mujer añosa como factor de riesgo. *Diagnóstico* 16: 147-151

11. GONZÁLES, G.F., COYOTUPA, J., KANEKU, L. & GUERRA-GARCÍA, R. 1981. Relationship between blood serotonin and serum growth hormone in basal conditions in natives at low and high altitude. *IRCS Medical Sciences* 9: 262

12. GONZÁLES, G.F., GENG, V., SEMINARIO, J. & EXEBIO, A. 1986. El sexo femenino: el sexo fuerte. I. Estudios en gestantes añosas. *Diagnóstico* 17: 46-51

13. GONZÁLES, G.F., RAMÍREZ, T. & CAJAHUAMAN, S. 1987. Estudios en recién nacidos de gestantes añosas de Cerro de Pasco (4340 m). *Diagnóstico* 19: 146-149.

14. GONZÁLES, G.F., RAMÍREZ, T., SARAVIA, E., CARRILLO, C. & HUAMAN, R. 1986a. *Incidencia de la macrosomía fetal en el recién nacido de altura y nivel del mar: Efecto de la edad materna.* IV Jornadas Científicas de la Universidad Peruana Cayetano Heredia, Lima-Perú. Resumen 12.

15. GONZÁLES, G.F., RAMÍREZ, T., SARAVIA, E., CARRILLO, C. & HUAMAN, R. 1986b. *Antropometría del recién nacido a nivel del mar y en la altura (4340 m).* IV Jornadas Científicas UPCH, Lima-Perú. Resumen 13.

16. GONZÁLES, G.F., SANTIAGO, L. & GOÑEZ, C. 1992. *Niveles de Prolactina y Progesterona durante el embarazo en la altura.* IV Congreso Peruano de Endocrinología. Lima. Resumen.

17. GUERRA-GARCÍA, R. 1986. *Problemas Poblacionales Peruanos II.* AMIDEP, Ed. Lima-Perú. 402 pp.

18. GUERRA-GARCÍA, R. & COYOTUPA, J. 1985. *Estudios endocinológicos en recién nacidos de Cerro de Pasco a 4340 m de altura.* III Congreso Nacional de Medicina de Altura. C. Pasco-Perú. Resumen.

19. GUERRA-GARCÍA, R., DE LA TORRE, J. & COYOTUPA, J. 1977. *Estudio de la función adrenal del recién nacido de Cerro de Pasco (4200 m) y de Lima (150 m).* VII Jornadas Peruanas de Endocrinología. Ica, Perú. pp. 67

20. GUERRA-GARCÍA, R., LOZANO, R. & CATERIANO, M. 1971. Bioquímica de la sangre materna y del cordón umbilical en Cerro de Pasco (4200 m). *Ginecología y Obstetricia (Lima, Perú)* 17: 67-78

21. HAAS, J.D., FRONGILLO, E.A., STEPICK, C.D., BEARD, J.L. & HURTADO, L. 1980. Altitude, ethnic and sex difference in birth weight and length in Bolivia. *Human Biol.* 52: 459-477

22. KADAR, K. & SALDAÑA, M. 1971. La placenta en la altura. I. Características macroscópicas y morfometría. *Ginecología y Obstetricia (Lima, Perú)* 17: 3-23

23. KRUGER, H., ARIAS-STELLA, J. & SIALER, L. 1967. El recién nacido y el cociente placentario en las grandes alturas. *Ginecología y Obstetricia (Lima, Perú)* 13: 139

24. LLERENA, L.A., MUÑOZ, J.M. & MUÑOZ, T. 1971. Acidos grasos no esterificados en suero de gestantes, recién nacidos y hombres normales de altura. *Ginecología y Obstetricia (Lima,Perú)* 17: 103-115

25. MULCAHY, R., MURPHY, J. & MARTIN, F. 1970. Placental changes and maternal weight in smoking and non smoking mothers. *Am. J. Obst. Gynecol.* 106: 703-704.

26. OJEDA, E., SECLEN, S., CARRILLO, C. & VILLENA, A. 1992. *Despistaje de diabetes gestacional en mujeres nativas de altura.* IV Congreso Peruanxo de Endocrinología. Lima, Perú. Resumen.

27. PASSANO, S. 1983. *Características de las gestantes y de los recién nacidos en Puno.* Tesis Doctoral, Universidad Peruana Cayetano Heredia, Lima.

28. PRITCHARD, J., MAC DONALD, P. 1980. *Obstetricia.* Williams, Salvat ed. México. 2a ed.: pp. 106

29. RAMÍREZ, T., CAJAHUAMAN, S., GONZÁLES, G.F. & CARRILLO, C. 1987. El peso de la placenta en las grandes alturas. *Diagnóstico (Lima)* 19: 74-76.

30. RECAVARREN, S. 1979. *La placenta de altura.* II Jorn. Científicas UPCH, Lima. Abst 104.

31. RODRÍGUEZ, W .1974. *Altitud y Hormonas de la Unidad Feto-Placentaria.* Tesis Doctoral, Lima: Universidad Nacional Mayor de San Marcos.

32. SALDAÑA, M., KADAR, K. & RECAVARREN, S. 1971. La placenta en la altura. II. Estudio ultraestructural cuantitativo de placentas de Cerro de Pasco (4340 m), Puno (3850 m) y Lima (150 m). *Ginecología y Obstetricia (Lima, Perú)* 17: 25-35.

33. SOBREVILLA, L.A. 1971. Análisis matemático de la relación ponderal placenta: recién nacido en la altura. *Ginecología y Obstetricia (Lima, Perú)* 17: 37-43.

34. SOBREVILLA, L.A. 1973. Embarazo y Parto en los Andes: Cambios fisiológicos y alteraciones de la reproducción humana. *In*: Ed. L. Sobrevilla, *Fisiología de la Reproducción y Atención Integral de la Madre.* Lima, Perú: Universidad Peruana Cayetano Heredia: pp. 137-154

35. SOBREVILLA, L.A, CASSINELLI, M.T., CARCELEN. A. & MÁLAGA, J. 1971. Tensión de oxígeno y equilibrio ácido-base de madre y feto durante el parto en la altura. *Ginecología y Obstetricia (Lima, Perú)* 17: 45-66

36. SOBREVILLA, L.A., ROMERO, I. & KRUGER, F. 1971. Estriol levels of cord blood, maternal venous blood and amniotic fluid at delivery at high altitude. *Am. J. Obst. Gynecol.* 110: 596

37. SOBREVILLA, L.A., ROMERO, I., KRUGER, F. & WHITTEMBURY, J. 1968. Low estrogen excretion during pregnancy at high altitude. *Am. J. Obstet. Gynecol.* 102: 828

38. SOTOMAYOR, T. 1978. Hemorragia retiniana del recién nacido de altura. *In: Actas de las Primeras Jornadas de Medicina y Cirugía de altura.* La Oroya, Perú: pp. 153-165.

39. WILHELM, J., LÓPEZ, G., GIL, K., DONAYRE, M., AREVALO, J., RAMIREZ, C., CARRILLO, C., GONZÁLES, G.F. 1991. La edad materna como factor de riesgo en el embarazo en la selva del Perú. *Diagnóstico* 28: 80-84

GLUCOSE HOMEOSTASIS AT HIGH ALTITUDE

John R. Sutton, Fausto Garmendia

Abstract

The effect of acute and chronic hypoxia in sea level and Andean man concerning glucose homeostasis is reviewed. Glucose concentrations has found to be lower in the high altitude dweller (HAD) but they may also lower in the sea level dweller chronically exposed to altitude for several weeks to months. It may be due to a preferencial fatty acid oxidation and not to an impaired gluconeogenesis. The HAD shows a very dynamic situation in glucose homeostasis with an augmented glucose kinetics.

Although the resting growth hormone (GH) was elevated as was the plasma free fatty acids (FFA), both were supressible with glucose load. Despite that GH may be at a different set point in the HAD, it responded to the normal physiological regulators of exercise and glucose.

An elevation in serum GH may potentiate its somatotrophic role; alternatively, it may be having a selective metabolic role. The elevated plasma FFA in the HAD could be the result of the GH which will mobilize FFA from adipose tissue to be used as the principal energy substrate under hypoxic conditions.

Key words: Glucose homeostasis, growth hormone, free fatty acids, chronic hypoxia, Andes, high altitude.

Resumen

Se revisan los efectos de la hipoxia aguda y crónica a nivel del mar y en el hombre andino relativos a la homeostasis de la glucosa. Si bien se ha encontrado una baja concentración de glucosa en los residentes permanentes de altura (HAD), ésta es también baja en el individuo de nivel del mar expuesto crónicamente a la altura por algunas semanas o meses. Esto podría deberse a la preponderancia de la oxidación de ácidos grasos y no a una gluconeogénesis menoscabada. Los HAD presentan una homeostasis de la glucosa sumamente dinámica con una cinética de glucosa aumentada.

Aunque la hormona de crecimiento (GH) en reposo se encontraba elevada, así como los ácidos grasos libres (FFA), ambos disminuían con una carga de glucosa. No obstante la GH podría tener un umbral de respuesta diferente en los HAD, la respuesta se conserva en presencia de los reguladores fisiológicos normales: glucosa y ejercicio.

Un aumento de la GH sérica podría potenciar su rol somatotrófico; alternativamente, podría estar cumpliendo un rol metabólico selectivo. Los FFA elevados en plasma en HAD podrían ser el resultado de la GH, que mobilizaría los FFA del tejido adiposo para ser utilizado como el sustrato energético principal en condiciones de hipoxia.

Palabras claves: Homeostasia de la glucosa, hormona de crecimiento, ácidos grasos libres, hipoxia crónica, Andes, altura.

Résumé

Cet article révise les effets de l'hypoxie aiguë et chronique au niveau de la mer et chez l'homme andin relatifs à l'homéostasie du glucose. Bien que l'on ait trouvé une faible concentration de glucose chez les résidents permanents en altitude (HAD), celle-ci est également faible chez l'individu qui vit au niveau de la mer, exposé de façon chronique à l'altitude durant quelques semaines ou mois. Cela serait dû à la prépondérance de l'oxydation des acides gras et non pas à une gluconéogenèse diminuée. Les HAD présentent une homéostasie du glucose extrêmement dynamique accompagnée d'une cinétique du glucose augmentée.

Bien que l'hormone de croissance (GH) au repos soit élevée, ainsi que les acides gras libres (FFA), ces deux éléments diminuaient avec une charge de glucose. Cependant la GH pourrait avoir un seuil de réponse différent chez les HAD, la réponse reste la même en présence des régulateurs physiologiques normaux : glucose et exercice. Une augmentation de la GH sérique pourrait renforcer son rôle somatotrophique; de façon alternée cela pourrait jouer un rôle métabolique sélectif. Les FFA qui ont un taux plasmatique élevé de HAD pourraient être le résultat de la GH qui mobiliserait les FFA du tissu adipeux pour être utilisé comme sustrat énergétique principal en condition d'hypoxie.

Mots clés : Homéostasie du glucose, hormone de croissance, acides gras libres, hypoxie chronique, Andes, altitude.

INTRODUCTION

It is a great pleasure to write a chapter in this book to honour the 70th Birthday of Dr. Carlos (Choclo) Monge. Choclo has made a lifetime contribution to our understanding of high altitude adaptation. In this chapter we shall focus primarily on the studies that originated in the Andes concercing glucose homeostasis and the effect of acute and chronic hypoxia in sea level man and constrast this to observations on Andean man born and resident for numerous generations at high altitude.

. Plasma Glucose and Prolonged Exercise at Sea Level

During sub-maximal exercise circulating concentrations of glucose remain relatively constant. This is due to the balance between peripheral glucose uptake by exercise muscle (RD) and the addition to the plasma glucose pool of glucose from hepatic glycogenolysis (RA). Thus, stability of the circulating glucose is dependent on a rather unique matching between glucose utilization and glucose production from the liver. When RA is greater than RD then circulating glucose concentrations will increase. This is often the case in high intensity and supramaximal exercise and results in hyperglycemia which is of no clinical consequence. By contrast when RD exceeds RA as with prolonged moderate intensity exercise it is possible that hypoglycemia will develop. In any situation where liver glycogenolysis is depleted *e.g.* with prolonged fasting, during exercise RD will often exceed RA and as a result hypoglycemia will occur. Interestingly enough if even lower intensity exercise is continued for a prolonged period *e.g.* 24 hours, plasma glucose tends to level off and shows no further decrease after the first 10 to 12 hours. This is due to the increase in gluconeogenesis. Although the initial signals to increasing hepatic glucose production are not fully understood it is thought that both the feed forward and feed back mechanism probably exist.

Levine and colleagues first reported hypoglycemia during the Boston Marathon (6) and Sutton and colleagues showed both a normal and elevated plasma glucose following a marathon. By contrast joggers entering fun runs could become hypoglycemic and this may lead to confusion in the diagnosis of those runners who collapse, many of whom are also hyperthermic. During prolonged laboratory exercise Felig and colleagues (4) demonstrated that hypoglycemia (plasma glucose less than 45 mg/100 ml) occurred frequently and furthermore the administration of oral glucose given to maintain plasma glucose at euglycemic levels did not effect the time to exhaustion. These observations were in contrast to the early work of Christiansen and Hansen who found that the administration of oral glucose did prolong time to exhaustion (3).

Hormonal Control Mechanisms

There is a redundancy of hormonal mechanisms involved in glucose homeostasis, Insulin, glucagon and the catecholamines: epinephrine, norepinephrine and the sympathetic system discharge are important in the acute responses to exercise. Cortisol and growth hormone are also important in glucose homeostasis but more so over a longer time frame (14). All these hormonal changes may be important in both acute and the chronic exposure to high altitude. Figure 1 demonstrates the intracellular and extracellular fuel sources during exercise, the fat and carbohydrate present in muscle and glucose being transported from the liver following hepatic glycogenalysis. Lipolysis in adipose tissue will result in the formation of glycerol and free fatty acids and in combination with albumin free fatty acids are transported to muscle. In this diagram the effects of catecholamines, glucagon and cortisol, all of which increase with exercise also increase hepatic glycogenolysis and adipose lipolysis are demonstrated. By contrast insulin will enhance muscle glucose uptake but inhibit both hepatic glycogenolysis and adipose tissue lipolysis. However, insulin usually decreases with exercise. Thus the integrated hormonal response to exercise is one which facilitates the increased availability of blood borne energy substrates.

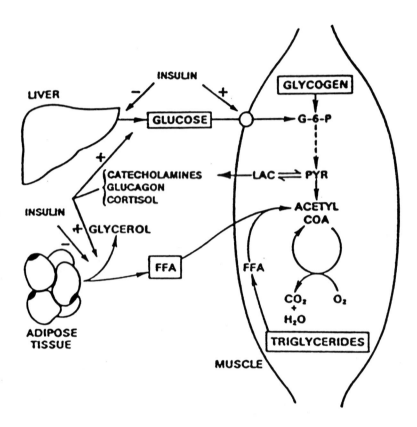

Fig. 1 - Intracellular and extracellular fueld source during exercise.

ACUTE HYPOXIA

With acute hypoxia at a simulated altitude of 4550 m (P_1O_2 83 mmHg) subjects of average fitness exercised for 20 minutes at 50% of their sea level VO_2 max and at altitude at abouth 80% of their VO_2 max. Plasma glucose showed a marked increase in concentration (10). This was seen in concert with similar increases in blood lactate and increases in free fatty acids but decreases in plasma insulin. Figure 2 summarised the effects of acute hypoxia on glucose and the hormonal responses to submaximal exercise. More recently on Pikes Peak similar changes in plasma glucose have been shown by Brooks and colleagues (1) and in that study tracers were used and it was demonstrated that the acute increase in plasma glucose was due to an increase in the appearance rate of glucose due one asumes to augmented hepatic glycogenolysis.

CHRONIC HYPOXIA IN SEA LEVEL DWELLERS

An additional study was performed on the sea level dwellers after they had spent three months above 4500 metres in the Cordillera Vilcabamba of Peru. The fasting resting glucose was only marginally lower to the previous

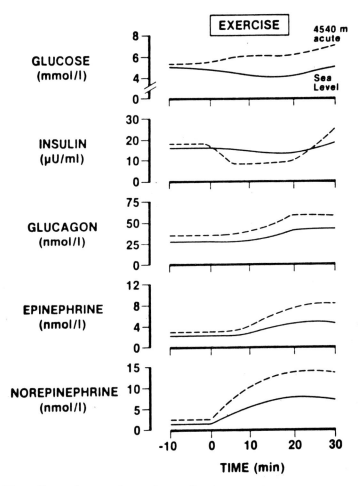

Fig. 2 - **The effect of acute hypoxia on the hormonal responses to submaximal exercise.**

findings at sea level. But the increase with exercise was greater. These findings are in somewhat of a contrast to the recent observations by Brooks *et al.* on Pikes Peak at 4300 metres (1). After 3 weeks at 4300 metres the resting plasma glucose concentration had fallen significantly from 85.8 to 70.8 mg/ 100 mls. With exercise the plasma concentration increased to 84.1 mg/ 100 ml but in no way reflected the more than twofold increase in exercise appearance rate (1).

GLUCOSE HOMEOSTASIS IN PERMANENT HIGH ALTITUDE RESIDENTS

It has been known for some time that plasma glucose is lower in high altitude dweller (HAD) than in their sea level counterparts. Picon-Reategui suggested there is a lower set point for glucose in the high altitude dweller (7). Plasma insulin and glucagon appeared to be normal and this suggested some change at the post receptive level. Plasma free fatty acid concentrations were normal (8) will increase (9) in the fasting state at rest but on exercise show a greater increase compared with sea level residents (2). The plasma glucose response to maximal exercise in sea level dwellers at sea level and after 3 months at or above 4540 m is seen in contrast with the permanent high altitude dwellers (Fig. 3)

PLASMA GLUCOSE AT ALTITUDE

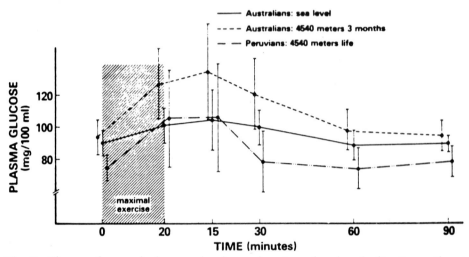

Fig. 3 - Plasma glucose during maximal exercise at sea level and after 3 months at or above 4540 m compared with high altitude permanent residents of Morococha (4540 m).

An additional intriguing finding by Garmendia and Sutton (11) in the Peruvians living at Morococha (4540 m) was the elevated growth hormone at rest. The physiological responsiveness of growth hormone to normal perterbation was further examined by exercise and (Fig. 4) the administration of an oral glucose load (Figure 5). This demonstrated that although the resting growth hormone was elevated as was the plasma free fatty acids in the high altitude dweller both were supressible with a glucose load. Furthermore, with maximal but not submaximal exercise there was a further increase in serum growth hormone concentrations. Thus, although growth hormone may be at a different set point in the high altitude residents it was suggested that it responded to the normal physiological regulators of exercise and glucose. It would therefore seem that the hypothalamic control of growth hormone secretion may well have a higher set point in the high altitude dweller when compard to his sea level counterpart (2). The prolonged elevation of serum growth hormone following maximal exercise is also intriguing and similar to previous findings at sea level in exhausted unfit or obese individuals (15). Such a finding could result from an increased pituitary release of the hormone, a delay in its metabolic clearance, or some combination of factors. The prolonged

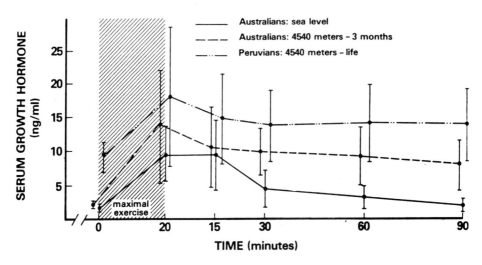

Fig. 4 - Serum growth hormone in response to maximal exercise at sea level, after 3 months at or above 4540 compared with high altitude permanent residents of Morococha (4540 m).

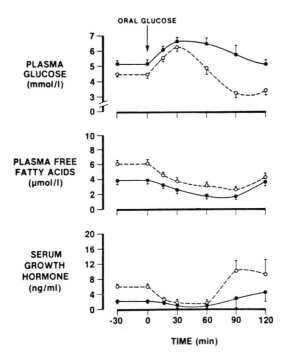

Fig. 5 - Plasma glucose and serum growth hormone response to an oral glucose load in permanent high altitude resident of Morococha (4540 m).

elevation following exercise could be due to a decreased metabolic clearance. For example, the elevation of testosterone (13) with exercise is due to a decrease in the metabolic clearance of the hormone, and not and an increased production.

An elevation in serum growth hormone may have some importance in a somatotrophic role, *i.e.* in maintaining organ hypertrophy of heart and lungs which is found in high altitude Peruvians. Alternatively, the elevated growth hormone may be important in a selective metabolic role. For instance, the elevated plasma FFA in the HAD could be the result of the result of the growth hormone which will mobilize FFA from adipose tissue to be used as the principal energy substrate under hypoxic conditions (5).

In summary, glucose concentrations are lower in the high altitude dweller but they may also lower in the sea level dweller chronically exposed to altitude for several weeks to months. This is not due to an impaired gluconeogenesis which was suggested by Capderou and colleagues studying the permanent altitude dwellers in Bolivia, more certainly in the sea level dweller exposed to high altitude it may be due to a preferential fatty acid oxidation. However, it has also become clear from the recent and detailed studies of Brooks and colleagues that in spite of the depressed plasma glucose concentration in the proloned exposure to altitude with the use of tracers they have shown that a very dynamic situation in glucose homeostasis exists. In these altitude dwellers the lower plasma glucose concentration belies a much augmented glucose kinetics with a dramatic increase in glucose appearance and disappearance rate but the net at rest and on exercise with the net result being a significant reduction in plasma glucose concentrations.

Finally the observation of elevated serum growth hormone in the high altitude permanent residents was demonstrated to be under normal physiological regulation.

REFERENCES

1. BROOKS, G.A., BUTTERFIELD, G.E., WOLFE, R.R., GROVES, B.M., MAZZEO, R.S., SUTTON, J.R., WOLFEL, E.E. & REEVES, J.T. 1991. Increased dependence on blood glucose after acclimatization to 4,300 m. *J. Appl. Physiol.* 70(2): 919-927.

2. CAPDEROU, A., POLIANSKI, J., MENSCH-DECHENE, J., DROUET, L., ANTEZANA, G., ZELTER, M. & LOCKHART, A. 1977. Splanchnic blood flow, O_2 consumption, removal of lactate, and output of glucose in highlanders. *J. Appl. Physiol: respirat environ exercise physiol* 43: 204-210.

3. CHRISTENSEN, E.H. & HANSEN, O. 1939. Arbeitsfahigkeit und ernahrung. *Scand. Arch. Physiol.* 81: 160-171.

4. FELIG, P., CHERIF, A., MINAGAWA, A. & WAHREN, J. 1982. Hypoglycemia during prolonged exercise in normal men. *N. Engl. J. Med.* 306: 895-900.

5. JONES, N.L., ROBERTSON, D.G., KANE, J.W. & HART, R.A. 1972. Effect of hypoxia on free fatty acid metabolism during exercise. *J. Appl. Physiol.* 33: 733.

6. LEVINE, S.A., GORDON, B. & DERICK, C.L. 1924. Some changes in the chemical constituents of the blood following a marathon race. *J. Amer. Med. Assoc.* 82: 1778-1779.

7. PICON-REATEGUI, E. 1963. Intravenous glucose tolerance test at sea level and at high altitudes. *J. Clin Endocrinol Metab.* 23: 1256-1261.

8. RAYNAUD, J., DROUET, J.P., MARTINEAUD, J.P., BORDACHAR, J., COUDERT, J. & DURAND, J. 1981. Time course of plasma growth hormone during exercise in humans at altitude. *J. Appl. Physiol: Respirat environ exercise physiol.* 50: 229-233.

9. STOCK, M.J., CHAPMAHN, J.L., STIRLING, J.L. & CAMPBELL, I.J. 1978. Effects of exercise, altitude and food on blood hormone and metabolic levels. *J. Appl. Physiol: respirat environ exercise physiol* 45: 350-354.

10. SUTTON, J.R. 1977. Effect to acute hypoxia on the hormone response to exercise. *J. Appl. Physiol.* 42: 587.

11. SUTTON, J.R. & GARMENDIA, F. 1982. Hormonal responses to exercise at altitude in sea level and mountain man. *In*: W. Brendel & R.A. Zink (eds), *High altitude physiology and medicine.* New York: Springer-Verlag: 165-171.

12. SUTTON, J.R., COLEMAN, M.J., MILLAR, A.P., LAZARUS, L. & RUSSO, P. 1972. The medical problems of mass participation in athletic competition. the «City to Surf» Race. *Med J. Aust.* 2: 127-133.

13. SUTTON, J.R., COLEMAN, M.J. & CASEY, J.H. 1978. Testosterone production rate during exercise. *In*: F. Landry & WAR Orban (eds), 3rd *International symposium on biochemistry of exercise.* Miami Fl: Symposia specialist Inc: 227-234.

14. SUTTON, J.R., FARRELL, P.A. & HARBER, V.J. 1989. Hormonal adaptation to physical activity. *In*: C. Bouchard, B. McPherson, R.J. Shepherd, T. Stephens & J.R. Sutton (eds), *Exercise, Fitness and Health. Champaign*, Illinois: Human Kinetics: 217-259.

15. SUTTON, J.R., YOUNG, J.D., LAZARUS, L., HICHIE, J.B. & MAKSVYTIS, J. 1969. The hormonal response to physical exercise. *Aust Ann Med.* 18: 84-90.

AVIAN EMBRYONIC RESPONSES TO HYPOXIA: DIFFERENCES BETWEEN DOMESTICATED CHICKEN AND WILD BIRD EMBRYOS

Cynthia Carey

Abstract

Responses of chicken embryos to hypoxia have received a great deal of study, while characteristics of embryos of wild birds at high altitudes have received relatively little attention. Chicken embryos have relatively poor tolerance to hypoxia; embryos of most wild birds studied to date develop normally in gaseous conditions that would be lethal for chicken embryos. Most responses of chicken embryos to hypoxia are in the same direction as, but fall short of, those of wild avian embryos. While use of chicken embryos is useful for developing methods and for understanding how an organism ill-equipped to deal with hypoxia functions in acute or chronic hypoxic conditions, study of embryos of wild birds adapted to high altitude provides a more complete picture of the wealth of mechanisms that avian embryos use for coping with hypoxia.

Key words: Hypoxia, barometric pressure, avian embryo, oxygen consumption, hematocrit, chorioallantoic membrane, gas exchange, blood gas tensions, citrate synthase.

Resumen

Las respuestas a la hipoxia del embrión de pollo han sido bien estudiados mientras que las características de los embriones de aves silvestres de la altura no lo han sido tanto. Los embriones de pollo tienen una tolerancia relativamente baja a la hipoxia; los embriones de la mayor parte de aves silvestres hasta ahora estudiadas se desarrollan normalmente en gases que serían letales para embriones de pollo. Las respuestas a la hipoxia en el embrión de pollo van en la misma dirección -aunque sin llegar- que las de los embriones de aves silvestres. Mientras que el uso del embrión de pollo es útil para el desarrollo de metodologías y para el conocimiento de cómo un organismo pobremente equipado funciona en condiciones de hipoxia aguda o crónica, el estudio de aves silvestres adaptadas a la altura nos da una visión más completa de la riqueza de mecanismos que usan los embriones de aves para manejar la hipoxia.

Palabras claves: Hipoxia, presión barométrica, embrión de aves, consumo de oxígeno, hematocrita. membrana chorioalantoidea, intercambio gaseoso, presiones gaseosas en la sangre, citrato sintetasa.

Résumé

   Les réactions physiologiques de l'embryon de poulet à l'hypoxie ont été très bien étudiées, tandis que l'étude des caractéristiques des embryons d'oiseaux d'altitude a retenu relativement peu l'attention. Les embryons de poulets ont une tolérance assez basse à l'hypoxie; les embryons de la plupart des oiseaux sauvages étudiés jusqu'à présent se développent normalement dans des conditions atmosphériques qui seraient considérées comme létales pour des embryons de poulet. La plupart des réactions à l'hypoxie chez l'embryon de poulet vont dans le même sens - bien que de façon limitée - que ceux des embryons d'oiseaux sauvages d'altitude.

   Tandis que l'utilisation de l'embryon de poulet est utile pour le développement de méthodologies et pour la connaissance du fonctionnement d'un organisme pauvrement équipé pour l'hypoxie quand celle-ci est aiguë ou chronique, l'étude des oiseaux sauvages adaptés à l'altitude permet une vision plus complète de la richesse des mécanismes utilisés par les embryons pour lutter contre l'hypoxie.

Mots clés : Hypoxie, pression barométrique, embryon d'oiseaux, consommation d'oxygène, hématocrite, membrane allantochoriale, échange gazeux, pressions gazeuses dans le sang, citrate synthase.

INTRODUCTION

   In this tribute to Dr. Carlos Monge-C., I would first like to salute his important contributions to the field of high altitude physiology and to thank him for all he taught me. In this paper, I would like to present a synopsis of current information relating to a concept that I believe has been important to Dr. Monge and has been illustrated in his work. The concept is that the most useful information concerning mechanisms by which animals adjust to an environmental hazard, such as hypoxia, is obtained by studying wild animals that have lived for generations with the hazard, rather than by studying acute or chronic responses of domesticated animals or other animals that have had minimal exposure to the environmental factor in their evolutionary history. My goal in this paper is to illustrate this concept by comparing responses to hypoxia of chicken embryos *(Gallus domesticus)* to characteristics of embryonic wild birds which experience not only hypoxia but also other unusual gaseous conditions during incubation. Data on embryos of wild birds are gathered mainly from studies by Dr. Monge in collaboration with Fabiola León-Velarde, other co-workers from his *Laboratorio de Biofísica*, and myself (25, 24).

BACKGROUND

   Since birds breed in a remarkable diversity of habitats, avian eggshell structure and embryonic physiology serve as excellent tools for identifying key patterns of adaptation to hazardous environments. Although adult behavior can protect avian eggs from thermal extremes and predators, avian embryos are more exposed to variation of the physical environment than are those of viviparous vertebrates. Further, avian eggs are unique in vertebrate reproduction since they exchange gases, but not solids or liquids (with the exception of eggs of a few species laid in contact with liquid water (35), with the environment (40). And since gases are exchanged between avian embryos and their environment principally by the process of diffusion, rather than by convection as used by adult birds and mammals (40, 41), avian eggs can be used to understand how diffusive respiratory systems can be modified in diverse environments.

The gradual reduction in barometric pressure with increasing elevation in montane habitats provides an environmental gradient that poses progressively severe problems for gas exchange. Since wild birds are known to breed successfully in montane areas extending to at least 4900 and 6500 m in the Andes and Himalayas, respectively (29), and since biogeographers believe that many avian species have moved up and down altitudinal gradients throughout their evolutionary history due to competition, predation, or availability of new habitats as mountain ranges were created (21), avian eggs have most certainly been shaped by selection from geographically variable aspects of the physical environment. Furthermore, since embryos of species breeding naturally in high montane areas may be exposed to some of the most extreme hypoxic conditions that vertebrates may naturally encounter, they can provide information about mechanisms of adjustment to hypoxia that may be unique in vertebrates.

Therefore, it would seem logical that responses of avian embryos to hypoxia would be most appropriately studied with eggs from wild montane species. However, a number of potentially troublesome problems confront investigators who attempt to study eggs of wild birds. First, most populations of birds, even those breeding near the equator (16) breed seasonally, rather than continuously. Therefore, eggs are not necessarily available on a year-round basis and investigators have to coordinate their research with breeding schedules that may vary each year according to rainfall and/or snow melt patterns. Travel and working conditions at high altitudes may pose logistical barriers. Nests can be hard to find, the age of eggs difficult to determine, and sample sizes may be small. Furthermore, since low barometric pressure can exert a variety of direct and indirect effects, it is difficult in some cases to know *exactly* which physical factor served as the selective agent. Finally, characteristics of eggs laid at high altitude should ideally be compared to those of conspecific populations breeding at lower altitudes. Unfortunately, very few species breed over entire altitudinal gradients of high mountain ranges, such as the Andes or Himalayas. For instance, the rufous-collared sparrow (*Zonotrichia capensis*) is the only species breeding at all elevations from sea level to over 4800 m in the Peruvian Andes (27; Carey *et al.*, unpubl. observations). A few other species, such as American coots (*Fulica americana peruviana*), breed both at sea level and in the puna (the high, dry grassland habitat above 3400 m in the Peruvian Andes), but not at intermediate altitudes (27). The most common pattern is that species breed either just at lower altitudes or just at higher altitudes: red-winged blackbirds (*Agelaius phoenicius*) breed from sea level to a moderate altitudinal limit (3050 m; 6) and Puna teal (*Anas versicolor puna*), Andean gulls (*Larus serranus*) and Himalayan monal (*Lophophorus impejanus*) do not breed breed at altitudes below 3500 m (27, 18). Termination of breeding at moderate altitudes by low altitude species is not necessarily due to any physiological problem related to low barometric pressure or hypoxia; it may be due to persistence of snow cover into the breeding season, lack of food, or absence of suitable vegetation or other requirements for nest-building.

For these and other reasons, few studies have been done on wild birds. Numerous investigators (see partial listing in Reference section) have chosen chicken embryos for testing responses of avian embryos to incubation in conditions of chronic (for the duration of the incubation period) or acute (for a period of hours) hypoxia. Use of chicken eggs for studying these responses has, of course, a number of benefits: large sample sizes of known-aged eggs are available at all times of the year. Travel and logistical problems are minimized since studies can be conducted in any laboratory with a barometric pressure chamber or a supply of hypoxic gas. Taken as a whole, the results of these studies indicate that domestic chicken embryos are remarkably sensitive to hypoxia (23). Hatchability of chicken eggs is decreased 10% at 305 m, 20% at 610 m, and 32% at 2346 m relative to sea level (15, 14). Commercial breeds in the United States rarely hatch at all above 3000 m (23). Acclimatization of stock to high altitude produces only modest improvements in hatchability: hatchability of eggs of sea level stock transported to 3229 m was only 3%; this value increased to 42% after 12 generations (33). Eggs produced by descendants of the Castillian chickens introduced to the Andes by the Spaniards about 400 years ago exhibit only about 50% hatchability at 3000 m (20) . In contrast, hatchability of eggs laid by wild species between 3000 and 4400 m appears to be above 90% (4, 7, 9; unpubl. observations).

In comparing responses to hypoxia of embryonic wild birds with those of domestic chicken embryos, it is important to remember that some differences between the two groups are likely to exist because one is comparing characteristics of species which have evolved at high altitude for centuries, if not thousands of years, to acute and chronic responses of chicken embryos. No studies of which I am aware have tested wild bird embryos under conditions of acute or chronic hypoxia, and the «recent» creation of *Gallus domesticus* by human selection, coupled with the sensitivity of this group to hypoxia, means that no high altitude populations of *Gallus domesticus* have had the equivalent amount of time at high altitudes to evolve as have wild birds. Although small numbers of *Gallus gallus* and *Gallus inauris* exist in the Himalayas and Andes, respectively, and may have evolved in these locations for centuries (31; Wilhem, in 20), information on their eggs and embryos is inadequate to determine how their characteristics compare with those of *Gallus domesticus* and whether their characteristics would accurately reflect those of *Gallus domesticus* if populations of this latter species had had the same evolutionary time at high altitude as other avian species in those mountain ranges. Additionally, differences between the two groups may also exist because hypoxia is usually the only experimental variable in tests with chicken embryos, whereas eggshells and embryos of wild birds have undoubtedly evolved in response to more than one selective pressure in the montane environment. Furthermore, it must not be assumed that all characteristics of montane embryos are genotypic just because the species have had evolutionary time with which to adjust to the high altitude environment. As we shall see below, some characteristics of wild embryos are phenotypic and readily modifiable upon exposure to lowland environments.

In light of their apparent sensitivity to hypoxia, it is appropriate to evaluate to what extent domesticated chicken embryos exposed to chronic or acute hypoxia provide an adequate model for completely and accurately understanding the mechanisms by which all avian embryos cope with hypoxia and whether data gathered on hypoxic chicken embryos can be assumed to represent the characteristics of species that have evolved at high altitudes. It is not known exactly why hatchability of chicken embryos decreases with altitude. While several theories have been advanced (23), most studies point to problems of gas exchange (39). In order to understand how gas exchange of avian embryos is influenced by barometric pressure, I would like to digress briefly to explain several principles before proceeding to a comparison of characteristics of chicken and wild bird embryos.

GAS EXCHANGE OF AVIAN EMBRYOS AT HIGH ALTITUDE

Avian embryos exchange O_2, CO_2, and water vapor between the atmosphere and the interior of the shell. Oxygen diffuses through minute pores in the shell into the egg down a concentration gradient established by the metabolism of the embryo, whereas CO_2 and water vapor travel out of the shell through these same pores down partial pressure gradients set up by the CO_2 production of the embryo and the humidity of the interior of the egg and the nest environment, respectively (40). Factors which govern the rate of diffusion of each of these gases have been described by a modification of the Fick equation (40, 42). Oxygen diffuses through the shell, through two shell membranes and the chorioallantoic membrane, and then into the blood from which it ultimately diffuses into the tissues. Estimates are that about 1/3 of the resistance to diffusion of O_2 from atmosphere to the blood exists in the shell and outer shell membrane, whereas about 2/3 of the resistance resides in the «inner barrier» comprised of the inner shell membrane and chorioallantoic membrane (28). Key points at which adjustments to hypoxia might occur are: shell conductance to oxygen, resistance of the inner barrier to O_2 diffusion, vascularity of the chorioallantoic membrane, oxygen capacity of the blood, oxygen affinity of hemoglobin for oxygen as affected by intracellular organic phosphates and hemoglobin structure, rate of blood flow and variation in distribution of blood, mitochondrial structure and function, and other cellular and biochemical parameters. I would like to review some of the existing evidence available on these subjects. In most cases, data are available for both chicken and embryos of wild species, but in others, data are available for only one group.

COMPARISON OF CHICKEN AND WILD BIRD EMBRYOS
Eggshell Conductances

Rahn and Ar (30) were the first to realize that eggshells of eggs transported to high altitude had a higher conductance to gases than at sea level. This effect could benefit the embryo by increasing flux of O_2 inward into the egg, thus in part offsetting the decrease in ambient P_{O2} (39), it would also increase rates water vapor and CO_2 losses. Therefore, the shell structure of both domesticated and wild birds breeding at altitude has been under selection from mutually antagonistic forces: the shell must minimize water and CO_2 losses while affording diffusion of sufficient O_2 to support growth and maintenance costs. There is space in this review to mention only that the adjustments in shell structure made by chickens laying at 3800 m in the White Mountains, *Gallus gallus* at 3500 m in the Himalayas, and Castillian chickens at 3900 m in the Peruvian Andes are similar to those made by wild birds laying at similar altitudes (24, 5).

Metabolism and Growth

Even in normoxic conditions, chicken embryos in the later stages of incubation are thought to be oxygen-limited and to receive insufficient O_2 to support metabolism and growth because they have outgrown the diffusing capacity of the shell for O_2 (22, 38). Incubation in hyperoxic conditions results in larger embryos and higher metabolic rates than in normoxia (39, 22, 36). Oxygen consumption (VO_2) of chicken embryos acutely exposed to any PIO_2 less than 149 torr is invariably lower than those of controls (39, 38). For instance, CO_2 production of 16-19 day embryos exposed to PIO_2 of 89.8 torr for 4 hours was reduced to 69% of control values (39). If eggs were exposed to an identical PIO_2 (90 torr) by either exposing the eggs to reduced fractional O_2 composition or to low barometric pressure, the VO_2 of the embryos at low barometric pressure was higher than that of the embryos exposed to a lower fractional O_2 content (420 and 264 ml.day-1, respectively) because of the effect of barometric pressure on increasing gas conductance of the shell (39). Reduction of the shell surface area by 25-50% by covering it with a material that is relatively impermeable to gases caused a significant reduction in embryonic weight by day 18 (37, 22). Oxygen consumption of chicken stock acclimatized to 3800 m for at least 15 years was reduced to 58% of sea level eggs at an equivalent age, growth rates were reduced, and hatching masses were smaller, and incubation periods prolonged compared to sea level values (41).

While embryos of two species have exhibited depressed VO_2 at altitude (coot and Andean gull embryos at 4150 and 4650 m, respectively; 8; León-Velarde *et al.*, unpubl. data) and incubation periods of coot eggs at 4150 m are probably prolonged beyond the lowland average (8), most data on montane species available to date indicate no effect of hypoxia or barometric pressure on metabolism, growth, or development. Incubation periods and hatchling masses of red-winged blackbirds, white-crowned sparrows (*Zonotrichia leucophrys oriantha*) and horned larks (*Eremophila alpestris*) did not vary significantly between sea level and 2900, 3475, and 3600 m, respectively (12). Oxygen consumption of red-winged blackbird embryos did not vary significantly over a 2900 m altitudinal gradient, and the slope of the regression line defining the relation between VO_2 and embryonic mass of Puna teal embryos at 4150 m was steeper (0.72) than even that of lowland coot embryos (0.54) of equivalent size (12, 10, 11). Oxygen consumption of white-tailed ptarmigan embryos (*Lagopus leucurus*) measured at 4300 m did not differ significantly from those of embryos of the same species which had been incubated at 1600 m for at least the last half of incubation (Carey & Martin, unpubl. data).

Hematocrits

Chicken embryos exposed to hypoxia produce more red blood cells than controls 3, 37). The hemopoietic response of chicken embryos to hypoxia does not appear to be improved by years of acclimatization of their stock to high altitude, since the hematocrit of day 20 embryos (40.0%) from stock maintained at 3800 m for at least 14 years (3) was similar to the hematocrits (40.7%) obtained from similarly-aged embryos from lowland stock subjected to restricted oxygen flux through the shell (37).

Hematocrits of Puna teal, coot and white-tailed ptarmigan embryos incubated naturally at 4150, 4150 and 3775-4100 m, respectively, are higher (40-45%) than any published value for avian embryos, including embryos of bar-headed geese (*Anser indicus*) acclimated to 1500 m for years (34). While blood properties of hypoxic chicken embryos do not rise above control levels until 1-2 days prior to hatching (3, 37), hematocrits of montane coot and ptarmigan embryos are significantly above lowland levels for most of incubation (10, Carey and Martin, unpubl. data). Hematocrits of montane and lowland ptarmigan ultimately match just before hatching (Carey and Martin, unpubl. data). The high hematocrit of white-tailed ptarmigan embryos is reversible: values fall to levels equivalent to those of lowland willow ptarmigan embryos (*Lagopus lagopus*) of equivalent size if eggs are incubated at 1600 m for at least 1 week (Carey and Martin, unpubl. data).

Hemoglobin

Hypoxia induces chicken embryos to replace embryonic hemoglobin with adult hemoglobin at a faster rate than do normoxic embryos (2). No comparable data are available from embryos of wild species. Adults of several species that fly at very high altitudes have been found to have amino acid compositions of hemoglobin that differ by at least several amino acids from those of lowland birds (17). Electrophoretic mobility of hemoglobin, a method which will not detect differences in neutral amino acids content, of montane white-tailed ptarmigan embryos does not differ from that of their lowland relatives, willow ptarmigan (*Lagopus lagopus;* Carey and Martin, unpubl. data).

Chorioallantoic Membrane

Chicken embryos incubated in chronic hypoxia increase the number of arterioles and venules in the membrane (13). While only preliminary data are available on wild birds, it appears that chorioallantoic membranes of Andean gull embryos incubated at 4650 m are thicker, have a thicker capillary plexus, and are more vascularized than similarly-sized lowland coot and willow ptarmigan embryos (Carey *et al.*, unpubl. data). Approximately 50% of the total blood flow in normoxic chicken embryos is estimated to be contained in the chorioallantoic membrane, vein and artery at any given time (32), but blood flow distribution was altered when 16-day old chicken embryos were subjected to hypoxia (Ar, unpubl. data). Using a hydrogen washout, non-invasive technique, Ar showed that chorioallantoic blood flow was maintained at a relatively higher level per unit oxygen uptake than in normoxia. While data on blood distribution of wild birds are not yet available, the increase in chorioallantoic vascularity at high altitude could foster either a greater degree of blood shunting to the membrane or a higher total blood volume. On a further note regarding blood flow, heart rate of chicken embryos exposed to hypoxia decreased relative to normoxic embryos at the same developmental stage (18). Heart rate of white-tailed ptarmigan embryos naturally incubated at 3600-4100 m was significantly higher than those of white-tailed ptarmigan embryos that had been incubated at 1600 m for the last half of incubation (Carey *et al.*, unpubl. data).

Preliminary data show that the increased numbers of venules and arterioles in the chorioallantoic membrane of white-tailed ptarmigan embryos incubated between 3600-4100 m relative to those of willow ptarmigan embryos incubated at 750 m is a phenotypic, rather than genetic characteristic. The increase does not occur if white-tailed ptarmigan embryos are incubated at 1600 m for the last two weeks of incubation (Carey *et al.*, unpubl. data).

Citrate Synthase

No data on this enzymatic marker of cellular aerobic capacity exist on chicken embryos, as far as I know. While Leon-Velarde *et al.* (in press) found no significant differences in activities of hexokinase, hydroxy-acyl dehydrogenase, or citrate synthase between montane and lowland adult coots, citrate synthase in heart and pectoralis muscle of white-tailed ptarmigan embryos from 3600-4100 m were significantly than those of lowland willow ptarmigan embryos during the last half of incubation (Carey *et al.*, unpubl. data). This relative increase is clearly also phenotypic, rather than genetic, since the difference failed to appear in the latter stages of incubation if white-tailed ptarmigan embryos were incubated at 1600 m for two weeks, or was reversible if an older embryo was removed from the montane nest and was incubated at 1600 m for at least a week (Carey *et al.*, unpubl. data).

Importance of phenotypic adjustments to altitude

When white-tailed ptarmigan embryos were incubated at 1600 m for two weeks starting early in incubation, they failed to develop the higher hematocrit and citrate synthase levels characteristic of their siblings incubated normally at 3600-4100 m (Carey & Martin, unpubl data). Data are too preliminary to determine if they also failed to exhibit blood concentrations of 2,3 DPG or chorioallantoic membrane vascularity changes similar to those of their montane siblings. When oxygen consumption of the embryos incubated at 1600 m was measured at 1600 m and then at 4300 m on the same day, VO_2 of the embryos at 4300 m was about 50% of the value at 1600 m, with each embryo used as its own comparison (Carey *et al.*, unpubl. data). These results do not prove that hematocrit or citrate synthase levels were solely responsible for, or even involved in, the inability of the transferred embryos to maintain the same oxygen consumption at 4300 m that they had at 1600 m, because many other phenotypic adjustments on the organ, tissue, and cellular level are certainly essential for maintaining VO_2 at high altitude. But they do suggest that a suite of adjustments, some of which are phenotypic, others of which may prove to be genetic especially at higher altitudes, have been developed by wild birds breeding at high altitude, that are truly beneficial and necessary for supplying and utilizing oxygen at normal levels.

CONCLUSION

Other than heart rate, the adjustments of chicken embryos to hypoxia differ from characteristics of wild avian embryo only in degree, rather than direction. Even so, it is important that research on wild avian embryos be encouraged, despite the difficulties, so that the full range of possible adaptations of avian embryos to hypoxia may be described.

ACKNOWLEDGEMENTS

Research described herein of C. Carey and colleagues was supported by National Geographic Society Grants 2863-84, 3254-86, 3736-88, and 4489-91. Support for the writing of this review was provided by National Science Foundation Grant IBN-9201396.

REFERENCES

1. AR, A., PAGANELLI, C.V., REEVES, R.B., GREENE, D.B. & RAHN, H. 1974. The avian egg: water vapor conductance, shell thickness and functional pore area. *Condor* 76:153-158.

2. BAUMANN, R., PADEKEN, S., HALLER, E.S. & BRILMAYER, T. 1983. Effects of hypoxia on oxygen affinity, hemoglobin pattern, and blood volume of early chicken embryos. *Amer J Physiol* 244: R733-R741.

3. BURTON, R.R. & SMITH, A.H. 1969. Induction of cardiac hypertrophy and polycythemia in the developing chick at high altitude. *Fed Proce* 28: 1170-1177.

4. CAREY, C. 1991. Respiration of avian embryos at high altitudes. *Acta XX Congressus Internationalis Ornithologici.* Wellington: New Zealand Ornithological Congress Trust Board: 265-278.

5. CAREY, C. 1986. Tolerance of variation in eggshell conductance, water loss, and water content by red-winged blackbird embryos. *Physiol Zool* 59:109-122.

6. CAREY, C., GARBER, S.D., THOMPSON, E.L. & JAMES, F.C. 1983. Avian reproduction over an altitudinal gradient. II. Physical characteristics and water loss of eggs. *Physiol Zool* 56: 340-352.

7. CAREY, C., LEÓN-VELARDE, F., CASTRO, G. & MONGE, C. 1987. Shell conductance, daily water loss, and water content of Andean gull and Puna ibis eggs. *J Exper Zool [Supplement* 1]: 247-252.

8. CAREY, C., LEÓN-VELARDE, F., DUNIN-BORKOWSKI, O., BUCHER, T.L., DE LA TORRE, G., ESPINOZA, D. & MONGE, C. 1989a. Variation in eggshell characteristics and gas exchange of montane and lowland coot eggs. *J Comp Physiol B* 159: 389-400.

9. CAREY, C., , DUNIN-BORKOWSKI, & MONGE, C. 1989b. Shell conductance, daily water loss, and water content of Puna teal eggs. *Physiol Zool* 62: 83-95.

10. CAREY, C., DUNIN-BORKOWSKI, O., LEÓN-VELARDE, F., ESPINOZA, D. & MONGE, C. 1993a. Blood gases, pH and hematology of montane and lowland coot embryos. *Respir Physiol* (In press).

11. CAREY, C., DUNIN-BORKOWSKI, O., LEÓN-VELARDE, F., ESPINOZA, D. & MONGE, C. 1993b. Gas exchange and blood gases of Puna teal embryos in the Peruvian Andes (In press).

12. CAREY, C., THOMPSON, E.L., VLECK, C.M. & JAMES, F.C. 1982. Avian reproduction over an altitudinal gradient: incubation period, hatchling mass, and embryonic oxygen consumption. *Auk* 99: 710-718.

13. DUSSEAU, J.W. & HUTCHINS, P.M. 1989. Microvascular responses to chronic hypoxia by the chick chorioallantoic membranes: a morphometric analysis. *Microvasc Research* 37: 138-147.

14. FRANCIS, D.W. 1972. Effects of atmospheric stresses on the performance of poultry. *New Mexico Agricultural Experiment Station Bulletin* 601: 56.

15. FRANCIS, D.W., BERNIER, P.E. & HUTTO, D.C. 1967. The effect of altitude on the hatchability of chicken eggs. *Poultry Science* 46: 1384-1389.

16. HARRIS, M.P. 1981. The waterbirds of Lake Junin, central Peru. *Waterfowl* 32: 137-145.

17. HIEBL, I., SCHNEEGANSS, D. & BRAUNITZER, G. 1987. High-altitude respiration of birds. The primary structures of the major and minor hemoglobin-components of adult Andean goose (*Ckhloephaga melanoptera*, Anatidae): the mutation Leu-Ser in position 55 of the b-chains. *Biol Chem Hoppe-Seyler* 368: 1559-1569.

18. INSKIPP, C. & INSKIPP, T. 1991. *A Guide to the Birds of Nepal.* Washington, D.C.: Smithsonian Institution Press; pp.1-400.

19. LAUGHLIN, K. F. 1978. The effects of restricted gas exchange on embryonic heart rate. *in:* J. Piiper (ed.), *Respiratory Function in Birds, Adult and Embryonic.* Berlin: Springer-Verlag: 298-303.

20. LEÓN-VELARDE, F., WHITTEMBURY, J., CAREY, C. & MONGE, C. 1984. Permeability of eggshells of native chickens in the Peruvian Andes. *In:* R. Seymour (ed.), *Respiration and Metabolism of Embryonic Vertebrates.* Dordrecht: Dr. W. Junk Publishers: 245-257.

21. MAYR, E. & DIAMOND, J.M. 1976. Birds on islands in the sky: Origin of the montane avifauna of Northern Melanesia. *Proc Nat Acad Sc USA:* 73:1765-1769.

22. METCALFE, J., STOCK, M.K. & INGERMANN, R.L. 1984. The effect of oxygen on growth and development of the chick embryo. *In:* R.S. Seymour (ed.), *Respiration and Metabolism of Embryonic Vertebrates.* Dordrecht: Dr. W. Junk: 205-219.

23. MORENG, R.E. 1983. Incubation and growth of fowls and turkeys in high altitude environments. *World Poultry Science Association Journal* 39: 47-51.

24. MONGE, C. & LEÓN-VELARDE, F. 1991. Physiological adaptation to high altitude: oxygen transport in mammals and birds. *Physiol Rev* 71: 1135-1172.

25. MONGE, C., LEÓN-VELARDE, F. & GÓMEZ DE LA TORRE, G. 1988. Laying eggs at high altitude. *News in Physiological Science* 3: 69-71.

26. PAGANELLI, C.V., AR., A., RAHN, H. & WANGENSTEEN, O.D. 1975. Diffusion in the gas phase: the effects of ambient pressure and gas composition. *Respir Physiol* 25: 247-258.

27. PARKER, T.A., PARKER, S. A. & PLENGE, M. A. 1982. *An Annotated Checklist of Peruvian Birds.* Buteo Books, Vermillion, South Dakota.

28. PIIPER, J., TAZAWA, H., AR, A. & RAHN, H. 1980. Analysis of chorioallantoic gas exchange in the chick embryo. *Resp Physiol* 39:2

29. RAHN, H. 1977. Adaptation of the avian embryo to altitude: the role of gas diffusion through the egg shell. *In:* A. S. Paintal & P. Gill-Kimar (eds.), *Respiratory Adaptations, Capillary Exchange, and Reflex Mechanisms.* Delhi: Vallabhbhai Patel Chest Institute, University of Delhi: 94-105.

30. RAHN, H. & AR, A. 1974. The avian egg: incubation time and water loss. *Condor* 76:147-152.

31. RAHN, H., CAREY, C., BALMAS, K., BHATIA, B. & PAGANELLI, C.V. 1977. Reduction of pore area of the avian eggshell as an adaptation to altitude. *Proc Nat Acad Sc USA* 74: 3095-3098.

32. RAHN, H., MATALON, S. & SOTHERLAND, P.R. 1985. Circulatory changes and oxygen delivery in the chick embryo prior to hatching. *In:* K. Johansen & W. W. Burggren (eds.), *Cardiovascular shunts, Alfred Benzon Symposium 21.* Copenhagen: Munksgaard: 179-198.

33. SMITH, A.H., ABPLANALP, H., HARWOOD, L.M. & KELLEY, C.F. 1959. Poultry at high altitudes. *California Agriculture* 13: 8-16.

34. SNYDER, G.K., BLACK, C. P., BIRCHARD, G. F. & LUCICH, R. 1982. Respiratory properties of blood from embryos of highland vs. lowland geese. *J Appl Physiol* 53: 1432-1438.

35. SOTHERLAND, P.R., ASHEN, M.D., SHUMAN, R.D. & TRACY, C.R. 1984. The water balance of bird eggs incubated in water. *Physiol Zool* 57: 338-348.

36. STOCK, M.K. & METCALFE, J. 1987. Modulation of growth and metabolism of the chick embryo by a brief (72-hour) change in oxygen availability. *J Exper Zool* [Suppl. 1]: 351-356.

37. TAZAWA, H., MIKAMI, T. & YASHIMOTO, C. 1971. Effect of reducing the shell area on the respiratory properties of chicken embryonic blood. *Respir Physiol* 13: 352-360.

38. TAZAWA, H., HASHIMOTO, Y., NAKAZAWA, S. & WHITTOW, G.C. 1992. Metabolic responses of chicken embryos and hatchlings to altered O_2 environments. *Respir Physiol* 88: 37-50.

39. VISSCHEDIJK, A.H.J., AR, A., RAHN, H. & PIIPER, J. 1980. The independent effects of atmospheric pressure and oxygen partial pressure on gas exchange of the chicken embryo. *Respir Physiol* 39: 33-44.

40. WANGENSTEEN, O.D. & RAHN, H. 1970-1971. Respiratory gas exchange by the avian embryo. *Respiration Physiology* 11: 31-45.

41. WANGENSTEEN, O.D., RAHN, H., BURTON, R.R. & SMITH, A.H. 1974. Respiratory gas exchange of high altitude chick embryos. *Respir Physiol* 11: 61-70..

42. WANGENSTEEN, O.D., WILSON, D. & RAHN, H. 1970-1971. Diffusion of gases across the shell of the hen's egg. *Respir Physiol* 11: 16-20.

THE MONGE LEGACY: LEARNING FROM HYPOXIA ADAPTED ANIMALS AND MAN

Peter W. Hochachka

Abstract

Three themes interweave through the literature on animal studies of hypoxia defense mechanisms. The first assumes that hypoxia is a survivable stress and gains most of its insights from studies of hypoxia (even anoxia) tolerant species. The second theme aims at protecting or reversing the effects of oxygen limitation and its data base arises largely from research on hypoxia sensitive systems. A third, more recently developing theme is to be found at the interface of these two quite distinct approaches and its main goal is the management and manipulation of hypoxia defense mechanisms found in hypoxia tolerant systems, in order to supply intervention guidelines for the clinical research community. Currently, four well described such hypoxia defense strategies are (i) the use of functionally advantageous metabolic pathways, (ii) the suppression of metabolism coordinately with suppression of energy demand, (iii) the maintenance of coupled metabolism-membrane functions, and (iv) the maintenance of conditions allowing for subsequent recovery. This paper systematically (i) reviews the potential for effective transfer to more hypoxia sensitive systems of each of these kinds of defenses and (ii) evaluates each in terms of its current usefulness for design of intervention strategies.

Key words: Hypoxia defense, hypobaric metabolism, hypoxia adaptation.

Resumen

Existen tres temas que se interrelacionan en la literatura sobre los mecanismos de defensa de animales sometidos a hipoxia. El primero asume que la hipoxia es una presión ambiental sobrevivible y llega a muchas de sus conclusiones a partir de estudios en animales tolerantes a la hipoxia (incluso la anoxia). El segundo tema tiene como objetivo la protección o reversión de los efectos de la limitación de oxígeno y su base de datos surge de las investigaciones realizadas en sistemas sensibles a la hipoxia. Un tercer tema, de reciente desarrollo, se encuentra en la interfase de estas dos distintas aproximaciones y su objetivo principal es el manejo y manipulación de los mecanismos de defensa contra la hipoxia que poseen los sistemas tolerantes a la hipoxia, de manera tal de producir líneas de intervención para la comunidad de investigación clínica. En la actualidad se describen cuatro estrategias de defensa contra la hipoxia: (i) el uso de vías metabólicas funcionalmente ventajosas, (ii) la supresión del metabolismo de manera coordinada con la supresión de la demanda de energía, (iii) el mantenimiento de las funciones acopladas de metabolismo-membrana, y (iv) el mantenimiento de condiciones que permitan la recuperación subsecuente.

Este trabajo sistemáticamente (i) revisa el potencial para la transferencia efectiva de estos tipos de defensa a sistemas sensibles a la hipoxia y (ii) evalúa cada uno de ellos en términos de su utilidad para el diseño de estrategias de intervención.

Palabras claves: Defensa contra la hipoxia, metabolismo hipobárico, adaptación a la hipoxia.

Résumé

Trois thèmes sont en interelation dans la littérature sur les mécanismes de défense des animaux soumis à l'hypoxie. Le premier assume que l'hypoxie est une pression du milieu ambiant tolérable et arrive à la plupart de ses conclusions en se servant d'études d'animaux tolérants à l'hypoxie (y compris l'anoxie). Le second thème traite de la protection ou de la réversion des effets de la limitation de l'oxygène, et sa banque de données vient des recherches réalisées sur des systèmes sensibles à l'hypoxie. Un troisième thème, de développement récent, se trouve à l'intersection de ces deux approches et son objectif essentiel est le maniement et la manipulation des mécanismes de défense contre l'hypoxie que possèdent les systèmes tolérants à l'hypoxie, de façon à produire des lignes d'intervention pour la communauté de recherche clinique. Actuellement, on décrit quatre stratégies de défense contre l'hypoxie : (i) l'usage des voies métaboliques fonctionnellement avantageuses ; (ii) la supression du métabolisme de manière coordonnée avec la suppression de la demande d'énergie; (iii) le maintien des fonctions couplées métabolisme-membrane, et (iv) le maintien des conditions qui permettent la récupération. Ce travail de façon systématique (i) révise le potentiel de transformation effective de ces types de défense à des systèmes sensibles à l'hypoxie et (ii) pour chacun d'entre eux, évalue son utilité pour lélaboration des stratégies d'intervention.

Mots clés : Défense contre l'hypoxie, métabolisme hypobarique, adaptation à l'hypoxie.

HYPOXIA PHYSIOLOGY AND PATHOPHYSIOLOGY

In 1974 Sir Hans Krebs presented an interesting little paper on occasion of the 65th birthday of C. Ladd Prosser, in which he reiterated the August Krogh principle and illustrated it with examples that went initially from biochemistry (31) and ultimately all the way to animal behaviour (32). There are two basic tenents to the Krogh principle: (i) that organisms can be used as an experimental parameter per se (a practice that indeed pervades all of comparative physiology and biochemistry) and (ii) that for each major biomedical problem nature has invented an organism or organisms that are particularly well suited for its analysis. For some two decades now, we and other biologists have been applying this same approach to unravelling hypoxia defense mechanism, using hypoxia tolerant animals as Kroghian examples of nature's best choice of organisms for analyzing this problem area (23). When, more recently, we turned our attention to metabolic defense adaptations against hypoxia in the human species, we were astonished to discover that the field of hypobaric hypoxia studies of man was already pervaded (indeed one could say, dominated) by a remarkably similar approach. Its origins, as far as I can tell, go back at least 4 or more decades to the work of the senior Monge and his colleagues, culminating in an incisive little book in 1948 (36), and it has been sustained and nurtured ever since by his son, to whom this paper is dedicated. Their approach (37; 50) certainly displays a key Kroghian feature - that of using the high altitude human (naturally adapted through varying time periods at altitude) as a valid experimental parameter, pregnant with information that would be otherwise inaccessible to science. Although their approach lacks a phylogenetically extensive interspecies frame of reference, and is missing a large animal-derived data base, it contains an additional novel feature; namely, transferability to clinically important O_2-limitation problems in general. In this regard it again displays a fascinating parallelism with current developments in studies of hypoxia tolerant animals.

Even a cursory library search on animal studies of hypoxia will show that three themes are intertwined through the literature over the last two decades. One dominant theme is that hypoxia is a survivable stress, proof of which is demonstrated by numerous hypoxia (even anoxia) tolerant species (23). Studies here are really dealing with what is normal physiology for these species. The second theme focusses more upon hypoxia sensitive systems in which research is dealing primarily with pathophysiology and the main goal of research is defense, protection, or reversal of debilitating effects of O_2 limitation (51; 40). The third (and more recently developing) theme lies at the interface of these two quite distinct research approaches; it aims to explore the possibilities of useful transfer of defense strategies of hypoxia tolerant species to the clinical researchers, as guidelines to intervention (18). Such goals are formally analogous to Monge's within-species approach, but are not easily realized. In research papers, it is often difficult to bluntly evalutate the status of theme three. Often the research scientist is either too close to his or her own research or too cautious to be concerned with whether or not a clinical researcher could use some of nature's blueprints of hypoxia defense as an intervention strategy in clinical settings. In turn, the clinical researcher may find it difficult to pick through the details of the pure science contributions to see what, if anything, could be transferred to more purely medical goals. Since Carlos Monge has taught me that intellectual provocation is the elixir of science, I reasoned that for this volume I would cast caution to the wind, and would systematically work through the main thematic contributions of research on hypoxia tolerant organisms with one goal in mind: evaluate the current transferability status. Or, to put it another way, what lessons or insights - if any - arise from these various studies? What should the clinical researcher be watching for? What is potentially transferable - from natural defense strategies of hypoxia tolerant systems, evolved in animals or man, to medical intervention strategies?

THE USE OF ENERGETICALLY MORE USEFUL METABOLIC PATHWAYS

One of the first points of departure for reseachers in this area is the realization that the main energetic problem of O_2 limitation arises from undesirable features of anaerobic metabolism: its yield of ATP is low, its use of fuel is inefficient, and it is self-polluting, generating undesirable and potentially noxious end products. Many hypoxia tolerant organisms, as a result, adapt to hypoxia in part at least through the utilization of alternative fermentative pathways which avoid or minimize some of the above problems.

The main pathways that are theoretically available to animals are (25):

1. glucose ---------> lactate

2. glucose ---------> ethanol

3. glucose ---------> succinate

4. glucose ---------> opines (octopine, strombine, alanopine, tauropine)

5. glucose ---------> propionate and acetate

6. glucose ---------> other short chain volatile fatty acids

7. aspartate ---------> succinate

8. glutamate --------> succinate

The first, anaerobic glycolysis, of course, is the main fermentation pathway in mammalian (including human) tissues. However, theoretically, pathways 3, 5, 6, 7, and 8 are possible in a number of tissues. Harnessing these pathways in diseases caused or complicated by hypoxia may yield two advantages: (i) more ATP/mole glucose metabolized and (ii) production of ATP both in the cytosol (at conventional sites of anaerobic ATP synthesis) and in the mitochondria (for example, at fumarate reductase and succinate thiokinase).

Conditions that minimize their use normally are either substrate limitations or very low enzyme capacities; both limitations in principle could be assaulted. Whereas clinical applications here may be difficult, they should probably be reviewed and evaluated. The use of glucose — succinate fermentation pathways are too common in nature (and are too readily imitated by preferential fuel delivery) and their advantages are too obvious to be ignored by clinical researchers.

Whereas purely anaerobic pathways are excellent short term solutions to O_2 lack, for higher organisms they are pathetically inadequate for chronic hypoxia. Hence, another line of research with hypoxia tolerant organisms looks more restrictively at efficiency *advantages of different aerobic metabolic pathways* (19; 20; 21). What are the possibilities here? To put this question into perspective, we should recall that oxidation yields about 36 ATP/glucose, but that no laws of chemistry or physics dictate this evolved stoichiometry (2). If not, one may wonder why 36, why not a higher number, say 50? Although this question has been pondered (16) at the moment there is no known way for improving the basic stoichiometries of oxidation of different kinds of fuels. There are however three well known ways for improving overall efficiency of tissue metabolic and work functions (27):

    1. improving cell work/ATP

    2. improving cell ATP/O_2

    3. improving the ratio of aerobic/anaerobic pathway contributions to ATP formation.

For the first what is required is management of cell ATPases, since some of these may be more efficient than others. For example, one Ca++ ATPase isoform pumps 2 ions/ATP while a second isoform pumps only 1 Ca++/ATP; favoring the first under O_2 limiting conditions could be energetically quite advantageous. Theoretically, this problem could be assaulted using endocrinological , molecular biology, or pharmaceutical tools. Or all of these at once (14). To date, this has not been adequetely explored either by theoreticians or by more practical-minded researchers.

The second kind of efficiency adjustment (up regulating cell ATP produced/O_2 used) in its simplest form means preferential catabolism of carbohydrate, instead of fat. Fatty acid metabolims uses O_2 less efficiently than does glucose oxidation; in principle, the difference is minimally about 10%, but in practice the O_2 wasting effect of free fatty acids is larger and leads to 25-60% less ATP/O_2 than with glucose oxidation (46; 29; 6). An exciting recent demonstration of this adaptational strategy arises from studies of heart metabolism in Andean natives, adapted to hypobaric hypoxia through generational time. Using Positron Emission Tomography (PET) techniques, this study confirmed that in normoxic lowlanders, following an overnight fast for metabolic standardization, the contribution of glucose to cardiac energy demands is a modest fraction of that required; under these conditions, it is known from many earlier studies that the preferred fuels for heart metabolism are free fatty acids (3; 9). In contrast, under the same conditions, the heart of Quechua natives (living at between 3700 and 5000 m) shows a much stronger preference for glucose, at least when the subject is at rest (28). Although this adaptation represents only a 25-60% improvement in ATP yield per O_2 used, the advantage is evidently large enough to have been selected and relatively firmly fixed in the physiological make-up of altitude adapted Quechuas, since even after 3 weeks deacclimation at sea level, only one subject was found to 'resolve' and express typical lowlander glucose uptake rates; the rest of the group studied, showed some reduction in glucose preference, but glucose still accounted for an unusually large fraction of cardiac energy needs.

Because this hypoxia adaptation strategy occurs in the human species and evidently is at least partially adjustable on a short term basis (28), there is urgent need to learn how to manipulate and manage the response in diseases or other clinical situations involving O_2 limitation. Coarse-level endocrine regulation mechanisms coupled with substrate-based finer (moment-to-moment) controls of fuel preferences in many mammalian (and indeed human) tissues and organs are well developed areas in biochemistry (3) and are indeed coming along even in molecular biology (12; 35). Thus, this is an area where transfer of a natural hypoxia defense strategy into a clinical intervention strategy is not only desirable; it should be achievable on the basis of already available knowledge.

The third kind of efficiency adjustment (maximizing the ratio of aerobic/anaerobic metabolism) under hypoxic conditions is again particularly noteworthy because one of the best research examples of it comes from studies of humans - again, the hypobaric hypoxia adaptations of high altitude natives (10; 49; 27; 34). Major advantages arising from this hypoxia adaptation include: (a) vastly improved yield of ATP/mole of glucose used (aerobic metabolism yields 36 ATP/glucose; anaerobic glycolysis yields 2 ATP/glucose), (b) decreased production of anaerobic end products and hence decreased self-pollution effects (such as acidosis, osmotic perturbations, and so forth), and (c) improved efficiency of fuel use (much less glucose is needed for the same energy turnover using aerobic pathways than using anaerobic glycolysis).

Of the above three efficiency strategies, maximizing the ratio of aerobic/anaerobic contributions to ATP synthesis is considered by far the most effective because of (by far) the greatest pay off (18 fold improvement in energy yield, for example, compared with the fractional gains arising from preferential oxidation of glucose over fat). As far as we know, however, there is a down side to this response to hypoxia: because the availability of O_2 is low and may be limiting, maximizing aerobic/anaerobic metabolism may be achievable only with simultaneous down regulation of overall (maximum) metabolic rate. While this may explain the perplexing observation that despite high endurance under hypobaric hypoxia, altitude adapted natives typically display low maximum aerobic metabolic capacities (27; 30), further work is clearly required to unravel the details of this problem. Nevertheless, because exactly this kind of hypoxia defense is already known to be used by man (in life-long hypobaric hypoxia exposure), I am again led to the opinion that the trasferability potential (laboratory to clinic) here is very high.

THE END PRODUCTS PROBLEM

One of the more intractable areas of research on hypoxia tolerant animals is that focussing on the problem of self-pollution or end product accumulation during anaerobic metabolism. Most workers consider the most deleterious end product to be H+ and the dominant themes explored are (i) ways to minimize the debilitating effects of acidosis, and (ii) ways to use H+ to advantage (24; 48). To put this into perspective, we should point out that H+ comes into play both in ATP production (in anaerobic pathways) and in ATP utilization (in ATPase reactions) in the following ways (24):

At steady state, here written for a relatively high pH, ATP production by glycolysis

glucose + n ADP + n Pi ------->2 anion end products + n ATP

is coupled to ATP utilization

ATP + H_2O -------> ADP + Pi + H+

and proton production arises mainly from the latter process. At low pH, glycolysis per se also generates some H+ ions, while ATP hydrolysis proceeds with an equivalent lesser H+ release than at more alkaline pH. Thus under all conditions, the net metabolic reaction is

glucose -------->2 anionic end products + 2 H+

while the value of n (the energy yield in terms of moles ATP/mole glucose) ranges from 2 (for the glucose—lactate pathway) to values as high as 6 (for glucose—propionate fermentation). As with the ATP stoichiometry of metabolic pathways, the inherent H+ stoichiometries of anaerobic pathways are not really adjustable and thus there is not much room for improvement here. Nevertheless, the potential for using H+ consuming metabolic reactions for minimazing the effects of H+ production during anaerobiosis must be seriously considered. Additionally, there is need for reviewing the possibilities of potential beneficial effects of H+. In naturally hypoxia tolerant systems, the main use of H+ seems to be as a coarse control mechanism - usually in down regulation of metabolism (13). The degree to which this could be used in clinical situations needs further exploration. Tentatively it appears that the transferability potential of this area is still low, but that research developments here should be closely monitored. This is because intracellular pH in essentially any tissue can now be monitored accurately noninvasively with the use of Nuclear Magnetic Resonance spectroscopy; hence, if the smallest metabolite in the cell - the H+ ion - can be harnessed to good ends, the means for monitoring it are already in hand (see 34, for literature).

SUPPRESSION OF ATP TURNOVER AS AN HYPOXIA DEFENSE STRATEGY

In comparative studies of hypoxia tolerant cells, organs, and organisms, a universal defense mechanism that emerges involves metabolic suppression. One of the leading physiologists of our time (the Viking, Kjell Johansen) referred to this phenomenon as 'switching down to the pilot light' in order to emphasize that the defense strategy involves down regulating metabolism to a new set point well below the normoxic minimum or maintenance level (23). The main goal of much recent work·in this area is to evaluate mechanisms of control in general and especially mechanisms of controlled metabolic suppression. In invertebrate systems, our understanding of the molecular basis for the defense is reasonably advanced and seemingly revolves around phosphorylation - dephosphorylation of key enzymes in energy yielding pathways (42). What is still missing in these analyses, however, is knowledge of the signal components and the signal transduction pathways by which metabolic suppression is achieved.

In fishes, metabolic suppression capacities correlate with hypoxia tolerance (as expected from numerous other studies) and in at least one cell type (fast twtich glycolytic muscle) free ADP and H+ may play pivotal roles in down regulation of metabolism (44; 47).

In mammals the situation is unfortunately not yet very clear, though recent evidence suggests its occurence even in the human brain (26). A phenomenon receiving especial attention is the frequently observed close relationship between perfusion and metabolic rate. Two issues here are notably outstanding; namely, what mechanisms regulate perfusion under normoxic or hypoxic conditions and what mechanisms regulate metabolism as a consequence (41). Although many studies have been devoted to sorting out these relationships, there is surprisingly poor understanding of the phenomenon. My personal opinion of the current status of this area of research is that we have a long way to go before manipulation and management of the response is achievable. Nevertheless, because the desired target (tissue metabolism) in theory can be manipulated indirectly (by control of perfusion), the flow-metabolism interface should be attracting more and more attention from clinical researchers.

METABOLISM-MEMBRANE COUPLING DURING HYPOXIA

Although metabolic suppression as an hypoxia defense strategy is widely recognized and (at least on the basis of current studies) seems to be universally expressed in all hypoxia tolerant systems (17; 42), it is often overlooked that energy demand must be simultaneously and coordinately down regulated. In fact, down regulation of energy demand may well be the pivotal piece of this hypoxia adaptation strategy. Since in many cells, the maintenance of electrochemical gradients under various conditions represents an important part of the tissue's energy demands, much attention has been devoted to unravelling mechanisms by which metabolic and membrane functions remain integrated during hypoxic stress. In hypoxia tolerant systems, such as the brain in species such as carp and turtles, the mechanisms of defense are gradually being clarified (43; 7; 8; 33; 39) and raise the hope that manipulation (i) of membrane ion-specific channels, transporters, or pumps, (ii) of release of excitatory neurotransmitters (which under hypoxic conditions can take on excitotoxic characteristics (see 51), and (iii) of basal membrane leakiness may allow the development of theoretical intervention strategies that may be of use to the clinical researcher.

INTEGRATIONIST VS REDUCTIONIST APPROACHES

Tradionally, the experimental fountainhead in hypoxia research has been the piece-by-piece dissection of hypoxia responses in sensitive vs tolerant systems. This represents the time-honored and reductionist approach of much of biochemistry, molecular biology, and physiology. However, *in vivo* principles and properties of hypoxia defense may differ from *in vitro* isolated systems. This is particularly clearly illustrated in studies of diving in marine mammals where the first line of defense against potential O_2 limitation during diving is a distinctly whole-organism level reflex response: diving bradycardia and peripheral vasoconstrictions in order to maintain blood pressure and redistribute cardiac output (see 21). The biological design of the diving response allows 'physiological level' protection to a few preferentially perfused tissues and organs (heart, brain, adrenal gland, locomotory muscles, placenta), while peripheral tissues are left to fend for themselves. Biochemical mechanisms protecting against hypoxia are crucially important in the latter tissues, but may be of minimal significance in the former.

While many exciting developments are being reported at ever increasing rates in this field (4; 1; 11; 15), it is probable that major insights are yet to come. Marine mammals like the large seals are such exquisite masters of O_2 management that they can breath-hold dive for periods of up to 2 hours (!) and swim to depths of over 1.5 km (!) compared to terrestrial species such as man that normally can manage a minute or two at best. The complete blueprint outlining how one air breathing warm bodied animal can so out-perform another is not yet available (21; 22). Hence, for the clinical researcher, the best advise may be to watch this field with an acute eye, but the time is not yet ripe for trying to imitate in the clinic the O_2 management strategies of large seals.

RECOVERY FROM IMPOSED OXYGEN LIMITATION

As mentioned above the August Krogh principle - that for every major biomedical problem nature has evolved a best animal for its scientific resolution - has pervaded much of the literature on naturally hypoxia tolerant animals. However, this paradigm becomes rather less useful in confronting issues of recovery and reperfusion after severe hypoxic or ischaemic episodes. This is because hypoxia tolerant animals may well have entirely unique recovery and reperfusion problems. For this reason, in much of the literature on recovery defense mechanisms, the paradigm is largely abandoned and most of the studies deal directly with issues of recovery and protection in relatively hypoxia sensitive cells; indeed, in some cases, the study specifically selects for mitochondria-rich cells that are super-sensitive to O_2 lack.

Developments here while most exciting cannot be readily packaged into preconceived hypotheses. Many of the results are indeed so surprising that they challenge our understanding (and indeed raise questions as to how acute is our knowledge of how the cell works and how best to protect it from O_2 limitation). This is particularly notable in studies of glycine and alanine protection of renal cells against hypoxic damage (45); the protective effects are striking and undeniable, but the mechanism of protection remains at this writing a complete mystery. For the clinical researcher, this field (of exogenous ligand protection against O_2 lack), while incomplete and rapidly developing, nonetheless is loaded with potential for clinical application and one to be closely watched.

Earlier in this review I made reference to the possibility of putting H+ production during hypoxia to good use, a concept that is explored at a whole-organism level by Wasserman et al. (48). The pH paradox is a specific example of a similar positive effect of H+ - in this case, in recovery of hepatocytes following exposure to O_2 limitation (5). This kind of effect would seem to be in critical need of evaluation using more integrated systems; it too in principle is of clinical significance, since extracellular pH can be manipulated fairly readily while intracellular pH can be monitored noninvasively.

Finally, as in other areas of post-hypoxic response, some surprising metabolic requirements may arise in recovery periods that are not evident from cursory examination. This has been closely analyzed (38) for one system (recovery in pure fast twitch glycolytic muscle). The results show how the need for glycogen resynthesis is integrated with the potentially conflicting need to regain normoxic adenylate and phosphagen status; while they may be unique to this tissue, the take-home message is that they could not have been predicted from previous data or from previous control theory. Thus the study uncovers an unexpected requirement for similar analyses with other tissues and organs. In order to design management strategies following exposure to O_2 lack it is patently advantageous to know how the metabolic requirements of the recovery period differ from other normoxic metabolic periods.

SUMMARY AND DEDICATION TO CARLOS MONGE

As pointed out above, in 1974 Sir Hans Krebs presented a paper of unusual interest to comparative physiologists in a symposium honoring the famous comparative physiologist, C. Ladd Prosser. In it, he argued that choice of experimental system in biology and medicine is sometimes crucial to solving the problem at hand. He reminded us that some of his own discoveries (including the citric acid or Krebs cycle of oxidative metabolism) and numerous other biomedical advances would not have been made without such strategic decisions on experimental systems to be used. This experimental paradigm, termed the August Krogh principle, in fact has served as the point of departure for a large part of the field of study of hypoxia tolerant animal systems. A measure of the success of such endeavour is being able to succintly summarize the dominant hypoxia defense mechanisms as four simple principles:

(i) the principle of using biochemically advantageous pathways of ATP utilization and ATP production,

(ii) the principle of metabolic suppression coordinated with suppression of energy demand,

(iii) the principle of protecting (maintaining) coupled metabolism-membrane functions, and

(iv) the principle of maintaining conditions during the O_2 limitation stress which are commensurate with subsequent recovery.

With these in hand, biologists now find themselves focussing on how these four fundamental defense mechanisms are used, when, and by which hypoxia tolerant tissues, organs, or organisms. It is particularly interesting that, while working mainly within a one-species (i.e. mankind) framework, both the senior and the junior Monge have been ploughing a remarkably similar furough for the better part of an entire century. Like classical comparative biologists, they have been emphasizing different adaptation levels (often of our own species) as an experimental parameter per se. Like classical comparative biologists, their work strives to better understand hypobaric hypoxia defense strategies and the adaptational limits. Like classical comparative biologists, who look for broad frameworks from specific experimental results, their work aims not only to better understand high altitude medicine but also to improve our understanding of analagous clinical problems in general and to challenge the clinical research community in particular.

It seems to me that the time is now ripe for our clinically oriented colleagues to rise to this challenge; it is time to pick up the theme and to seriously consider the possibilities for transfer of natural hypoxia defense strategies of animals and man into management, manipulation, and intervention strategies for various diseases either caused or complicated by O_2 limitation.

The challenge of this next huge stride in the field - daring to take it - that to me is the main Monge legacy.

ACKNOWLEDGEMENTS

This work was supported by NSERC (Canada). I thank all of my students, postdoctoral fellows, and collaborators who over the years have helped me to see connections and interactions which I otherwise would have overlooked. In particular, I thank Choclo who showed me more clearly than ever before how science in small nations can remain very competitive with science in large ones.

REFERENCES

1. ANDREWS, R.D., JONES, J.R., THORSON, P.T., WILLIAMS, J., OLIVER, G.W., MORRIS, P.A. COSTA, D.P. & LE BOEUF, B.J. 1991. Heart rate responses in freely diving northern elephant seals. *9th Biennial Conf. Biol. Marine Mammals*: 2.

2. ATKINSON, D.E. 1977. *Cellular Energy Metabolism and its Regulation.* New York: Academic Press: pp 1-293.

3. BARRETT, E.J., SCHWARTZ, R.G., FRANCIS, C.K. & ZARET, B.L. 1984. Regulation by insulin of myocardial glucose and fatty acid metabolism in the conscious dog. *J. Clin. Invest.* 74: 1073-1079.

4. CASTELLINI, M.A., KOOYMAN G.L., & PONGANIS, P.J. 1992. Metabolic rates of freely diving Weddell seals: Correlations with oxygen stores, swim velocity, and diving duration. *J. Exp. Biol.* 165: 181-194.

5. CURRIN, R.T., GORES, G.J., THURMAN, R.G. & LEMASTERS, J.L. 1991. Protection by acidotic pH against anoxic killing in perfused rat liver: evidence for a pH paradox. *FASEB J.* 5: 207-210.

6. DAUT, J. & ELZINGA, G. 1989. Substrate dependence of energy metabolism in isolated guinea pig cardiac muscle: a microcalorimetric study. *J. Physiol.* 413: 379-387.

7. DOLL, C.S., HOCHACHKA, P.W. & REINER, P.B. 1991a. Effects of anoxia and metabolic arrest on turtle and rat cortical neurons. *Am. J. Physiol.* 260: R747-R755.

8. DOLL, C.S., HOCHACHKA, P.W. & REINER, P.B. 1991b. Channel arrest: implications from membrane resistance. *Am. J. Physiol.* 261:R1321-R1324.

9. DRAKE, A. 1985. Substrate utilization in the myocardium. *Basic Res. Cardiol.* 19: 1-11.

10. EDWARDS, H.T. 1936. Lactic acid in rest and work at high altitude. *Am. J. Physiol.* 116: 367-375.

11. FEDAK, M.A. & THOMPSON, D. 1991. Profound bradycardia during foraging dives in grey seals. *9th Biennial Conf. Biol. Marine Mammals*: 21.

12. GOODRIDGE, A.G. 1990. The new metabolism: molecular genetics in the analysis of metabolic regulation. *FASEB J.* 4: 3099-3110.

13. HAND, S.C. 1992. pHi and anabolic arrest during anoxia in Artemia franciscana embryos. *In:* P.W. Hochachka, P.L.Lutz, T.Sick, M.Rosenthal, and G.van den Thillart (eds.), *Surviving Hypoxia.* Boca Raton, Florida: CRC Press, pp. 171-188.

14. HARDEVELD, C., van & SIMONIDES, W.S. 1992. *In:* P.W. Hochachka *et al.* (eds.), *Surviving Hypoxia.* Boca Raton, Florida: CRC Press, in press.

15. HINDELL, M.A., SLIP, D.J., BURTON, H.R. & BRYDEN, M.M. 1992. Physiological implications of continuous, prolonged, and deep dives of the southern elephant seal (Mirounga leonina). *Can. J. Zool.,* 70: 370-379.

16. HOCHACHKA, P.W. 1980. *Living Without Oxygen.* Cambridge, Mass.: Harvard Univ. Press: pp 1-181.

17. HOCHACHKA, P.W. 1986. Defense strategies against hypoxia and hypothermia. *Science,* 231: 234-241.

18. HOCHACHKA, P.W. 1987. Metabolic arrest. *Intensive Care Med.* 12: 127-133.

19. HOCHACHKA, P.W. 1992a. Principles of physiological and biochemical adaptation. High altitude man as a case study. *In:* S.C.Wood, R.E.Weber, A.R.Hargens, and R.W.Millard (eds.), *Physiological Adaptations in Vertebrates.* New York: Marcel Dekker, Inc.: 21-35.

20. HOCHACHKA, P.W. 1992b. Adaptability of metabolic efficiencies under chronic hypoxia in man. *In:* P.W. Hochachka, *et al.* (eds.), *Surviving Hypoxia.* Boca Raton, Florida: pp. 127-135.

21. HOCHACHKA, P.W. 1992c. Metabolic biochemistry and the making of a mesopelagic mammal. *Experientia,* 48: 570-575.

22. HOCHACHKA, P.W. & FOREMAN, R.A. III. 1993. Phocid and cetacean blueprints of muscle metabolism. *Can. J. Zool.,* in press.

23. HOCHACHKA, P.W. & GUPPY, M. 1987. *Metabolic Arrest and the Control of Biological Time.* Cambridge, Mass.: Harvard Univ. Press: pp 1-227.

24. HOCHACHKA, P.W. & MOMMSEN, T.P. 1981. Protons and anaerobiosis. *Science* 219: 1391-1397.

25. HOCHACHKA, P.W. & SOMERO, G.N. 1984. *Biochemical Adaptation.* Princeton, N.J.: Princeton Univ. Press: pp 1-537.

26. HOCHACHKA, P.W., CLARK, C.M., BROWN, W.D., STANLEY, C., STONE, C.K., NICKLES, R.J., ZHU, G.G., ALLEN, P.S. & HOLDEN, J.E. 1994. The brain at high altitude: Hypometabolism as a defense against chronic hypoxia? *J. Cerebral Bl. Flow & Metabolism,* in press.

27. HOCHACHKA, P.W., STANLEY, C., MATHESON, G.O., MCKENZIE, D.C., ALLEN, P.S. & PARKHOUSE, W.S. 1991. Metabolic and work efficiencies during exercise in Andean natives. *J. Appl. Physiol.* 70: 1720-1730.

28. HOLDEN, J., BROWN, D., STANELY, C., STONE, C. & HOCHACHKA, P.W. 1993. Elevated glucose preference of heart metabolism in altitude natives: A metabolic defense adaptation against chronic hypoxia. *J. Appl. Physiol.,* submitted.

29. HUTTER, J.F., PIPER, H.M. & SPIKECKERMANN, P.G. 1985. Influence of free fatty acids on myocardial oxygen consumption and ischemic injury. *Am. J. Physiol.* 249: H723-H728.

30. KAYSER, B., HOPPLER, H., CLASSEN, H. & CERRETELLI, P. 1991. Muscle structure and performance capacities of Himalayan Sherpas. *J. Appl. Physiol.* 70: 1938-1942.

31. KREBS, H.A. 1975. The August Krogh principle: For many problems there is an animal on which it can be most conveniently studied. *J. Exp. Zool.* 194: 221-226.

32. KREBS, H.A. & KREBS, J. 1980. The "August Krogh principle". *Comp. Biochem. Physiol.* 67B: 379-380.

33. LUTZ, P.L. 1992. Anoxic defense mechanisms in the vertebrate brain. *Ann. Rev. Physiol.* 54: 619-637.

34. MATHESON, G.O., ALLEN, P.S., ELLINGER, D.C., HANSTOCK, C.C., GHEORGHIU, D., MCKENZIE, D.C., STANELY, C., PARKHOUSE, W.S. & HOCHACHKA, P.W. 1991. Skeletal muscle metabolism and work capacity: a 31P-NMR study of Andean natives and lowlanders. *J. Appl. Physiol.* 70: 1963-1976.

35. MCGRANE, M.M., YUN, J.S., PATEL, Y.M. & HANSON, R.W. 1992. Metabolic control of gene expression: in vivo studies with transgenic mice. *Trends Biochem. Sci.* 17: 40-44.

36. MONGE, C. 1948. *Acclimatization in the Andes.* Baltimore: Johns Hopkins Univ. Press: pp 1-148.

37. MONGE, C. & LEÓN-VELARDE, F. 1991. Physiological adaptation to high altitude: Oxygen transport in mammals and birds. *Physiol. Reviews* 71: 1135-1172.

38. MOYES, C.D., SCHULTE, P.M. & HOCHACHKA, P.W. 1992. Recovery metabolism of trout white muscle: role of mitochondria. *Am. J. Physiol.* 262: R295-R304.

39. NILSON, G.E. 1992. Neurotransmitters and anoxia resistance - Comparative physiological and evolutionary perpsectives. *In:* P.W. Hochachka *et al.* (eds.), *Surviving Hypoxia.* Boca Raton, Florida: CRC Press, pp. 401-413.

40. SNYDER, S.H. & BREDT, D.S. 1992. Biological roles of nitric oxide. *Sci. Amer.* 266: 68-77.

41. STAINSBY, W.N., O'DROBINAK D.M., BRECHUE, W.F. & BARCLAY, J.K. 1992. Metabolism-perfusion relationships in mammalian skeletal muscle. *In:* P.W. Hochachka *et al.* (eds.), *Surviving Hypoxia.* Boca Raton, Florida: CRC Press, pp. 341-348.

42. STOREY K.B. & STOREY, J.M. 1990. Facultative rate depression: molecular regulation and biochemical adaptation in anaerobiosis, hibernation, and estivation. *Quart. Rev. Biol.* 65: 145-174.

43. SUÁREZ, R.K., DOLL, C.J., BUIE, E., WEST, T.G., FUNK, G.D. & HOCHACHKA, P.W. 1989. Turtles and rats: a biochemical comparison of anoxia tolerant and anoxia sensitive brains. *Am. J. Physiol.* 257: R1083-R1088.

44. THILLART, G.,van den, WAARDE, A.,van, MULLER, H.J., ERKELENS, C., ADDINK, A. & LUGTENBURG, J. 1989. Fish muscle energy metabolism measured by in vivo 31P-NMR during anoxia and recovery. *Am J. Physiol.* 256: R922-R929.

45. VENKATACHALAM, M.J. & WEINBERG, J.M. 1992. Structural effects of intracellular amino acids during ATP depletion. *In:* P.W.Hochachka *et al.* (eds.), *Surviving Hypoxia.* Boca Raton: Florida: CRC Press, pp. 473-494.

46. VIK-MO, H. & MOJS, O.D. 1981. Influence of free fatty acids on myocardial oxygen consumption and ischemic injury. *Am. J. Cardiol.* 48: 361-365.

47. WAARDE, A.,van, THILLART, G., van den, ERKELENS, C., ADDINK, A. & LUGTENBURG, J. 1990. Functional coupling of glycolysis and phosphocreatine utilization in anoxic fish muscle: an in vivo 31P-NMR study. *J. Biol. Chem.* 265: 914-923.

48. WASSERMAN, K., HANSE, J.E. & SUE, D.Y. 1991. Facilitation of oxygen consumption by lactic acidosis during exercise. *News Physiol. Sci.* 6:29-34.

49. WEST, J. 1986. Lactate during exercise at extreme altitudes. Fed. Proc. 45: 2953-2957.

50. WINSLOW, R.M. & MONGE, C. 1987. *Hypoxia, Polycythemia, and Chronic Mountain Sickness.* Baltimore: Johns Hopkins Univ. Press: pp 1-231.

51. ZITVIN, J.A. & CHOI, D.W. 1991. Stroke therapy. *Sci. Amer.* 265: 56-63.